EVERYMAN'S LIBRARY

461

Everyman, I will go with thee, and be thy guide,
In thy most need to go by thy side

SAINT THOMAS MORE, born in London 1478. Educated at Oxford 1492–3; studied at the Inns of Court 1494–c. 1498. Became the friend of Erasmus 1497. Retired to the Charterhouse c. 1499–c. 1503. Member of Parliament 1504. First marriage 1505; second marriage 1511. *Utopia* published at Louvain 1516. Speaker of the House of Commons 1523; Lord Chancellor 1529–32. *Dialogue of Comfort* written in the Tower 1534. Martyred for refusing to acknowledge Henry VIII as head of the Church 6th July 1535. Beatified by Leo XIII 1886; canonized by Pius XI 1935.

MORE'S UTOPIA

AND A DIALOGUE OF COMFORT

INTRODUCTION BY
JOHN WARRINGTON

LONDON J. M. DENT & SONS LTD
NEW YORK E. P. DUTTON & CO INC

INTRODUCTION

THOMAS MORE was born at Milk Street in the city of London on 7th February 1478, the son of John More who was later a judge of the King's Bench. His education was begun at St Anthony's School in Broadstreet ward, and about 1490 he was received as a page into the household of John Morton, Archbishop of Canterbury, who in 1493 was created cardinal. Here More gave evidence of that gaiety and ready wit which characterized all his life and writings. 'For the cardinal,' says his son-in-law and biographer, William Roper, 'would often make trial of his present wit, especially at Christmas merriments, when . . . he alone made more sport than all the players beside.'

Two years later, by Morton's advice, More was sent to Oxford to Canterbury Hall,[1] where he studied the classics and made his first contact with the new learning of which in later years he proved himself one of the most brilliant exponents. In 1494 he was entered as a law student at New Inn and in 1496 transferred to Lincoln's Inn. Having been called to the Bar he was appointed reader at Furnival's Inn; but now he passed through a spiritual crisis.

The Catholic Church has been accused in more than one period of setting her face against material progress, of discouraging and even persecuting a new spirit in the arts and sciences. The charge is foolish, for churchmen in the highest places have been in every age, and in none more than the Renaissance, munificent patrons of scholarship and art. But the Church would have her sons walk warily in their new-found enthusiasms, and her caution has been too often justified by events. Material achievement has sometimes been the prelude to spiritual ruin, and a too ready trust in human reasoning has led to the denial of eternal truths. More, especially after his first meeting with Erasmus in 1497, was drawn on the one hand to the fresh fields of humanism; but he was no less powerfully attracted by the bonds of love to Christ. Accordingly, in or about 1499, he retired to the London Charterhouse where he lived for some four years, without vows, but in seclusion, seeking through prayer and penance to learn his true vocation. He was at length persuaded by his confessor, Dean Colet, that his proper course lay in the world and as a married man. Nevertheless, he

---

[1] Later absorbed into Christ Church.

seems to have retained until the last a yearning for the cloister; for while in the Tower shortly before his martyrdom he said to his daughter: 'I assure thee . . . that if it had not been for my wife and you, my children, whom I account the chief part of my charge, I would not have failed long ere this to have closed myself in as strait a room as this, and straiter too.' It is certain that in his long retreat More reconciled once and for all what was best in the new learning with the ancient doctrine of the Church.

In 1504, having been returned to Parliament, he was instrumental in persuading the Commons to oppose the exactions of Henry VII, who took revenge on More's father with a heavy fine; and More himself was preparing to seek refuge overseas when Henry died in 1509. Thomas More was twice married, first in 1505 to a daughter of John Colt of New Hall in Essex. She bore him three daughters and a son, but died in 1511. In the same year, in order that his home should have a mistress and his children a mother's care, he married a widow, Alice Middleton, some years his senior. With this lady he did not find the unalloyed happiness of his first union. She was querulous, having little sympathy with her husband's character, and no understanding of the problems of her age. To the end she was ever ready with a 'Tilly-vally!' in the several crises of his life and the still greater crisis of his death. She was, however, a good wife and mother, and More himself a devoted husband and father. His domestic life is one of the most attractive elements of Sir Thomas's character, and Erasmus in a letter to Ulrich von Hutten gives this charming picture of his home:

There is not any man living so loving to his children as he, and he loveth his old wife as if she were a young maid, and such is the excellency of his temper, that whatsoever happeneth that could not be helped, he loveth it as if nothing could happen more happily. You would say there were in that place Plato's academy, but I do the house injury in comparing it to Plato's academy, wherein there was only disputations of numbers, and geometrical figures, and sometimes of moral and virtues. I should rather call his house a school or university of Christian religion, for there is none therein but readeth or studieth the liberal sciences; their special care is piety and virtue, there is no quarrelling or intemperate words heard, none seem idle, which household discipline that worthy gentleman doth not govern by proud and lofty words, but with all kind and courteous benevolence; everybody performeth his duty; yet is there always alacrity; neither is sober mirth anything wanting.

As with his family, so with his friends he was gracious, gentle, and beloved. Erasmus wrote to the Bishop of

Cracow: 'In Moro mihi videor extinctus adeo μία ψυχή juxta Pythagoram duobus erat.'

More had returned to the Bar; his success was immediate, and he was engaged as counsel in every case of importance. The new king, Henry VIII, and Cardinal Wolsey tried without success to lure him from the law to the royal court and politics. He was, however, employed upon a number of foreign embassies, and honours were rapidly heaped upon him. In 1510 he became under-sheriff of London; in 1518 Master of Requests and Privy Councillor; knight and sub-treasurer to the king in 1521; and in 1523 Speaker of the House of Commons. Amidst all the work which these offices and his own practice entailed Sir Thomas More never relaxed his studies, his literary pursuits in defence of Catholic doctrine, his domestic ties, and least of all his life of prayer. In 1516 he had completed his most famous work, *Utopia*, which was published the same year under the supervision of Erasmus at Louvain. Since Plato's *Republic* it has been a favourite exercise of thoughtful men to draw a picture of a state governed by ideal laws and institutions. Since the eighteenth century, however, says Judge O'Hagan,[1] 'these sports of the imagination have taken a very different form. They have been transmuted into proposals to carry such chimeras into actual practice. They have found fanatical advocates of what we now term Socialism and Communism. . . . Underlying these proposals there is always one radical fallacy, namely, that they not only invent ideal institutions for mankind, but invent an ideal mankind for their institutions.' We learn from Roper that it was after More's appointment as Chancellor of the Duchy of Lancaster in 1525 that the king began to take a special delight in his company.

'The king's custom was . . . to send for Sir Thomas into his traverse, and there, sometimes in matters of astronomy, geometry, and divinity, and such other sciences to sit and confer with him; otherwhiles also in the clear nights he would have him walk with him on the leads, there to discourse of the diversity of the courses, motions, and operations of the stars as well fixed as the planets; and because he was of a very pleasant disposition, it pleased his majesty and the queen at supper-time, commonly to call him to hear his pleasant jests.' More was now living at Chelsea, and this constant attendance on the king kept him from his family and other things by far the better. He contrived to evade the royal invitations; but now Henry began to come in person to Chelsea 'and be merry with him; whither on a time unlooked for, he came and dined at his house, and after dinner walked with him the space of an hour, holding his arm about his neck most lovingly in the

---

[1] *Irish Monthly Magazine*, 1876.

garden.' Sir Thomas, however, knew the hearts of men; for being congratulated upon so high an honour, he replied: 'I may tell you I have no cause to be proud thereof; for if my head would win him a castle in France, it should not fail to go off.' Nor was he deceived by the outward prosperity of the kingdom. 'I pray God,' he said to Roper, 'that some of us may not live to see the day in which all this will be changed, and in which we will be glad to be permitted to possess our own churches and our own religion in peace.'

Thus matters stood when the affair of the divorce burst upon Europe.

'It seems his [the king's] marriage with his brother's wife has crept too near his conscience.'

'No, his conscience has crept too near another lady.'

Shakespeare, *Henry VIII.*

In 1529 Anne Boleyn won the disgrace of Wolsey from her infatuated paramour; and now Sir Thomas More was chosen to succeed the cardinal as Lord High Chancellor of England. He proved himself one of the best in an illustrious line of men who have occupied the woolsack. Not only did he clear the large arrears of causes left unheard by his predecessor, but he also, three centuries before it came to pass, attempted the fusion of common law and equity. So long as the case of the divorce was undetermined by the Holy See Sir Thomas More continued in the service of his king. But as soon as it became clear that Rome would not accede to the royal lust, he had to choose between Christ and the world. The issue was never for a moment in doubt. 'We may not look at our pleasure,' he had declared, 'to go to heaven in feather beds, it is not the way. For our Lord Himself went thither with great pain, and by many tribulations, which is the path wherein He walked thither, and the servant may not look to be in better case than his master.' He asked to be relieved of his office, and his resignation was accepted in 1532. He abandoned honours and dignities with more readiness than other men embrace them, and retired to Chelsea, his family, his books, and communion with God. 'Tilly-vally, Mr More,' exclaimed his wife, 'will you sit and make goslings in the ashes?'

The king had decreed his own divorce by the mouth of Cranmer, and More had refused the royal command to be present at the coronation of the adulteress. Henry, not satisfied with his victory, now lusted for the goods of the Church, and for blood besides. He therefore claimed to be head of the Church in England and denied the Roman jurisdiction. This was schism, total separation from the body of the Catholic Church; yet it was ratified by Parliament without a dissenting voice, and to declare a contrary opinion was made high treason.

Historians have expressed surprise that the English people were ready, at the command of a tyrant mad with self-will and unbridled passions, to deny their ancient faith, especially when the Church was, to outward appearance, in a flourishing condition. It should be remembered, however, that the English generally are a docile race, ever ready to obey, and if needs be suffer, at the bidding of their rulers, good or bad.

For Sir Thomas More the supreme crisis was at hand. The oath of the royal supremacy was tendered to the clergy, and all but the Bishop of Rochester and the monks of the Charterhouse submitted. It was considered that if More should take the oath, such was his prestige, none other of the laity would refuse. Accordingly, on 13th April, he was commanded to appear at Lambeth. As was his custom, he went to Chelsea Church where he confessed, heard Mass, and received Communion. The path before him was clear, but it was not easy, and his son-in-law, who accompanied him, tells us that he left home with a heavy heart. He sat for a long while silent in the boat, and then at last he spoke: 'My son, I thank our Lord that the field is won.'

Twice he refused to deny his Master, while the vicar of Croydon 'called for a cup of beer at the buttery bar and drank very familiarly.' After four days he was once more summoned to abjure the ancient faith; once more he refused, and was committed to the Tower. Here, alone with Christ, he awaited the fulfilment of God's will. After a month of rigorous confinement Sir Thomas was visited by his daughter Margaret, to whom he said: 'Methinks God, by this imprisonment, maketh me one of His wantons,[1] and setteth me upon His lap, and dandleth me, even as He hath done all His best friends.' Lady More came after the manner of Xanthippe to Socrates. Her mind was in the house at Chelsea, not on the everlasting hills.

Sir Thomas More's long confinement was due to a legal difficulty. The Act of Parliament declaring the king head of the Church had, as we have seen, made the denial of that supremacy high treason. Merely to refuse the oath amounted to no more than misprision of treason punishable with imprisonment and forfeiture of goods. The king's party hoped that Sir Thomas, given time, would change his mind, or that some means of encompassing his destruction might be found. More had occupied much of his time writing the *Dialogue of Comfort against Tribulation*. In this work Antonio, an old man, and his nephew Vincent, both Hungarians, discuss the approaching invasion of the Turks. 'We who know the end

---

[1] i.e. favourite children.

of the story,' writes M. Brémond, 'feel a thrill every time the Grand Turk appears. We know the tyrant's name,' More simply adds: 'There is no born Turk so cruel to Christian folk as is the false Christian that falleth from the faith.' The dialogue, like the introduction to *Utopia*, is a personal revelation.

And now Henry ordered that he should be deprived of books and writing materials. The solicitor-general, moreover, one Rich, visited him and tried to ensnare him into treasonable utterance. It was in vain; but his enemies determined to proceed against him by means of perjury and a carefully selected jury.

The trial of Sir Thomas More opened at Westminster Hall on 7th May 1535, but was adjourned and resumed on 1st July. So futile was the case against him and so conclusive his defence that an acquittal seemed inevitable. At this juncture Rich left his place as crown counsel at the Bar, entered the witness box, and swore on oath that the accused had uttered treasonable words. More preserved his calm and dignity, saying only: 'In truth, Mr Rich, I am more sorry for your perjury than for my peril.' He was sentenced to be hanged, drawn, and quartered, but according to the custom for men of his rank the sentence was commuted to death by beheading. The wonderful scene between Sir Thomas and his best-beloved Margaret at Tower Wharf after the trial has passed into legend. On the evening before his execution he sent her his hair shirt and discipline together with a letter:

I cumber you, good Margaret, much, but I would be sorry if it should be any longer than to-morrow. For to-morrow is St Thomas' Eve, and the Octave of St Peter, therefore to-morrow long I to go to God, that were a day very meet and convenient for me. And I never liked your manners better than when you kissed me last. For I like when daughterly love and dear charity hath no leisure to look to worldly courtesy.

Early next morning, 6th July, More was brought to execution. His imprisonment had weakened him and the scaffold had been hastily built. Wherefore, 'Assist me up,' he said to the Lieutenant of the Tower, 'and in coming down I will shift for myself.' When his head was already on the block he uttered the most famous of all his sayings: 'Wait till I put my beard aside, for that hath done no treason.'

Lord Campbell has said of the character of Sir Thomas More that it comes as near to perfection as our nature will permit. Dean Swift places Sir Thomas with Junius and Marcus Brutus, Socrates, Epaminondas, and the younger Cato, 'a sextumvirate to which all the ages of the world cannot add a seventh.'

Yet More is greater than all that. He is, perhaps, the supreme instance of nature perfected by grace. His natural talents were ennobled by a life of unsullied virtue, and that life in turn was crowned by a most glorious martyrdom. To-day he has a message for men whose claims to enlightenment are little justified by events. In the first place, contrary to a strange but persistent belief, goodness is not synonymous with gloom; sanctity is rather the companion of 'sober mirth.' Again, a high order of intelligence is not incompatible with religious belief and a life consistent with that belief. But more important still is the consideration that, when in the name of human wisdom individuals or governments deny the authority of Christ, making their own interests and ambitions the criterion of good and evil and their own conceit the arbiter of their acts, they walk contrary to the nature of man with results that need no comment in our day.

Aye, flattering fortune, look you never so fair,
Nor never so pleasantly begin to smile,
As though thou wouldest my ruins all repair,
During my life thou shalt not me beguile.
Trust I shall, God, to enter in a while
Thy haven of heaven sure and uniform,
Ever after Thy calm look I for no storm.

                                    Written by More with a coal in the Tower.

UTOPIA consists of two books, the second written abroad in 1515 and the first a year later after Sir Thomas More's return to England. It is in the form of a dialogue between the author and one Raphael Hythloday, an imaginary traveller who has visited strange lands.

The first book is critical. It presents a picture of English social life at the beginning of the sixteenth century, on the eve of the Reformation. Tyranny and corruption are everywhere; but the fundamental evil, in More's opinion, is the misuse of private property. The concentration of riches, especially of land, in the hands of a few powerful corporations, e.g. the Church, had led to the dispossession of the poor, and that in turn to unemployment and want with its resulting wave of crime and the savage laws with which society retaliated.

In the second book we are shown the opposite picture of an ideal society in an imaginary island. Here tyranny and luxury have been abolished, private property is unknown, and manual labour is looked upon as the sole occupation profitable to the state.

Superficially considered, *Utopia* appears to be based upon the *Republic* of Plato and early Christian practices, and it shows the influence of St Augustine's *De Civitate Dei*. The work is, however, no mere adaptation. For not only does More confront all the serious evils of his day, religious, social, and political, but he considers philosophically their remedy, and that in a manner far in advance of the period at which he wrote. He saw, says Jusserand,[1] long before Drummond, the evolutionary truth that the ascent of man has been marked by the triumph of altruistic over egoistic sentiments. And Lord Campbell [2] remarks on More's sensitive imagination, his familiarity with the principles of government, his knowledge of the strings of human action, and the felicity of his expression.

Utopia has been interpreted to condone every kind of political theory directed to the transference of power and wealth to self-styled reformers; and More himself has been accused of inconsistency and the lack of those intellectual qualities which others of his commentators have extolled in him. Thus he has been claimed as a forerunner of Karl Marx on the strength of his advocacy of communal property. It must, however, be remembered that More expressly rejects such a system, answering Raphael's arguments with 'I am of a contrary opinion'; and he believes that the abolition of private property will lead to bloodshed and plunder. He was opposed not to private property as such, but to its misuse.

In the *Supplycacyon of Soulys* he denies the theory that manual labour alone is profitable to society, but this does not prove inconsistency. The Utopians are ideal beings, not inhabitants of our workaday world. Moreover, some years intervened between *Utopia* and the *Supplycacyon*, and he may well have changed his views. Again, it has been pointed out that More attends too much to the material property of his citizens at the expense of their liberty: slavery is an essential feature of Utopia. This slavery, however, is rather of a penal nature, for specified crimes, and not irrevocable. It is administered by wise and beneficent rulers, and preserves the essential dignity of human nature. Christianity has never taught that freedom is the liberty to follow every whim.

Whether or not these arguments are sound, the reader of *Utopia* must bear in mind that the work is a social satire. 'More hovers so perpetually on the confines of jest and earnest, passes so naturally from one to the other, that the reader is in constant suspense whether his jest be serious or his seriousness a jest.' [3] And this is borne out by the

[1] *The English Novel in the Time of Shakespeare*, 1890.
[2] *Lives of the Chancellors*.
[3] J. B. Sherren, *The Reign of Henry VIII*, vol. i (ed. Gairdner, 1884).

statement of Thomas Fuller who records that after *Utopia's* publication certain worthy divines were anxious to send missionaries at once to win so excellent a people for the Faith.

THE DIALOGUE OF COMFORT was written by St Thomas More in 1534 whilst in the Tower awaiting martyrdom. Two Hungarians, Anthony and his nephew Vincent, discuss an impending invasion by the Turks, who here represent the enemies of the Catholic Church. The younger man is fearful lest the persecutions which follow the power of the infidel may cause him to abandon or to compromise his faith. Anthony encourages him to remain steadfast, showing that all the goods of this world, whether of mind or body, and life itself are not worth the loss of eternal life. Tribulation, indeed, is but a means to draw man closer to God. The highest motive and the strongest incentive to perseverance is the Passion of our Lord Jesus Christ; and the final chapter, in which His sufferings are considered, is perhaps the most beautiful and most moving meditation on the Passion in any language.

The dialogue affords us a vision of More's own soul beset with doubts and fears, yet full of tranquillity, gentleness, and his old 'sober mirth' in the dark night before his supreme sacrifice.

JOHN WARRINGTON.

SELECT BIBLIOGRAPHY

1. *Utopia*. (*a*) The Latin text was first published at Louvain in 1516. A second edition appeared at Paris in 1517, and a third at Basle in 1518.

(*b*) The first English translation was that of Ralph Robinson, published in 1551. Reprints followed in 1556, 1597, 1624 and 1639. Of the modern editions the best is that of G. Sampson and A. Guthkelch (1910) which includes the Latin text. A finely printed edition is that issued by the Golden Cockerel Press in 1929.

(*c*) Other translations were those of Gilbert Burnet (1684), edited (with poems) by Sir Sidney Lee (1906); Sir Arthur Cayley (with the history of Richard III and Latin poems) (1808); V. Paget (1909) and G. C. Richards (1923).

(*d*) Critical Studies: K. Kautsky, *Thomas More and his Utopia* (English translation by H. J. Stenning, 1927); R. W. Chambers, *The Saga and Myth of Sir Thomas More* (1927); W. E. Campbell, *More's Utopia and his Social Teaching* (1930).

2. *A Dialogue of Comfort against Tribulation* (1553); English Catholic Library, 1847.

3. LATIN WORKS. *Thomae Mori Lucubrationes* (Basle, 1563); *Thomae Mori Omnia opera* (Louvain, 1565, 1566); *Thomae Mori Opera omnia* (Frankfort, 1689). The following Latin works were published separately: *Luciani compluria opuscula ab Erasmo et Thoma Moro in latinorum linguam traductio* (Paris, 1506; Venice, 1516, 1517; Basle, 1528); *Epigrammata Thomae Mori* (Basle, 1518, 1520); *Thomae Mori Epistola ad Germanium Brixium* (1520); *Eruditissimi viri G. Rossei opus quo repellitur Lutheri calumnias* (1523); *Epistola T. Mori ad Academiam Oxon.* (1663).

4. ENGLISH WORKS. Ed. W. Rastell, 1557, edited in facsimile with a modern version by W. E. Campbell with Introductions by R. W. Chambers and Notes by A. W. Reed, 7 vols., 1931– ; T. E. Bridgett, *The Wisdom and Wit of Blessed Thomas More*, 1892. The following English works appeared separately: *A Merry Jest* (1510); *Life of Johan Picus Erle of Myrandula* (1510), ed. J. M. Rigg (1890); *Supplycacyon of Soulys* (1530); *Dialogue of Images* (1529, 1530); *Confutation of Tyndale's Answer to the Dialogue* (1532, 1533); *Debellacyon of Salem and Bizance* (1533); *Apology of Sir Thomas More* (1533), ed. A. J. Tafts for the Early English Text Society, 1929; *Sir Thomas More's Answer to Tyndale's 'Supper of the Lord'* (1534).

5. LIVES. E. Heywood, *Il Moro*, 1556; T. Stapleton, *Tres Thomae*, Douai, 1588 (English translation by P. E. Hallett, 1928); W. Roper, *The Life, Arraignement, and Death of that Mirrour of all true honour and vertue, Syr Thomas More*, 1626 (ed. E. V. Hitchcock for the Early English Text Society, 1935); Cresaere More, 1631 (ed. J. Hunter, 1828); F. Seebohm, *The Oxford Reformers of 1498*, 1867, 1887; T. E. Bridgett, 1887; W. H. Hutton, 1895; H. Brémond (English translation by H. Child, 1924); E. M. G. Routh, *Sir Thomas More and his Friends*, 1934; R. W. Chambers, 1935; A. Cecil, *A Portrait of Thomas More*, 1936.

See also W. Smyth, *Twelve Merry Jests of the Widow Edith*, 1525 (ed. W. C. Hazlitt: *Shakespeare Jest Books*, vol. iii, 1864); F. Watson, *Vives and the Renaissance Education of Women*, 1912; Elizabeth Rogers, *The Correspondence of Sir Thomas More*, 1947.

CONTENTS

PAGE

TO THE RIGHT HONOURABLE, AND HIS VERY
SINGULAR GOOD MASTER,

MASTER WILLIAM CECIL,

ESQUIRE,

ONE OF THE TWO PRINCIPAL SECRETARIES TO THE KING'S MOST EXCEL-
LENT MAJESTY,

RALPH ROBINSON WISHETH CONTINUANCE OF HEALTH
WITH DAILY INCREASE OF VIRTUE AND HONOUR

UPON a time when tidings came to the city of Corinth that
King Philip, father to Alexander surnamed the Great, was
coming thitherward with an army royal to lay siege to the city,
the Corinthians being forthwith stricken with great fear,
began busily and earnestly to look about them and to fall to
work on all hands. Some to scour and trim up harness, some
to carry stones, some to amend and build higher the walls,
some to rampiere and fortify the bulwarks and fortresses,
some one thing and some another for the defending and
strengthening of the city. The which busy labour and toil of
theirs when Diogenes the philosopher saw, having no profitable
business whereupon to set himself on work (neither any man
required his labour and help as expedient for the commonwealth in that necessity), immediately girded about him his
philosophical cloak, and began to roll and tumble up and
down hither and thither upon the hillside that lieth adjoining
to the city his great barrel or tun, wherein he dwelled, for
other dwelling-place would he have none. This seeing one
of his friends, and not a little musing thereat, came to him:
and, I pray thee, Diogenes, quoth he, why dost thou thus,
or what meanest thou hereby? Forsooth I am tumbling my
tub too, quoth he, because it were no reason that I only
should be idle, where so many be working. In semblable
manner, right honourable sir, though I be, as I am indeed, of

1

much less ability than Diogenes was to do anything that
shall or may be for the advancement and commodity of the
public wealth of my native country, yet I, seeing every sort
and kind of people in their vocation and degree busily occupied about the commonwealth's affairs, and especially
learned men daily putting forth in writing new inventions
and devices to the furtherance of the same, thought it my
bounden duty to God and to my country so to tumble my
tub, I mean so to occupy and exercise myself in bestowing
such spare hours as I, being at the beck and commandment
of others, could conveniently win to myself, that though no
commodity of that my labour and travail to the public weal
should arise, yet it might by this appear that mine endeavour
and goodwill hereunto was not lacking.

To the accomplishment, therefore, and fulfilling of this my
mind and purpose, I took upon me to turn and translate out
of Latin into our English tongue the fruitful and profitable
book which Sir Thomas More, knight, compiled and made of
the new isle Utopia, containing and setting forth the best
state and form of a public weal, a work (as it appeareth)
written almost forty years ago by the said Sir Thomas More
the author thereof.   The which man, forasmuch as he was a
man of late time, yea almost of this our days, and for the
excellent qualities wherewith the great goodness of God had
plentifully endowed him, and for the high place and room
whereunto his prince had most graciously called him, notably
well known, not only among us his countrymen, but also in
foreign countries and nations; therefore I have not much to
speak of him.   This only I say: that it is much to be lamented
of all, and not only of us Englishmen, that a man of so incomparable wit, of so profound knowledge, of so absolute learning,
and of so fine eloquence was yet nevertheless so much blinded,
rather with obstinacy than with ignorance, that he could not
or rather would not see the shining light of God's holy truth
in certain principal points of Christian religion; but did rather
choose to persevere and continue in his wilful and stubborn

obstinacy even to the very death. This I say is a thing much
to be lamented. But letting this matter pass, I return again
to *Utopia*. Which (as I said before) is a work not only for
the matter that it containeth fruitful and profitable, but also
for the writer's eloquent Latin style pleasant and delectable.
Which he that readeth in Latin, as the author himself wrote
it, perfectly understanding the same, doubtless he shall take
great pleasure and delight both in the sweet eloquence of the
writer and also in the witty invention and fine conveyance or
disposition of the matter, but most of all in the good and
wholesome lessons which be there in great plenty and abundance. But now I fear greatly that in this my simple translation, through my rudeness and ignorance in our English
tongue, all the grace and pleasure of the eloquence wherewith
the matter in Latin is finely set forth may seem to be utterly
excluded and lost, and therefore the fruitfulness of the matter
itself much peradventure diminished and appaired.

For who knoweth not, which knoweth anything, that an
eloquent style setteth forth and highly commendeth a mean
matter? Whereas on the other side rude and unlearned
speech defaceth and disgraceth a very good matter. According as I heard once a wise man say, a good tale evil told
were better untold, and an evil tale well told needeth none
other solicitor. This thing I, well pondering and weighing
with myself, and also knowing and acknowledging the barbarous rudeness of my translation, was fully determined never to
have put it forth in print, had it not been for certain friends of
mine, and especially one whom above all other I regarded, a
man of sage and discreet wit and in worldly matters by long
use well experienced, whose name is George Tadlowe, an
honest citizen of London, and in the same city well accepted
and of good reputation, at whose request and instance I first
took upon my weak and feeble shoulders the heavy and
weighty burden of this great enterprise. This man with
divers other, but this man chiefly (for he was able to do more
with me than many other), after that I had once rudely

brought the work to an end, ceased not by all means possible continually to assault me until he had at the last, what by the force of his pithy arguments and strong reasons, and what by his authority so persuaded me, that he caused me to agree and consent to the imprinting hereof. He therefore, as the chief persuader, must take upon him the danger which upon this bold and rash enterprise shall ensue. I, as I suppose, am herein clearly acquit and discharged of all blame. Yet, honourable sir, for the better avoiding of envious and malicious tongues, I (knowing you to be a man not only profoundly learned and well affected towards all such as either can or will take pains in the well bestowing of that poor talent which God hath endued them with, but also for your godly disposition and virtuous qualities not unworthily now placed in authority and called to honour) am the bolder humbly to offer and dedicate unto your good mastership this my simple work. Partly that under the safe conduct of your protection it may the better be defended from the obloquy of them which can say well by nothing that pleaseth not their fond and corrupt judgments, though it be else both fruitful and godly, and partly that by the means of this homely present I may the better renew and revive (which of late, as you know, I have already begun to do) that old acquaintance that was between you and me in the time of our childhood, being then school-fellows together. Not doubting that you for your native goodness and gentleness will accept in good part this poor gift, as an argument or token that mine old goodwill and hearty affection towards you is not, by reason of long tract of time and separation of our bodies, anything at all quailed and diminished, but rather (I assure you) much augmented and increased. This verily is the chief cause that hath encouraged me to be so bold with your mastership, else truly this my poor present is of such simple and mean sort, that it is neither able to recompense the least portion of your great gentleness to me, of my part undeserved, both in the time of our old acquaintance and also now lately again bountifully shewed, neither yet

fit and meet for the very baseness of it to be offered to one so
worthy as you be. But Almighty God (who therefore ever be
thanked) hath advanced you to such fortune and dignity, that
you be of ability to accept thankfully as well a man's goodwill
as his gift. The same God grant you and all yours long and
joyfully to continue in all godliness and prosperity.

THOMAS MORE TO PETER GILES,

sendeth greeting

I AM almost ashamed, right well beloved Peter Giles, to send unto you this book of the Utopian commonwealth wellnigh after a year's space, which I am sure you looked for within a month and a half. And no marvel, for you knew well enough that I was already disburdened of all the labour and study belonging to the invention in this work, and that I had no need at all to trouble my brains about the disposition or conveyance of the matter, and therefore had herein nothing else to do, but only to rehearse those things which you and I together heard master Raphael tell and declare. Wherefore there was no cause why I should study to set forth the matter with eloquence, forasmuch as his talk could not be fine and eloquent, being first not studied for, but sudden and unpremeditate, and then, as you know, of a man better seen in the Greek language than in the Latin tongue. And my writing, the nigher it should approach to his homely, plain, and simple speech, so much the nigher should it go to the truth, which is the only mark whereunto I do and ought to direct all my travail and study herein. I grant and confess, friend Peter, myself discharged of so much labour, having all these things ready done to my hand, that almost there was nothing left for me to do. Else either the invention or the disposition of this matter might have required of a wit neither base neither at all unlearned, both some time and leisure, and also some study. But if it were requisite and necessary that the matter should also have been written eloquently and not alone truly, of a surety that thing could I have performed by no time nor study. But now seeing all these cares, stays, and lets were taken away, wherein else so much labour and study should have been employed, and that there remained no other thing for me to do but only to write plainly the matter as I heard it spoken, that indeed was a thing light and easy to be done.

Howbeit, to the dispatching of this so little business, my other cares and troubles did leave almost less than no leisure. Whiles I do daily bestow my time about law matters, some to plead, some to hear, some as an arbitrator with mine award to determine, some as an umpire or a judge, with my sentence finally to discuss; whiles I go one way to see and visit my friend, another way about mine own private affairs; whiles I spend almost all the day abroad among others, and the residue at home among mine own; I leave to myself, I mean to my book, no time. For when I am come home I must commune with my wife, chat with my children, and talk with my servants. All the which things I reckon and account among business forasmuch as they must of necessity be done, and done must they needs be, unless a man will be stranger in his own house. And in any wise a man must so fashion and order his conditions and so appoint and dispose himself that he be merry, jocund, and pleasant among them whom either nature hath provided or chance hath made or he himself hath chosen to be the fellows and companions of his life, so that with too much gentle behaviour and familiarity he do not mar them, and by too much sufferance of his servants make them his masters. Among these things now rehearsed stealeth away the day, the month, the year. When do I write then? And all this while have I spoken no word of sleep, neither yet of meat, which among a great number doth waste no less time than doth sleep, wherein almost half the lifetime of man creepeth away. I therefore do win and get only that time which I steal from sleep and meat. Which time, because it is very little, and yet somewhat it is, therefore have I once at the last, though it be long first, finished *Utopia*, and have sent it to you, friend Peter, to read and peruse, to the intent that if anything have escaped me you might put me in remembrance of it.

For though in this behalf I do not greatly mistrust myself

(which would God I were somewhat in wit and learning, as I am not all of the worst and dullest memory), yet have I not so great trust and confidence in it that I think nothing could fall out of my mind.   For John Clement, my boy, who, as you know, was there present with us, whom I suffer to be away from no talk wherein may be any profit or goodness (for out of this young-bladed and new-shot-up corn, which hath already begun to spring up both in Latin and Greek learning, I look for plentiful increase at length of goodly ripe grain), he, I say, hath brought me into a great doubt.   For whereas Hythloday (unless my memory fail me) said that the bridge of Amaurote which goeth over the river of Anyder is five hundred paces, that is to say half a mile, in length, my John saith that two hundred of those paces must be plucked away, for that the river containeth there not above three hundred paces in breadth; I pray you heartily call the matter to your remembrance.   For if you agree with him I also will say as you say and confess myself deceived.   But if you cannot remember the thing, then surely I will write as I have done and as mine own remembrance serveth me.   For as I will take good heed that there be in my book nothing false, so if there be anything doubtful I will rather tell a lie than make a lie, because I had rather be good than wily.   Howbeit, this matter may easily be remedied if you will take the pains to ask the question of Raphael himself by word of mouth, if he be now with you, or else by your letters.   Which you must needs do for another doubt also that hath chanced, through whose fault I cannot tell, whether through mine or yours or Raphael's.   For neither we remembered to inquire of him, nor he to tell us, in what part of the new world Utopia is situate.   The which thing I had rather have spent no small sum of money than that it should thus have escaped us, as well for that I am ashamed to be ignorant in what sea that island standeth whereof I wrote so long a treatise, as also because there be with us certain men, and especially one virtuous and godly man and a professor of divinity, who is exceeding desirous to go unto Utopia, not for a vain and curious desire to see news, but to the intent he may further and increase our religion which is there already luckily begun. And that he may the better accomplish and perform this his good intent he is minded to procure that he may be sent thither by the high bishop; yea, and that he himself may be made bishop of Utopia, being nothing scrupulous herein that he must obtain this bishopric with suit. For he counteth that a godly suit which proceedeth not of the desire of honour or lucre, but only of a godly zeal. Wherefore I most earnestly desire you, friend Peter, to talk with Hythloday, if you can, face to face, or else to write your letters to him, and so to work in this matter that in this my book there may neither anything be found which is untrue, neither anything be lacking which is true. And I think verily it shall be well done that you shew unto him the book itself. For if I have missed or failed in any point, or if any fault have escaped me, no man can so well correct and amend it as he can; and yet that can he not do unless he peruse and read over my book written. Moreover, by this means shall you perceive whether he be well willing and content that I should undertake to put this work in writing. For if he be minded to publish and put forth his own labours and travels himself, perchance he would be loath, and so would I also, that in publishing the Utopian weal-public I should prevent him and take from him the flower and grace of the novelty of this his history. Howbeit, to say the very truth, I am not yet fully determined with myself whether I will put forth my book or no. For the natures of men be so diverse, the phantasies of some so wayward, their minds so unkind, their judgments so corrupt, that they which lead a merry and a jocund life, following their own sensual pleasures and carnal lusts, may seem to be in a much better state or case than they that vex and unquiet themselves with cares and study for the putting forth and publishing of something that may be either profit or pleasure to others, which others nevertheless will disdainfully, scornfully, and unkindly accept the same. The most part of all be unlearned, and a great number hath learning in contempt. The rude and barbarous alloweth nothing but that which is very barbarous indeed. If it be one that hath a little smack of learning, he rejecteth as homely gear and common ware whatsoever is not stuffed full of old moth-eaten terms and that be worn out of use. Some there be that have pleasure only in old rusty antiquities, and some only in their own doings. One is so sour, so crabbed, and so unpleasant, that he can away with no mirth nor sport. Another is so narrow between the shoulders, that he can bear no jests nor taunts. Some silly poor souls be so afeard that at every snappish word their nose shall be bitten off, that they stand in no less dread of every quick and sharp word than he that is bitten of a mad dog feareth water. Some be so mutable and wavering, that every hour they be in a new mind, saying one thing sitting and another thing standing. Another sort sitteth upon their ale-benches, and there among their cups they give judgment of the wits of writers, and with great authority they condemn, even as pleaseth them, every writer according to his writing, in most spiteful manner mocking, louting, and flouting them, being themselves in the mean season safe and, as saith the proverb, out of all danger of gunshot. For why, they be so smug and smooth, that they have not so much as one hair of an honest man whereby one may take hold of them. There be, moreover, some so unkind and ungentle, that, though they take great pleasure and delectation in the work, yet for all that they cannot find in their hearts to love the author thereof nor to afford him a good word, being much like uncourteous, unthankful, and churlish guests, which when they have with good and dainty meat well filled their bellies, depart home, giving no thanks to the feast maker. Go your ways now, and make a costly feast at your own charges for guests so dainty mouthed, so divers in taste, and besides that of so unkind and unthankful natures. But nevertheless, friend Peter, do, I pray you, with Hythloday as I willed you before. And as for this matter I shall be at my liberty afterwards to take new advisement. Howbeit, seeing I have taken great pains and labour in writing the matter, if it may stand with his mind and pleasure I will, as touching the edition of publishing of the book, follow the counsel and advice of my friends and specially yours. Thus fare you well, right heartily beloved friend Peter, with your gentle wife, and love me as you have ever done, for I love you better than ever I did.

UTOPIA

THE COMMUNICATION OF
RAPHAEL HYTHLODAY,

Concerning the best state of a commonwealth

THE most victorious and triumphant king of England, Henry
the eighth of that name, in all royal virtues a prince most peer-
less, had of late in controversy with Charles, the right high
and mighty king of Castile, weighty matters and of great
importance; for the debatement and final determination
whereof the king's majesty sent me ambassador into Flanders,
joined in commission with Cuthbert Tunstall, a man doubtless
out of comparison and whom the king's majesty of late, to
the great rejoicing of all men, did prefer to the office of Master
of the Rolls.

But of this man's praises I will say nothing, not because
I do fear that small credence shall be given to the testimony
that cometh out of a friend's mouth; but because his virtue
and learning be greater and of more excellence than that I am
able to praise them, and also in all places so famous and so
perfectly well known that they need not, nor ought not, of
me to be praised, unless I would seem to shew and set forth
the brightness of the sun with a candle, as the proverb saith.

There met us at Bruges (for thus it was before agreed) they
whom their prince had for that matter appointed commis-
sioners, excellent men all. The chief and the head of them
was the Margrave (as they call him) of Bruges, a right honourable man: but the wisest and the best spoken of them was
George Temsice, Provost of Cassel, a man not only by
learning but also by nature of singular eloquence, and in the

laws profoundly learned; but in reasoning and debating of matters, what by his natural wit and what by daily exercise, surely he had few fellows. After that we had once or twice met, and upon certain points or articles could not fully and thoroughly agree, they for a certain space took their leave of us and departed to Brussels, there to know their prince's pleasure.

I, in the meantime (for so my business lay), went straight thence to Antwerp. While I was there abiding, oftentimes among other but which to me was more welcome than any other, did visit me one Peter Giles, a citizen of Antwerp; a man there in his country of honest reputation, and also preferred to high promotions, worthy truly of the highest, for it is hard to say whether the young man be in learning or in honesty more excellent. For he is both of wonderful virtuous conditions, and also singularly well learned, and towards all sorts of people exceeding gentle; but towards his friends so kind-hearted, so loving, so faithful, so trusty, and of so earnest affection, that it were very hard in any place to find a man that with him in all points of friendship may be compared. No man can be more lowly or courteous. No man useth less simulation or dissimulation; in no man is more prudent simplicity. Besides this, he is in his talk and communication so merry and pleasant, yea and that without harm, that, through his gentle entertainment and his sweet and delectable communication, in me was greatly abated and diminished the fervent desire that I had to see my native country, my wife, and my children, whom then I did much long and covet to see, because that at that time I had been more than four months from them.

Upon a certain day when I had heard the divine service in our Lady's Church—which is the fairest, the most gorgeous, and curious church of building in all the city, and also most frequented of people—and, the service being done, was ready to go home to my lodging, I chanced to espy this foresaid Peter talking with a certain stranger, a man well stricken in age, with a black sun-burned face, a long beard, and a cloak cast homely about his shoulders, whom by his favour and apparel forthwith I judged to be a mariner. But the said Peter, seeing me, came unto me and saluted me. And as I was about to answer him: See you this man? saith he (and therewith he pointed to the man that I saw him talking with before). I was minded, quoth he, to bring him straight home to you.

He should have been very welcome to me, said I, for your sake.

Nay, quoth he, for his own sake, if you knew him; for there is no man this day living that can tell you of so many strange and unknown peoples and countries as this man can. And I know well that you be very desirous to hear of such news.

Then I conjectured not far amiss, quoth I, for even at the first sight I judged him to be a mariner.

Nay, quoth he, there ye were greatly deceived. He hath sailed indeed, not as the mariner Palinurus, but as the expert and prudent prince Ulysses; yea, rather as the ancient and sage philosopher Plato. For this same Raphael Hythloday (for this is his name) is very well learned in the Latin tongue, but profound and excellent in the Greek language, wherein he ever bestowed more study than in the Latin, because he had given himself wholly to the study of philosophy; whereof he knew that there is nothing extant in Latin that is to any purpose, saving a few of Seneca's and Cicero's doings. His patrimony that he was born unto he left to his brethren (for he is a Portuguese born), and for the desire that he had to see and know the far countries of the world, he joined himself in company with Amerigo Vespucci, and in the three last voyages of those four that be now in print and abroad in every man's hands, he continued still in his company, saving that in the last voyage he came not home again with him. For he made such means and shift, what by entreatance, and what by importune suit, that he got licence of Master Amerigo (though it were sore against his will) to be one of the twenty-three which in the end of the last voyage were left in the country of Gulike.   He was therefore left behind for his mind sake, as one that took more thought and care for travelling than dying, having customarily in his mouth these sayings: He that hath no grave is covered with the sky, and, The way to heaven out of all places is of like length and distance.   Which fantasy of his (if God had not been his better friend) he had surely bought full dear.   But after the departing of Master Vespucci, when he had travelled through and about many countries with five of his companions Gulikians, at the last by marvellous chance he arrived in Taprobane, from whence he went to Calicut, where he chanced to find certain of his country ships, wherein he returned again into his country, nothing less than looked for.

All this when Peter had told me, I thanked him for his gentle kindness that he had vouchsafed to bring me to the speech of that man whose communication he thought should be to me pleasant and acceptable.   And therewith I turned me to Raphael; and when we had hailed each other and had spoken those common words that be customarily spoken at the first meeting and acquaintance of strangers, we went thence to my house, and there in my garden, upon a bench covered with green turves, we sat down talking together. There he told us how that, after the departing of Vespucci, he and his fellows that tarried behind in Gulike began by little and little, through fair and gentle speech, to win the love and favour of the people of that country, insomuch that within short space they did dwell amongst them not only harmless, but also occupying with them very familiarly.   He told us also that they were in high reputation and favour with a certain great man (whose name and country is now quite out of my remembrance) which of his mere liberality did bear the costs and charges of him and his five companions; and besides that gave them a trusty guide to conduct them in their journey (which by water was in boats and by land in wagons) and to bring them to other princes with very friendly commendations.

Thus after many days' journeys, he said, they found towns and cities and weal-publics, full of people, governed by good and wholesome laws. For under the line equinoctial, and on both sides of the same as far as the sun doth extend his course, lieth, quoth he, great and wide deserts and wildernesses, parched, burned, and dried up with continual and intolerable heat. All things be hideous, terrible, loathsome, and unpleasant to behold; all things out of fashion and comeliness, inhabited with wild beasts and serpents, or at the least wise with people that be no less savage, wild, and noisome than the very beasts themselves be. But a little farther beyond that, all things begin by little and little to wax pleasant; the air soft, temperate, and gentle; the ground covered with green grass; less wildness in the beasts. At the last shall ye come again to people, cities, and towns wherein is continual intercourse and occupying of merchandise and chaffare, not only among themselves and with their borderers, but also with merchants of far countries, both by land and water. There I had occasion, said he, to go to many countries on every side. For there was no ship ready to any voyage or journey, but I and my fellows were into it very gladly received. The ships that they found first were made plain, flat, and broad in the bottom, troughwise. The sails were made of great rushes, or of wickers, and in some places of leather. Afterwards they found ships with ridged keels and sails of canvas, yea, and shortly after, having all things like ours.

The shipmen also very expert and cunning, both in the sea and in the weather. But he said that he found great favour and friendship among them for teaching them the feat and the use of the lodestone, which to them before that time was unknown, and therefore they were wont to be very timorous and fearful upon the sea, nor to venture upon it, but only in the summer time. But now they have such a confidence in that stone, that they fear not stormy winter: in so doing

farther from care than danger.   Insomuch that it is greatly to
be doubted lest that thing, through their own foolish hardiness, shall turn them to evil and harm, which at the first was
supposed should be to them good and commodious.

But what he told us that he saw in every country where he
came, it were very long to declare.   Neither it is my purpose
at this time to make rehearsal thereof.   But peradventure in
another place I will speak of it, chiefly such things as shall be
profitable to be known, as in special be those decrees and
ordinances that he marked to be well and wisely provided and
enacted among such peoples as do live together in a civil policy
and good order.   For of such things did we busily inquire
and demand of him, and he likewise very willingly told us of
the same.   But as for monsters, because they be no news, of
them we were nothing inquisitive.   For nothing is more easy
to be found than be barking Scyllas, ravening Celænos, and
Læstrygons, devourers of people, and suchlike great and
incredible monsters.   But to find citizens ruled by good and
wholesome laws, that is an exceeding rare and hard thing.
But as he marked many fond and foolish laws in those new
found lands, so he rehearsed divers acts and constitutions
whereby these our cities, nations, countries, and kingdoms
may take example to amend their faults, enormities, and
errors.   Whereof in another place (as I said) I will entreat.

Now at this time I am determined to rehearse only that he
told us of the manners, customs, laws, and ordinances of the
Utopians.   But first I will repeat our former communication
by the occasion and (as I might say) the drift whereof he was
brought into the mention of that weal-public.   For, when
Raphael had very prudently touched divers things that be
amiss, some here and some there, yea, very many on both
parts; and again had spoken of such wise laws and prudent
decrees as be established and used, both here among us and
also there among them, as a man so perfect and expert in the
laws and customs of every several country, as though into
what place soever he came guestwise there he had led all his

life: then Peter, much marvelling at the man: Surely, Master Raphael, quoth he, I wonder greatly why you get you not into some king's court. For I am sure there is no prince living, that would not be very glad of you, as a man not only able highly to delight him with your profound learning and this your knowledge of countries and peoples, but also meet to instruct him with examples and help him with counsel. And thus doing, you shall bring yourself in a very good case, and also be of ability to help all your friends and kinsfolk.

As concerning my friends and kinsfolk, quoth he, I pass not greatly for them. For I think I have sufficiently done my part towards them already. For these things that other men do not depart from until they be old and sick, yea, which they be then very loath to leave when they can no longer keep, those very same things did I, being not only lusty and in good health, but also in the flower of my youth, divide among my friends and kinsfolk. Which I think with this my liberality ought to hold them contented, and not to require nor to look that besides this I should for their sakes give myself in bondage unto kings.

Nay, God forbid that, quoth Peter, it is not my mind that you should be in bondage to kings, but as a retainer to them at your pleasure. Which surely I think is the nighest way that you can devise how to bestow your time fruitfully, not only for the private commodity of your friends and for the general profit of all sorts of people, but also for the advancement of yourself to a much wealthier state and condition than you be now in.

To a wealthier condition, quoth Raphael, by that means that my mind standeth clean against? Now I live at liberty after mine own mind and pleasure, which I think very few of these great states and peers of realms can say. Yea, and there be enough of them that sue for great men's friendships, and therefore think it no great hurt if they have not me, nor three or four such other as I am.

Well, I perceive plainly, friend Raphael, quoth I, that you

be desirous neither of riches nor of power; and truly I have in no less reverence and estimation a man of your mind than any of them all that be so high in power and authority.   But you shall do as it becometh you: yea, and according to this wisdom, to this high and free courage of yours, if you can find in your heart so to appoint and dispose yourself that you may apply your wit and diligence to the profit of the weal-public, though it be somewhat to your own pain and hindrance. And this shall you never so well do, nor with so great profit perform, as if you be of some great prince's council, and put into his head (as I doubt not but you will) honest opinions and virtuous persuasions.   For from the prince, as from a perpetual well-spring, cometh among the people the flood of all that is good or evil.   But in you is so perfect learning that, without any experience, and again so great experience that without any learning you may well be any king's counsellor.

You be twice deceived, Master More, quoth he, first in me and again in the thing itself.   For neither is in me the ability that you force upon me, and if it were never so much, yet in disquieting mine own quietness I should nothing further the weal-public.   For, first of all, the most part of all princes have more delight in warlike matters and feats of chivalry (the knowledge whereof I neither have nor desire) than in the good feats of peace, and employ much more study how by right or by wrong to enlarge their dominions, than how well and peaceable to rule and govern that they have already. Moreover, they that be counsellors to kings, every one of them either is of himself so wise indeed that he needeth not, or else he thinketh himself so wise that he will not, allow another man's counsel, saving that they do shamefully and flatteringly give assent to the fond and foolish sayings of certain great men, whose favours, because they be in high authority with their prince, by assentation and flattery they labour to obtain. And verily it is naturally given to all men to esteem their own inventions best.   So both the raven and the ape think their own young ones fairest. Then if a man in such a company, where some disdain and have despite at other men's inventions and some count their own best, if among such men (I say) a man should bring forth anything that he hath read done in times past or that he hath seen done in other places, there the hearers fare as though the whole existimation of their wisdom were in jeopardy to be overthrown, and that ever after they should be counted for very dizzards, unless they could in other men's inventions pick out matter to reprehend and find fault at. If all other poor helps fail, then this is their extreme refuge. These things, say they, pleased our forefathers and ancestors; would God we could be so wise as they were. And, as though they had wittily concluded the matter, and with this answer stopped every man's mouth, they sit down again. As who should say it were a very dangerous matter if a man in any point should be found wiser than his forefathers were. And yet be we content to suffer the best and wittiest of their decrees to lie unexecuted: but if in anything a better order might have been taken than by them was, there we take fast hold, finding therein may faults. Many times have I chanced upon such proud, lewd, overthwart, and wayward judgments, yea, and once in England.

I pray you, sir, quoth I, have you been in our country?

Yea forsooth, quoth he, and there I tarried for the space of four or five months together, not long after the insurrection that the western Englishmen made against their king, which by their own miserable and pitiful slaughter was suppressed and ended. In the mean season I was much bound and beholden to the right reverend father, John Morton, Archbishop and Cardinal of Canterbury, and at that time also Lord Chancellor of England: a man, Master Peter (for Master More knoweth already that I will say), not more honourable for his authority than for his prudence and virtue. He was of a mean stature, and though stricken in age, yet bare he his body upright. In his face did shine such an amiable reverence as was pleasant to behold; gentle in communication, yet earnest, and sage.

He had great delight many times with rough speech to his suitors, to prove, but without harm, what prompt wit and what bold spirit were in every man. In the which, as in a virtue much agreeing with his nature so that therewith were not joined impudency, he took great delectation. And the same person, as apt and meet to have an administration in the weal-public, he did lovingly embrace. In his speech he was fine, eloquent, and pithy. In the law he had profound knowledge, in wit he was incomparable, and in memory wonderful excellent. These qualities, which in him were by nature singular, he by learning and use had made perfect. The king put much trust in his counsel, the weal-public also, in a manner, leaned unto him when I was there. For even in the chief of his youth he was taken from school into the court, and there passed all his time in much trouble and business, being continually tumbled and tossed in the waves of divers misfortunes and adversities. And so by many and great dangers he learned the experience of the world, which so being learned cannot easily be forgotten.

It chanced on a certain day, when I sat at his table, there was also a certain layman cunning in the laws of your realm. Who, I cannot tell whereof taking occasion, began diligently and earnestly to praise that strait and rigorous justice which at that time was there executed upon felons, who, as he said, were for the most part twenty hanged together upon one gallows. And, seeing so few escaped punishment, he said he could not choose but greatly wonder and marvel, how and by what evil luck it should so come to pass that thieves, nevertheless, were in every place so rife and so rank.

Nay, sir, quoth I (for I durst boldly speak my mind before the cardinal), marvel nothing hereat: for this punishment of thieves passeth the limits of justice, and is also very hurtful to the weal-public. For it is too extreme and cruel a punishment for theft, and yet not sufficient to refrain and withhold men from theft. For simple theft is not so great an offence that it ought to be punished with death. Neither there is any punishment so horrible that it can keep them from stealing which have no other craft whereby to get their living. Therefore in this point not you only but also the most part of the world be like evil schoolmasters, which be readier to beat than to teach their scholars. For great and horrible punishments be appointed for thieves, whereas much rather provision should have been made that there were some means whereby they might get their living, so that no man should be driven to this extreme necessity, first to steal and then to die.

Yes, quoth he, this matter is well enough provided for already. There be handicrafts, there is husbandry to get their living by, if they would not willingly be nought.

Nay, quoth I, you shall not escape so: for, first of all, I will speak nothing of them that come home out of the wars maimed and lame, as not long ago out of Blackheath field and a little before that out of the wars in France; such, I say, as put their lives in jeopardy for the weal-public's or the king's sake, and by reason of weakness and lameness be not able to occupy their old crafts, and be too aged to learn new: of them I will speak nothing, forasmuch as wars have their ordinary recourse. But let us consider those things that chance daily before our eyes.

First there is a great number of gentlemen which cannot be content to live idle themselves, like dors, of that which others have laboured for: their tenants, I mean, whom they poll and shave to the quick by raising their rents (for this only point of frugality do they use, men else, through their lavish and prodigal spending, able to bring themselves to very beggary); these gentlemen, I say, do not only live in idleness themselves, but also carry about with them at their tails a great flock or train of idle and loitering serving-men, which never learned any craft whereby to get their livings. These men, as soon as their master is dead, or be sick themselves, be incontinent thrust out of doors. For gentlemen had rather keep idle persons than sick men, and many times the dead man's heir is not able to maintain so great a house

and keep so many serving-men as his father did. Then in the
mean season they that be thus destitute of service either starve
for hunger or manfully play the thieves. For what would you
have them to do? When they have wandered abroad so long,
until they have worn threadbare their apparel and also appaired their health, then gentlemen, because of their pale and
sickly faces and patched coats, will not take them into service.
And husbandmen dare not set them a-work; knowing well
enough that he is nothing meet to do true and faithful service
to a poor man with a spade and a mattock for small wages and
hard fare, which, being daintily and tenderly pampered up
in idleness and pleasure, was wont with a sword and a buckler
by his side to jet through the street with a bragging look and
to think himself too good to be any man's mate. Nay, by
Saint Mary, sir, quoth the lawyer, not so. For this kind of
men must we make most of. For in them, as men of stouter
stomachs, bolder spirits, and manlier courages than handicraftsmen and plowmen be, doth consist the whole power,
strength, and puissance of our army, when we must fight in
battle.

Forsooth, sir, as well you might say, quoth I, that for war's
sake you must cherish thieves; for surely you shall never lack
thieves while you have them. No, nor thieves be not the
most false and faint-hearted soldiers, nor soldiers be not the
cowardliest thieves: so well these two crafts agree together.
But this fault, though it be much used among you, yet is it
not peculiar to you only, but common also almost to all
nations.

Yet France besides this is troubled and infected with a
much sorer plague. The whole realm is filled and besieged
with hired soldiers in peace time (if that be peace) which be
brought in under the same colour and pretence that hath
persuaded you to keep these idle serving-men. For these
wise fools and very archdolts thought the wealth of the whole
country herein to consist, if there were ever in a readiness a
strong and sure garrison, specially of old practised soldiers,

for they put no trust at all in men unexercised. And therefore they must be forced to seek for war, to the end they may ever have practised soldiers and cunning manslayers, lest that (as it is prettily said of Sallust) their hands and their minds, through idleness or lack of exercise, should wax dull. But how pernicious and pestilent a thing it is to maintain such beasts the Frenchmen by their own harms have learned, and the examples of the Romans, Carthaginians, Syrians, and of many other countries do manifestly declare. For not only the empire but also the fields and cities of all these by divers occasions have been overrunned and destroyed of their own armies beforehand had in a readiness. Now how unnecessary a thing this is hereby it may appear, that the French soldiers, which from their youth have been practised and inured in feats of arms, do not crack nor advance themselves to have very often got the upper hand and mastery of your new-made and unpractised soldiers. But in this point I will not use many words, lest perchance I may seem to flatter you. No, nor those same handicraftsmen of yours in cities, nor yet the rude and uplandish plowmen of the country, are not supposed to be greatly afraid of your gentlemen's idle serving-men, unless it be such as be not of body or stature correspondent to their strength and courage, or else whose bold stomachs be discouraged through poverty.

Thus you may see that it is not to be feared lest they should be effeminated if they were brought up in good crafts and laboursome works whereby to get their livings, whose stout and sturdy bodies (for gentlemen vouchsafe to corrupt and spill none but picked and chosen men) now, either by reason of rest and idleness be brought to weakness, or else by too easy and womanly exercises be made feeble and unable to endure hardness. Truly, howsoever the case standeth, this, methinketh, is nothing available to the weal-public, for war sake, which you never have but when you will yourselves, to keep and maintain an innumerable flock of that sort of men that be so troublesome and noyous in peace, whereof you ought to have a thousand times more regard, than of war. But yet this is not only the necessary cause of stealing. There is another, which, as I suppose, is proper and peculiar to you Englishmen alone.

What is that? quoth the cardinal.

Forsooth, my lord, quoth I, your sheep that were wont to be so meek and tame and so small eaters, now, as I hear say, be become so great devourers and so wild, that they eat up and swallow down the very men themselves. They consume, destroy, and devour whole fields, houses, and cities. For look in what parts of the realm doth grow the finest and therefore dearest wool, there noblemen and gentlemen, yea and certain abbots, holy men no doubt, not contenting themselves with the yearly revenues and profits that were wont to grow to their forefathers and predecessors of their lands, nor being content that they live in rest and pleasure nothing profiting, yea, much annoying the weal-public, leave no ground for tillage. They enclose all into pastures; they throw down houses; they pluck down towns, and leave nothing standing but only the church to be made a sheep-house. And as though you lost no small quantity of ground by forests, chases, lands, and parks, those good holy men turn all dwelling places and all glebeland into desolation and wilderness. Therefore that one covetous and insatiable cormorant and very plague of its native country may compass about and enclose many thousand acres of ground together within one pale or hedge, the husbandmen be thrust out of their own, or else either by covin and fraud or by violent oppression they be put besides it, or by wrongs and injuries they be so wearied, that they be compelled to sell all. By one means, therefore, or by other, either by hook or crook, they must needs depart away, poor, silly, wretched souls, men, women, husbands, wives, fatherless children, widows, woeful mothers with their young babes, and their whole household small in substance and much in number, as husbandry requireth many hands. Away they trudge, I say, out of their known and accustomed houses, finding no place to rest in. All their household stuff, which is very little worth though it might well abide the sale, yet being suddenly thrust out they be constrained to sell it for a thing of nought. And when they have wandered abroad till that be spent, what can they then else do but steal, and then justly pardy be hanged, or else go about a-begging? And yet then also they be cast in prison as vagabonds, because they go about and work not, whom no man will set a-work, though they never so willingly proffer themselves thereto.

For one shepherd or herdman is enough to eat up that ground with cattle, to the occupying whereof about husbandry many hands were requisite. And this is also the cause why victuals be now in many places dearer. Yea, besides this the price of wool is so risen, that poor folks, which were wont to work it and make cloth thereof, be now able to buy none at all. And by this means very many be forced to forsake work and to give themselves to idleness. For after that so much ground was enclosed for pasture an infinite multitude of sheep died of the rot, such vengeance God took of their inordinate and insatiable covetousness, sending among the sheep that pestiferous murrain which much more justly should have fallen on the sheepmasters' own heads. And though the number of sheep increase never so fast, yet the price falleth not one mite, because there be so few sellers; for they be almost all come into a few rich men's hands, whom no need forceth to sell before they lust, and they lust not before they may sell as dear as they lust.

Now the same cause bringeth in like dearth of the other kinds of cattle, yea, and that so much the more because that after farms plucked down and husbandry decayed there is no man that passeth for the breeding of young store. For these rich men bring not up the young ones of great cattle as they do lambs. But first they buy them abroad very cheap, and afterward, when they be fatted in their pastures, they sell them again exceeding dear. And therefore (as I suppose) the whole incommodity hereof is not yet felt; for yet they make dearth only in those places where they sell. But when they shall fetch them away from thence where they be bred faster than they can be brought up, then shall there also be felt great dearth, store beginning there to fail where the ware is bought. Thus the unreasonable covetousness of a few hath turned that thing to the utter undoing of your island, in the which thing the chief felicity of your realm did consist. For this great dearth of victuals causeth men to keep as little houses and as small hospitality as they possibly may, and to put away their servants; whither, I pray you, but a-begging, or else (which these gentle bloods and stout stomachs will sooner set their minds unto) a-stealing?

Now to amend the matter, to this wretched beggary and miserable poverty is joined great wantonness, importunate superfluity, and excessive riot. For not only gentlemen's servants, but also handicraftsmen, yea, and almost the plowmen of the country, with all other sorts of people, use much strange and proud newfangleness in their apparel, and too much prodigal riot and sumptuous fare at their table. Now bawds, queans, whores, harlots, strumpets, brothel-houses, stews; and yet another stews, wine-taverns, ale-houses, and tippling houses, with so many naughty, lewd, and unlawful games, as dice, cards, tables, tennis, bowls, quoits, do not all these send the haunters of them straight a-stealing, when their money is gone? Cast out these pernicious abominations; make a law that they which plucked down farms and towns of husbandry shall re-edify them, or else yield and uprender the possession thereof to such as will go to the cost of building them anew. Suffer not these rich men to buy up all to engross and forestall, and with their monopoly to keep the market alone as please them. Let not so many be brought up in idleness; let husbandry and tillage be restored; let clothworking be renewed, that there may be honest labours for this idle sort to pass their time in profitably, which hitherto either poverty hath caused to be thieves, or else now be either vagabonds or idle serving men, and shortly will be thieves.

Doubtless unless you find a remedy for these enormities you shall in vain advance yourselves of executing justice upon felons. For this justice is more beautiful in appearance and more flourishing to the shew than either just or profitable. For by suffering your youth wantonly and viciously to be brought up, and to be infected, even from their tender age, by little and little with vice, then, a God's name, to be punished when they commit the same faults after being come to man's state, which from their youth they were ever like to do; in this point, I pray you, what other thing do you than make thieves and then punish them?

Now as I was thus speaking, the lawyer began to make himself ready to answer, and was determined with himself to use the common fashion and trade of disputers, which be more diligent in rehearsing than answering, as thinking the memory worthy of the chief praise. Indeed, sir, quoth he, you have said well, being but a stranger and one that might rather hear something of these matters, than have any exact or perfect knowledge of the same, as I will incontinent by open proof make manifest and plain. For first I will rehearse in order all that you have said; then I will declare wherein you be deceived through lack of knowledge in all our fashions, manners, and customs; and last of all I will answer your arguments, and confute them every one. First therefore I will begin where I promised. Four things you seemed to me——

Hold your peace, quoth the cardinal, for it appeareth that you will make no short answer, which make such a beginning. Wherefore at this time you shall not take the pains to make your answer, but keep it to your next meeting, which I would be right glad that it might be even to-morrow next, unless either you or master Raphael have any earnest let. But now, Master Raphael, I would very gladly hear of you, why you think theft not worthy to be punished with death, or what other punishment you can devise more expedient to the

weal-public.   For I am sure you are not of that mind, that you
would have theft escape unpunished.   For if now the extreme
punishment of death cannot cause them to leave stealing,
then, if ruffians and robbers should be sure of their lives,
what violence, what fear, were able to hold their hands from
robbing which would take the mitigation of the punishment
as a very provocation to the mischief?

Surely, my lord, quoth I, I think it not right nor justice
that the loss of money should cause the loss of man's life.
For mine opinion is, that all the goods in the world are not
able to countervail man's life.   But if they would thus say,
that the breaking of justice and the transgression of the laws is
recompensed with this punishment, and not the loss of the
money, then why may not this extreme and rigorous justice
well be called plain injury?   For so cruel governance, so strict
rules and unmerciful laws be not allowable, that if a small
offence be committed, by and by the sword should be drawn.
Nor so stoical ordinances are to be borne withal, as to count all
offences of such equality, that the killing of a man or the
taking of his money from him were both a matter, and the one
no more heinous offence than the other, between the which
two, if we have any respect to equity, no similitude or equality
consisteth.   God commandeth us that we shall not kill.
And be we then so hasty to kill a man for taking a little
money?   And if any man would understand killing by this
commandment of God to be forbidden after no larger wise
than man's constitutions define killing to be lawful, then why
may it not likewise by man's constitutions be determined after
what sort whoredom, fornication, and perjury may be lawful?
For whereas, by the permission of God, no man hath power to
kill neither himself nor yet any other man, then, if a law made
by the consent of men concerning slaughter of men ought to
be of such strength, force, and virtue, that they which contrary to the commandment of God have killed those whom
this constitution of man commanded to be killed, be clean
quit and exempt out of the bonds and danger of God's

commandment, shall it not then, by this reason follow that
the power of God's commandment shall extend no further
than man's law doth define and permit? And so shall it come
to pass, that in like manner man's constitutions in all things
shall determine how far the observation of all God's commandments shall extend. To be short, Moses' law, though
it were ungentle and sharp, as a law that was given to bondmen, yea, and them very obstinate, stubborn, and stiff-necked,
yet it punished theft by the purse, and not with death. And
let us not think that God in the new law of clemency and
mercy, under the which He ruleth us with fatherly gentleness,
as His dear children, hath given us greater scope and licence
to the execution of cruelty one upon another.

Now ye have heard the reasons whereby I am persuaded
that this punishment is unlawful. Furthermore, I think
there is nobody that knoweth not how unreasonable, yea, how
pernicious a thing it is to the weal-public that a thief and an
homicide or murderer should suffer equal and like punishment. For the thief, seeing that man that is condemned for
theft in no less jeopardy nor judged to no less punishment
than him that is convict of manslaughter, through this cogi-
tation only he is strongly and forcibly provoked, and in a
manner constrained, to kill him whom else he would have but
robbed. For the murder being once done, he is in less fear
and in more hope that the deed shall not be betrayed or
known, seeing the party is now dead and rid out of the way,
which only might have uttered and disclosed it. But if he
chance to be taken and descried, yet he is in no more danger
and jeopardy than if he had committed but single felony.
Therefore while we go about with such cruelty to make
thieves afraid, we provoke them to kill good men.

Now as touching this question, what punishment were
more commodious and better, that truly in my judgment is
easier to be found than what punishment might be worse.
For why should we doubt that to be a good and a profitable
way for the punishment of offenders, which we know did in

times past so long please the Romans, men in the administration of a weal-public most expert, politic, and cunning? Such as among them were convict of great and heinous trespasses, them they condemned into stone quarries, and into mines to dig metal, there to be kept in chains all the days of their life. But as concerning this matter, I allow the ordinance of no nation so well as that which I saw, while I travelled abroad about the world, used in Persia among the people that commonly be called the Polylerites, whose land is both large and ample and also well and wittily governed, and the people in all conditions free and ruled by their own laws, saving that they pay a yearly tribute to the great king of Persia. But because they be far from the sea, compassed and enclosed almost round about with high mountains, and do content themselves with the fruits of their own land, which is of itself very fertile and fruitful, for this cause neither they go to other countries, nor other come to them. And according to the old custom of the land they desire not to enlarge the bounds of their dominions; and those that they have by reason of the high hills be easily defended, and the tribute which they pay to their chief lord and king setteth them quit and free from warfare. Thus their life is commodious rather than gallant, and may better be called happy or wealthy than notable or famous. For they be not known as much as by name, I suppose, saving only to their next neighbours and borderers.

They that in this land be attainted and convict of felony, make restitution of that which they stole to the right owner, and not (as they do in other lands) to the king, whom they think to have no more right to the thief-stolen thing than the thief himself hath. But if the thing be lost or made away, then the value of it is paid of the goods of such offenders, which else remaineth all whole to their wives and children. And they themselves be condemned to be common labourers; and, unless the theft be very heinous, they be neither locked in prison nor fettered in gyves, but be untied and go at large,

labouring in the common works.   They that refuse labour, or
go slowly and slackly to their work, be not only tied in chains,
but also pricked forward with stripes; but being diligent
about their work they live without check or rebuke.   Every
night they be called in by name, and be locked in their
chambers.   Beside their daily labour, their life is nothing
hard or incommodious.   Their fare is indifferent good, borne
at the charges of the weal-public, because they be common
servants to the commonwealth.   But their charges in all
places of the land are not borne alike, for in some parts that
which is bestowed upon them is gathered of alms.   And
though that way be uncertain, yet the people be so full of
mercy and pity, that none is found more profitable or plentiful.   In some places certain lands be appointed hereunto, of
the revenues whereof they be maintained; and in some places
every man giveth a certain tribute for the same use and
purpose.

Again, in some parts of the land these serving-men (for so
be these damned persons called) do no common work, but as
every private man needeth labourers, so he cometh into the
market-place and there hireth some of them for meat and
drink and a certain limited wages by the day, somewhat
cheaper than he should hire a free man.   It is also lawful for
them to chastise the sloth of these serving-men with stripes.
By this means they never lack work, and besides the gaining
of their meat and drink, every one of them bringeth daily
something into the common treasury.   All and every one of
them be apparelled in one colour.   Their heads be not polled
or shaven, but rounded a little above the ears, and the tip of
the one ear is cut off.   Every one of them may take meat and
drink of their friends, and also a coat of their own colour; but
to receive money is death, as well to the giver as to the
receiver.   And no less jeopardy it is for a free man to receive
money of a serving-man for any manner of cause, and likewise
for serving men to touch weapons.   The serving-men of every
several shire be distinct and known from other by their several

and distinct badges which to cast away is death, as it is also
to be seen out of the precinct of their own shire, or to talk
with a serving-man of another shire.   And it is no less danger
to them for to intend to run away than to do it indeed.   Yea,
and to conceal such an enterprise in a serving-man it is death,
in a free man servitude.   Of the contrary part, to him that
openeth and uttereth such counsels be decreed large gifts,
to a free man a great sum of money, to a serving-man freedom,
and, to them both, forgiveness and pardon of that they were of
counsel in that pretence.   So that it can never be so good for
them to go forward in their evil purpose as, by repentance, to
turn back.

This is the law and order in this behalf, as I have shewed
you.   Wherein what humanity is used, how far it is from
cruelty, and how commodious it is, you do plainly perceive,
forasmuch as the end of their wrath and punishment intendeth
nothing else but the destruction of vices and saving of men,
with so using and ordering them that they cannot choose but
be good, and what harm soever they did before, in the residue
of their life to make amends for the same.   Moreover it is so
little feared that they should turn again to their vicious
conditions, that wayfaring men will for their safeguard choose
them to their guides before any other, in every shire changing
and taking new; for if they would commit robbery they have
nothing about them meet for that purpose.   They may touch
no weapons; money found about them should betray the
robbery.   They should be no sooner taken with the manner,
but forthwith they should be punished.   Neither they can
have any hope at all to scape away by fleeing.   For how
should a man that in no part of his apparel is like other men
fly privily and unknown, unless he would run away naked?
Howbeit, so also fleeing he should be descried by the rounding
of his head and his ear mark.   But it is a thing to be doubted
that they will lay their heads together and conspire against the
weal-public.   No, no, I warrant you.   For the serving-men
of one shire alone could never hope to bring to pass such an

enterprise without soliciting, enticing, and alluring the serving-men of many other shires to take their parts. Which thing is to them so impossible, that they may not as much as speak or talk together or salute one another. No, it is not to be thought that they would make their own countrymen and companions of their counsel in such a matter, which they know well should be jeopardy to the concealer thereof and great commodity and goodness to the opener and detector of the same. Whereas, on the other part, there is none of them all hopeless or in despair to recover again his former state of freedom by humble obedience, by patient suffering, and by giving good tokens and likelihood of himself, that he will ever after that live like a true and an honest man. For every year divers of them be restored to their freedom through the commendation of their patience.

When I had thus spoken, saying moreover that I could see no cause why this order might not be had in England with much more profit than the justice which the lawyer so highly praised, Nay, quoth the lawyer, this could never be so stablished in England but that it must needs bring the weal-public into great jeopardy and hazard. And, as he was thus saying, he shaked his head and made a wry mouth, and so he held his peace. And all that were there present with one assent agreed to his saying.

Well, quoth the cardinal, yet it were hard to judge without a proof whether this order would do well here or no. But when the sentence of death is given, if then the king should command execution to be deferred and spared, and would prove this order and fashion, taking away the privileges of all sanctuaries, if then the proof should declare the thing to be good and profitable, then it were well done that it were stablished; else the condemned and reprieved persons may as well and as justly be put to death after this proof as when they were first cast. Neither any jeopardy can in the mean space grow hereof. Yea, and methinketh that these vaga-bonds may very well be ordered after the same fashion, against whom we have hitherto made so many laws and so little prevailed.

When the cardinal had thus said, then every man gave great praise to my sayings, which a little before they had disallowed. But most of all was esteemed that which was spoken of vagabonds, because it was the cardinal's own addition. I cannot tell whether it were best to rehearse the communication that followed, for it was not very sad; but yet you shall hear it, for there was no evil in it, and partly it pertained to the matter before said.

There chanced to stand by a certain jesting parasite or scoffer, which would seem to resemble and counterfeit the fool. But he did in such wise counterfeit, that he was almost the very same indeed that he laboured to represent. He so studied with words and sayings brought forth so out of time and place to make sport and move laughter, that he himself was oftener laughed at than his jests were. Yet the foolish fellow brought out now and then such indifferent and reasonable stuff, that he made the proverb true, which saith: He that shooteth oft, at the last shall hit the mark. So that when one of the company said that through my communication a good order was found for thieves, and that the cardinal also had well provided for vagabonds, so that only remained some good provision to be made for them that through sickness and age were fallen into poverty and were become so impotent and unwieldy that they were not able to work for their living: Tush, quoth he, let me alone with them; you shall see me do well enough with them. For I had rather than any good that this kind of people were driven somewhere out of my sight, they have so sore troubled me many times and oft when they have with their lamentable tears begged money of me: and yet they could never to my mind so tune their song that thereby they ever got of me one farthing. For evermore the one of these two chanced: either that I would not, or else that I could not because I had it not. Therefore now they be waxed wise; for when they see me go by, because they will not lose their labour, they let me pass and say not one word to me. So they look for nothing of me, no, in good sooth, no more than if I were a priest or a monk. But I will make a law, that all these beggars shall be distributed and bestowed into houses of religion. The men shall be made lay brethren, as they call them, and the women nuns.

Hereat the cardinal smiled, and allowed it in jest, yea, and all the residue in good earnest. But a certain friar, graduate in divinity, took such pleasure and delight in this jest of priests and monks, that he also being else a man of grisly and stern gravity, began merrily and wantonly to jest and taunt. Nay, quoth he, you shall not so be rid and dispatched of beggars unless you make some provision also for us friars.

Why, quoth the jester, that is done already, for my lord himself set a very good order for you when he decreed that vagabonds should be kept strait, and set to work; for you be the greatest and veriest vagabonds that be.

This jest also, when they saw the cardinal not disprove it, every man took it gladly, saving only the friar. For he (and that no marvel) being thus touched on the quick, and hit on the gall, so fret, so fumed, and chafed at it, and was in such a rage, that he could not refrain himself from chiding, scolding, railing, and reviling. He called the fellow ribald, villain, javel, backbiter, slanderer, and the child of perdition, citing therewith terrible threatenings out of Holy Scripture.

Then the jesting scoffer began to play the scoffer indeed, and verily he was good at that, for he could play a part in that play, no man better. Patient yourself, good master friar, quoth he, and be not angry, for Scripture saith: In your patience you shall save your souls.

Then the friar (for I will rehearse his own very words): No, gallows wretch, I am not angry, quoth he, or at the least wise I do not sin; for the Psalmist saith, Be you angry, and sin not. Then the cardinal spake gently to the friar, and desired him to quiet himself.

No, my lord, quoth he, I speak not but of a good zeal as I

ought, for holy men had a good zeal.   Wherefore it is said:
The zeal of thy house hath eaten me.   And it is sung in the
church.   The scorners of Elisha, while he went up into the
house of God, felt the zeal of the bald, as peradventure this
scorning villain ribald shall feel.

You do it, quoth the cardinal, perchance of a good mind
and affection; but methinketh you should do, I cannot tell
whether more holily, certes more wisely, if you would not
set your wit to a fool's wit, and with a fool take in hand a
foolish contention.

No, forsooth, my lord, quoth he, I should not do more
wisely.   For Solomon the wise saith: Answer a fool according to his folly, like as I do now, and do shew him the pit
that he shall fall into if he take not heed.   For if many
scorners of Elisha, which was but one bald man, felt the zeal
of the bald, how much more shall one scorner of many friars
feel, among whom be many bald men?   And we have also
the pope's bulls, whereby all that mock and scorn us be
excommunicate, suspended, and accursed.

The cardinal, seeing that none end would be made, sent
away the jester by a privy beck, and turned the communication to another matter.   Shortly after, when he was risen
from the table, he went to hear his suitors, and so dismissed us.

Look, Master More, with how long and tedious a tale I have
kept you, which surely I would have been ashamed to have
done, but that you so earnestly desired me, and did after such
a sort give ear unto it as though you would not that any parcel
of that communication should be left out.   Which though I
have done somewhat briefly, yet could I not choose but
rehearse it for the judgment of them which, when they had
disproved and disallowed my sayings, yet incontinent, hearing
the cardinal allow them, did themselves also approve the
same, so impudently flattering him, that they were nothing
ashamed to admit, yea, almost in good earnest, his jester's
foolish inventions, because that he himself by smiling at them
did seem not to disprove them.   So that hereby you may right

well perceive how little the courtiers would regard and esteem me and my sayings.

I ensure you, Master Raphael, quoth I, I took great delectation in hearing you; all things that you said were spoken so wittily and so pleasantly. And methought myself to be in the meantime not only at home in my country, but also through the pleasant remembrance of the cardinal, in whose house I was brought up of a child, to wax a child again. And, friend Raphael, though I did bear very great love towards you before, yet seeing you do so earnestly favour this man, you will not believe how much my love towards you is now increased. But yet, all this notwithstanding, I can by no means change my mind, but that I must needs believe that you, if you be disposed and can find in your heart to follow some prince's court, shall with your good counsels greatly help and further the commonwealth. Wherefore there is nothing more appertaining to your duty, that is to say to the duty of a good man. For whereas your Plato judgeth that wealpublics shall by this means attain perfect felicity, either if philosophers be kings, or else if kings give themselves to the study of philosophy, how far, I pray you, shall commonwealths then be from this felicity, if philosophers will vouchsafe to instruct kings with their good counsel?

They be not so unkind, quoth he, but they would gladly do it, yea, many have done it already in books that they have put forth, if kings and princes would be willing and ready to follow good counsel. But Plato doubtless did well foresee, unless kings themselves would apply their minds to the study of philosophy, that else they would never thoroughly allow the counsel of philosophers, being themselves before, even from their tender age, infected and corrupt with perverse and evil opinions. Which thing Plato himself proved true in King Dionysius. If I should propose to any king wholesome decrees, doing my endeavour to pluck out of his mind the pernicious original causes of vice and naughtiness, think you not that I should forthwith either be driven away or else made

a laughing-stock? Well, suppose I were with the French
king, and there sitting in his council while in that most secret
consultation, the king himself there being present in his own
person, they beat their brains, and search the very bottoms
of their wits to discuss by what craft and means the king may
still keep Milan and draw to him again fugitive Naples; and
then how to conquer the Venetians, and how to bring under
his jurisdiction all Italy; then how to win the dominion of
Flanders, Brabant, and of all Burgundy with divers other
lands whose kingdoms he hath long ago in mind and purpose
invaded.   Here while one counselleth to conclude a league
of peace with the Venetians, so long to endure as shall be
thought meet and expedient for their purpose, and to make
them also of their counsel, yea, and besides that to give them
part of the prey which afterward, when they have brought
their purpose about after their own minds, they may require
and claim again, another thinketh best to hire the Germans.
Another would have the favour of the Swiss won with money.
Another's advice is to appease the puissant power of the
emperor's majesty with gold as with a most pleasant and
acceptable sacrifice.   While another giveth counsel to make
peace with the king of Aragon, and to restore unto him his
own kingdom of Navarre as a full assurance of peace. Another
cometh in with his five eggs, and adviseth to hook in the
king of Castile with some hope of affinity or alliance, and to
bring to their part certain peers of his court for great pensions.
While they all stay at the chiefest doubt of all, what to do in
the mean time with England; and yet agree all in this to make
peace with the Englishmen, and with most sure and strong
bonds to bind that weak and feeble friendship, so that they
must be called friends, and had in suspicion as enemies;
and that therefore the Scots must be had in a readiness,
as it were in a standing, ready at all occasions, in aunters
the Englishmen should stir never so little, incontinent to
set upon them.   And moreover privily and secretly (for
openly it may not be done by the truce that is taken), privily,

therefore, I say, to make much of some peer of England that is banished his country, which must claim title to the crown of the realm and affirm himself just inheritor thereof, that by this subtle means they may hold to them the king, in whom else they have but small trust and affiance. Here, I say, where so great and high matters be in consultation, where so many noble and wise men counsel their king only to war, here if I, silly man, should rise up and will them to turn over the leaf, and learn a new lesson, saying that my counsel is not to meddle with Italy but to tarry still at home, and that the kingdom of France alone is almost greater than that it may well be governed of one man, so that the king should not need to study how to get more; and then should propose unto them the decrees of the people that be called the Achorians, which be situate over against the island of Utopia on the southeast side.

These Achorians once made war in their king's quarrel for to get him another kingdom which he laid claim unto and advanced himself right inheritor to the crown thereof by the title of an old alliance. At the last, when they had got it, and saw that they had even as much vexation and trouble in keeping it as they had in getting it, and that either their new conquered subjects by sundry occasions were making daily insurrections to rebel against them, or else that other countries were continually with divers inroads and foragings invading them, so that they were ever fighting either for them or against them, and never could break up their camps: seeing themselves in the mean season pilled and impoverished, their money carried out of the realm, their own men killed to maintain the glory of another nation; when they had no war, peace nothing better than war, by reason that their people in war had so inured themselves to corrupt and wicked manners, that they had taken a delight and pleasure in robbing and stealing; that through manslaughter they had gathered boldness to mischief; that their laws were had in contempt, and nothing set by or regarded; that their king, being troubled with the charge and governance of two kingdoms, could not nor was not able perfectly to discharge his office towards them both: seeing again, that all these evils and troubles were endless, at the last [they] laid their heads together, and like faithful and loving subjects gave to their king free choice and liberty to keep still the one of these two kingdoms, whether he would, alleging that he was not able to keep both, and that they were more than might well be governed of half a king, forasmuch as no man would be content to take him for his muleteer that keepeth another man's mules besides his. So this good prince was constrained to be content with his old kingdom and to give over the new to one of his friends. Who shortly after was violently driven out.

Furthermore if I should declare unto them that all this busy preparance to war, whereby so many nations for his sake should be brought into a troublesome hurly-burly, when all his coffers were emptied, his treasures wasted, and his people destroyed, should at the length through some mischance be in vain and to none effect, and that therefore it were best for him to content himself with his own kingdom of France as his forefathers and predecessors did before him, to make much of it, to enrich it, and to make it as flourishing as he could, to endeavour himself to love his subjects and again to be beloved of them, willingly to live with them, peaceably to govern them, and with other kingdoms not to meddle, seeing that which he hath already is even enough for him, yea, and more than he can well turn him to: this mine advice, Master More, how think you it would be heard and taken?

So God help me, not very thankfully, quoth I.

Well, let us proceed then, quoth he. Suppose that some king and his council were together whetting their wits and devising what subtle craft they might invent to enrich the king with great treasures of money. First one counselleth to raise and enhance the valuation of money when the king must pay any, and again to call down the value of coin to less than it is worth when he must receive or gather any. For thus great sums shall be paid with a little money, and where little is due much shall be received. Another counselleth to feign war, that when under this colour and pretence the king hath gathered great abundance of money, he may, when it shall please him, make peace with great solemnity and holy ceremonies, to blind the eyes of the poor community as taking pity and compassion forsooth upon man's blood, like a loving and a merciful prince. Another putteth the king in remembrance of certain old and moth-eaten laws that of long time have not been put in execution, which because no man can remember that they were made, every man hath transgressed. The fines of these laws he counselleth the king to require, for there is no way so profitable nor more honourable as the which hath a shew and colour of justice. Another adviseth him to forbid many things under great penalties and fines, specially such things as is for the people's profit not be used, and afterward to dispense for money with them, which by this prohibition sustain loss and damage. For by this means the favour of the people is won, and profit riseth two ways. First by taking forfeits of them whom covetousness of gains hath brought in danger of this statute, and also by selling privileges and licences, which the better that the prince is, forsooth the dearer he selleth them, as one that is loath to grant to any private person anything that is against the profit of his people, and therefore may sell none but at an exceeding dear price.

Another giveth the king counsel to endanger unto his grace the judges of the realm, that he may have them ever on his side, and that they may in every matter dispute and reason for the king's right; yea, and further to call them into his palace and to require them there to argue and discuss his matters in his own presence. So there shall be no matter of his so openly wrong and unjust wherein one or other of them, either because he will have something to allege and object, or that he is ashamed to say that which is said already, or else to pick a thank with his prince, will not find some hole open to set a snare in, wherewith to take the contrary part in a trip. Thus while the judges cannot agree amongst themselves, reasoning and arguing of that which is plain enough and bringing the manifest truth in doubt, in the mean season the king may take a fit occasion to understand the law as shall most make for his advantage, whereunto all other, for shame or for fear, will agree. Then the judges may be bold to pronounce on the king's side, for he that giveth sentence for the king cannot be without a good excuse. For it shall be sufficient for him to have equity on his part, or the bare words of the law, or a writhen and wrested understanding of the same, or else (which with good and just judges is of greater force than all laws be) the king's indisputable prerogative.

To conclude, all the counsellors agree and consent together with the rich Crassus, that no abundance of gold can be sufficient for a prince which must keep and maintain an army. Furthermore that a king, though he would, can do nothing unjustly; for all that all men have, yea, also the men themselves, be all his. And that every man hath so much of his own as the king's gentleness hath not taken from him. And that it shall be most for the king's advantage that his subjects have very little or nothing in their possession, as whose safeguard doth herein consist, that his people do not wax wanton and wealthy through riches and liberty, because where these things be, there men be not wont patiently to obey hard, unjust, and unlawful commandments; whereas, on the other part, need and poverty doth hold down and keep under stout courages, and maketh them patient perforce, taking from them bold and rebelling stomachs.

Here again, if I should rise up and boldly affirm that all these counsels be to the king dishonour and reproach, whose honour and safety is more and rather supported and upholden by the wealth and riches of his people than by his own treasures; and if I should declare that the commonalty chooseth their king for their own sake, and not for his sake, to the intent that through his labour and study they might all

live wealthily safe from wrongs and injuries; and that therefore the king ought to take more care for the wealth of his
people than for his own wealth, even as the office and duty
of a shepherd is, in that he is a shepherd, to feed his sheep
rather than himself.

For as touching this, that they think the defence and
maintenance of peace to consist in the poverty of the people,
the thing itself sheweth that they be far out of the way.
For where shall a man find more wrangling, quarrelling,
brawling, and chiding than among beggars? Who be more
desirous of new mutations and alterations, than they that
be not content with the present state of their life? Or,
finally, who be bolder stomached to bring all in a hurly-
burly (thereby trusting to get some windfall) than they that
have now nothing to lose? And if any king were so smally
regarded and so lightly esteemed, yea, so behated of his
subjects, that other ways he could not keep them in awe, but
only by open wrongs, by polling and shaving and by bringing
them to beggary, surely it were better for him to forsake his
kingdom than to hold it by this means, whereby though the
name of a king be kept, yet the majesty is lost. For it is
against the dignity of a king to have rule over beggars, but
rather over rich and wealthy men. Of this mind was the
hardy and courageous Fabricius when he said that he had
rather be a ruler of rich men than be rich himself. And,
verily, one man to live in pleasure and wealth while all others
weep and smart for it, that is the part, not of a king, but of a
jailer. To be short, as he is a foolish physician that cannot
cure his patient's disease unless he cast him in another sickness,
so he that cannot amend the lives of his subjects but by taking
from them the wealth and commodity of life, he must needs
grant that he knoweth not the feat how to govern men. But
let him rather amend his own life, renounce unhonest pleasures, and forsake pride; for these be the chief vices that cause
him to run in the contempt or hatred of his people. Let him
live of his own, hurting no man. Let him do cost not above

his power. Let him restrain wickedness. Let him prevent vices, and take away the occasions of offences by well ordering his subjects, and not by suffering wickedness to increase, afterwards to be punished. Let him not be too hasty in calling again laws which a custom hath abrogated, specially such as have been long forgotten and never lacked nor needed. And let him never, under the cloak and pretence of transgression, take such fines and forfeits as no judge will suffer a private person to take as unjust and full of guile.

Here if I should bring forth before them the law of the Macarians, which be not far distant from Utopia, whose king the day of his coronation is bound by a solemn oath that he shall never at any time have in his treasury above a thousand pound of gold or silver. They say a very good king, which took more care for the wealth and commodity of his country than for the enriching of himself, made this law to be a stop and a bar to kings from heaping and hoarding up so much money as might impoverish their people. For he foresaw that this sum of treasure would suffice to support the king in battle against his own people if they should chance to rebel, and also to maintain his wars against the invasions of his foreign enemies. Again, he perceived the same stock of money to be too little and insufficient to encourage and enable him wrongfully to take away other men's goods, which was the chief cause why the law was made. Another cause was this: He thought that by this provision his people should not lack money wherewith to maintain their daily occupying and chaffare. And seeing the king could not choose but lay out and bestow all that came in above the prescript sum of his stock, he thought he would seek no occasions to do his subjects injury. Such a king shall be feared of evil men and loved of good men. These, and such other information, if I should use among men wholly inclined and given to the contrary part, how deaf hearers think you should I have?

Deaf hearers doubtless, quoth I, and in good faith no marvel. And to be plain with you, truly I cannot allow that

such communication shall be used, or such counsel given, as
you be sure shall never be regarded nor received. For how
can so strange information be profitable, or how can they be
beaten into their heads whose minds be already prevented
with clean contrary persuasions? This school philosophy is
not unpleasant among friends in familiar communication, but
in the councils of kings, where great matters be debated and
reasoned with great authority, these things have no place.

That is it which I meant, quoth he, when I said philosophy
had no place among kings.

Indeed, quoth I, this school philosophy hath not, which
thinketh all things meet for every place. But there is another
philosophy more civil, which knoweth, as ye would say, her
own stage, and thereafter, ordering and behaving herself in
the play that she hath in hand, playeth her part accordingly
with comeliness, uttering nothing out of due order and fashion.
And this is the philosophy that you must use. Or else whiles
a comedy of Plautus is playing, and the vile bondmen scoffing
and trifling among themselves, if you should suddenly come
upon the stage in a philosopher's apparel, and rehearse out of
Octavia the place wherein Seneca disputeth with Nero, had it
not been better for you to have played the dumb person,
than, by rehearsing that which served neither for the time nor
place, to have made such a tragical comedy or gallimaufry?
For by bringing in other stuff that nothing appertaineth
to the present matter, you must needs mar and pervert the
play that is in hand, though the stuff that you bring be much
better. What part soever you have taken upon you, play that
as well as you can and make the best of it. And do not therefore disturb and bring out of order the whole matter because
that another which is merrier and better cometh to your
remembrance.

So the case standeth in a commonwealth, and so it is in the
consultations of kings and princes. If evil opinions and
naughty persuasions cannot be utterly and quite plucked
out of their hearts, if you cannot even as you would remedy

vices which use and custom hath confirmed, yet for this cause you must not leave and forsake the commonwealth. You must not forsake the ship in a tempest because you cannot rule and keep down the winds. No, nor you must not labour to drive into their heads new and strange information which you know well shall be nothing regarded with them that be of clean contrary minds. But you must with a crafty wile and a subtle train study and endeavour yourself, as much as in you lieth, to handle the matter wittily and handsomely for the purpose; and that which you cannot turn to good, so to order it that it be not very bad. For it is not possible for all things to be well unless all men were good, which I think will not be yet this good many years.

By this means, quoth he, nothing else will be brought to pass, but whiles that I go about to remedy the madness of others I should be even as mad as they. For if I would speak such things that be true I must needs speak such things; but as for to speak false things, whether that be a philosopher's part or no I cannot tell, truly it is not my part. Howbeit, this communication of mine, though peradventure it may seem unpleasant to them, yet can I not see why it should seem strange or foolishly newfangled. If so be that I should speak those things that Plato feigneth in his weal-public, or that the Utopians do in theirs, these things, though they were (as they be indeed) better, yet they might seem spoken out of place, forasmuch as here amongst us every man hath his possessions several to himself, and there all things be common. But what was in my communication contained that might not, and ought not, in any place to be spoken? Saving that to them which have thoroughly decreed and determined with themselves to run headlong the contrary way it cannot be acceptable and pleasant, because it calleth them back and sheweth them the jeopardies. Verily, if all things that evil and vicious manners have caused to seem inconvenient and nought should be refused as things unmeet and reproachful, then we must among Christian people wink at the most part of all those things which Christ taught us and so straitly forbade them to be winked at, that those things also which He whispered in the ears of his disciples He commanded to be proclaimed in open houses. And yet the most part of them is more dissident from the manners of the world nowadays than my communication was.

But preachers, sly and wily men, following your counsel (as I suppose) because they saw men evil willing to frame their manners to Christ's rule, they have wrested and wried His doctrine, and like a rule of lead have applied it to men's manners, that by some means, at the least way, they might agree together. Whereby I cannot see what good they have done, but that men may more securely be evil. And I truly should prevail even as little in kings' councils. For either I must say otherways than they say, and then I were as good to say nothing; or else I must say the same that they say, and (as Mitio saith in Terence), help to further their madness. For that crafty wile and subtle train of yours, I cannot perceive to what purpose it serveth, wherewith you would have me to study and endeavour myself, if all things cannot be made good, yet to handle them wittily and handsomely for the purpose, that as far forth as is possible they may not be very evil. For there is no place to dissemble in nor to wink in. Naughty counsels must be openly allowed and very pestilent decrees must be approved. He shall be counted worse than a spy, yea, almost as evil as a traitor, that with a faint heart doth praise evil and noisome decrees.

Moreover, a man can have no occasion to do good, chancing into the company of them which will sooner pervert a good man than be made good themselves, through whose evil company he shall be marred, or else, if he remain good and innocent, yet the wickedness and folly of others shall be imputed to him and laid in his neck. So that it is impossible with that crafty wile and subtle train to turn anything to better. Wherefore Plato by a goodly similitude declareth why wise men refrain to meddle in the commonwealth. For

when they see the people swarm into the streets, and daily wet
to the skin with rain, and yet cannot persuade them to go out
of the rain and to take their houses, knowing well that if they
should go out to them they should nothing prevail nor win
aught by it but with them be wet also in the rain, they do keep
themselves within their houses, being content that they be
safe themselves, seeing they cannot remedy the folly of the
people.

Howbeit, doubtless, Master More (to speak truly as my
mind giveth me), where possessions be private, where money
beareth all the stroke, it is hard and almost impossible that
there the weal-public may justly be governed and prosperously
flourish. Unless you think thus: that justice is there executed where all things come into the hands of evil men, or that
prosperity there flourisheth where all is divided among a few,
which few, nevertheless, do not lead their lives very wealthily,
and the residue live miserably, wretchedly, and beggarly.
Wherefore when I consider with myself and weigh in my
mind the wise and godly ordinances of the Utopians, among
whom with very few laws all things be so well and wealthily
ordered that virtue is had in price and estimation, and yet, all
things being there common, every man hath abundance of
everything. Again, on the other part, when I compare with
them so many nations ever making new laws, yet none of
them all well and sufficiently furnished with laws, where
every man calleth that he hath gotten his own proper and
private goods, where so many new laws daily made be not
sufficient for every man to enjoy, defend, and know from
another man's that which he calleth his own; which thing the
infinite controversies in the law, daily rising, never to be
ended, plainly declare to be true: these things (I say) when
I consider with myself, I hold well with Plato, and do nothing
marvel that he would make no laws for them that refused
those laws whereby all men should have and enjoy equal
portions of wealths and commodities.

For the wise man did easily foresee this to be the one and

only way to the wealth of a commonalty, if equality of all things should be brought in and stablished. Which, I think, is not possible to be observed where every man's good be proper and peculiar to himself. For where every man under certain titles and pretences draweth and plucketh to himself as much as he can, so that a few divide among themselves all the whole riches, be there never so much abundance and store, there to the residue is left lack and poverty. And for the most part it chanceth that this latter sort is more worthy to enjoy that state of wealth than the other be, because the rich men be covetous, crafty, and unprofitable. On the other part the poor be lowly, simple, and by their daily labour more profitable to the commonwealth than to themselves. Thus I do fully persuade myself that no equal and just distribution of things can be made, nor that perfect wealth shall ever be among men, unless this propriety be exiled and banished. But so long as it shall continue, so long shall remain among the most and best part of men the heavy and inevitable burden of poverty and wretchedness. Which, as I grant that it may be somewhat eased, so I utterly deny that it can wholly be taken away. For if there were a statute made that no man should possess above a certain measure of ground, and that no man should have in his stock above a prescript and appointed sum of money, if it were by certain laws decreed that neither the king should be of too great power, neither the people too haut and wealthy, and that offices should not be obtained by inordinate suit, or by bribes and gifts, that they should neither be bought nor sold, nor that it should be needful for the officers to be at any cost or charge in their offices (for so occasion is given to them by fraud and ravin to gather up their money again, and by reason of gifts and bribes the offices be given to rich men, which should rather have been executed of wise men) by such laws, I say, like as sick bodies that be desperate and past cure be wont with continual good cherishing to be kept and botched up for a time, so these evils also might be lightened and mitigated. But that they may be

perfectly cured, and brought to a good and upright state, it is
not to be hoped for, whiles every man is master of his own to
himself.   Yea, and whiles you go about to do your cure of one
part you shall make bigger the sore of another part, so the
help of one causeth another's harm, forasmuch as nothing can
be given to any one unless it be taken from another.

But I am of a contrary opinion, quoth I, for methinketh
that men shall never there live wealthily where all things be
common.   For how can there be abundance of goods or of
anything where every man withdraweth his hand from
labour?   Whom the regard of his own gains driveth not to
work, but the hope that he hath in other men's travails maketh
him slothful.   Then when they be pricked with poverty, and
yet no man can by any law or right defend that for his own
which he hath gotten with the labour of his own hands, shall
not there of necessity be continual sedition and bloodshed?
Specially the authority and reverence of magistrates being
taken away, which, what place it may have with such men
among whom is no difference, I cannot devise.

I marvel not, quoth he, that you be of this opinion.   For
you conceive in your mind either none at all, or else a very false
image and similitude of this thing.   But if you had been with
me in Utopia and had presently seen their fashions and laws,
as I did which lived there five years and more, and would never
have come thence but only to make that new land known
here, then doubtless you would grant that you never saw
people well ordered but only there.

Surely, quoth Master Peter, it shall be hard for you to make
me believe that there is better order in that new land than is
here in these countries that we know.   For good wits be as well
here as there, and I think our commonwealths be ancienter
than theirs.   Wherein long use and experience hath found out
many things commodious for man's life, besides that many
things here among us have been found by chance which no
wit could ever have devised.

As touching the ancientness, quoth he, of commonwealths,

then you might better judge, if you had read the histories and chronicles of that land, which if we may believe, cities were there before men were here. Now what thing soever hitherto by wit hath been devised or found by chance, that might be as well there as here. But I think verily, though it were so that we did pass them in wit, yet in study, in travail, and in laboursome endeavour they far pass us. For (as their chronicles testify) before our arrival there they never heard anything of us whom they call the ultra-equinoctials; saving that once about 1200 years ago, a certain ship was lost by the isle of Utopia which was driven thither by tempest. Certain Romans and Egyptians were cast on land, which after that never went thence. Mark now what profit they took of this one occasion through diligence and earnest travail. There was no craft nor science within the empire of Rome whereof any profit could rise, but they either learned it of these strangers, or else of them taking occasion to search for it, found it out. So great profit was it to them that ever any went thither from hence. But if any like chance before this hath brought any man from thence hither, that is as quite out of remembrance as this also perchance in time to come shall be forgotten, that ever I was there. And like as they quickly, almost at the first meeting, made their own whatsoever is among us wealthily devised, so I suppose it would be long before we would receive anything that among them is better instituted than among us. And this, I suppose, is the chief cause why their commonwealths be wiselier governed and do flourish in more wealth than ours, though we neither in wit nor riches be their inferiors.

Therefore, gentle Master Raphael, quoth I, I pray you and beseech you describe unto us the island. And study not to be short, but declare largely in order their grounds, their rivers, their cities, their people, their manners, their ordinances, their laws, and, to be short, all things that you shall think us desirous to know. And you shall think us desirous to know whatsoever we know not yet.

* C 461

There is nothing, quoth he, that I will do gladlier.   For all these things I have fresh in mind.   But the matter requireth leisure.

Let us go in, therefore, quoth I, to dinner; afterward we will bestow the time at our pleasure.

Content, quoth he, be it.   So we went in and dined. When dinner was done, we came into the same place again, and sat us down upon the same bench, commanding our servants that no man should trouble us.   Then I and Master Peter Giles desired Master Raphael to perform his promise. He, therefore, seeing us desirous and willing to hearken to him, when he had sit still and paused a little while musing and bethinking himself, thus he began to speak.

THE END OF THE FIRST BOOK

THE COMMUNICATION OF
RAPHAEL HYTHLODAY,

Concerning the beststate of a commonwealth containing the description of Utopia, with a large declaration of the politic government and of all the good laws and orders of the same land.

THE island of Utopia containeth in breadth in the middle part of it (for there it is broadest) 200 miles. Which breadth continueth through the most part of the land, saving that by little and little it cometh in and waxeth narrower towards both the ends. Which fetching about a circuit or compass of 500 miles, do fashion the whole island like to the new moon. Between these two corners the sea runneth in, dividing them asunder by the distance of eleven miles or thereabouts, and there surmounteth into a large and wide sea, which by reason that the land on every side compasseth it about and sheltereth it from the winds, is not rough nor mounteth not with great waves, but almost floweth quietly, not much unlike a great standing pool, and maketh wellnigh all the space within the belly of the land in manner of a haven, and to the great commodity of the inhabitants receiveth in ships towards every part of the land. The forefronts or frontiers of the two corners, what with fords and shelves and what with rocks, be very jeopardous and dangerous. In the middle distance between them both standeth up above the water a great rock, which therefore is nothing perilous because it is in sight. Upon the top of this rock is a fair and a strong tower builded, which they hold with a garrison of men. Other rocks there be lying hid under the water, which therefore be dangerous. The channels be known only to themselves, and therefore it seldom chanceth that any stranger, unless be he guided by an Utopian, can come into this haven, insomuch that they themselves could scarcely enter without jeopardy, but that their way is directed and ruled by certain landmarks standing on the shore. By turning, translating, and removing these marks into other places they may destroy their enemies' navies, be they never so many. The outside or utter circuit of the land is also full of havens, but the landing is so surely fenced, what by nature and what by workmanship of man's hand, that a few defenders may drive back many armies.

Howbeit, as they say and as the fashion of the place itself doth partly shew, it was not ever compassed about with the sea. But King Utopus, whose name as conqueror the island beareth (for before his time it was called Abraxa), which also brought the rude and wild people to that excellent perfection in all good fashions, humanity, and civil gentleness, wherein they now go beyond all the people of the world, even at his first arriving and entering upon the land, forthwith obtaining the victory, caused fifteen miles space of uplandish ground, where the sea had no passage, to be cut and digged up, and so brought the sea round about the land. He set to this work not only the inhabitants of the island (because they should not think it done in contumely and despite) but also all his own soldiers. Thus the work, being divided into so great a number of workmen, was with exceeding marvellous speed dispatched. Insomuch that the borderers, which at the first began to mock and to jest at this vain enterprise, then turned their derision to marvel at the success and to fear. There be in the island fifty-four large and fair cities, or shire towns, agreeing all together in one tongue, in like manners, institutions, and laws. They be all set and situate alike, and in all points fashioned alike, as far forth as the place or plot suffereth.

Of these cities they that be nighest together be twenty-four miles asunder. Again, there is none of them distant from the next above one day's journey afoot. There come yearly to

Amaurote out of every city three old men wise and well experienced, there to entreat and debate of the common matters of the land. For this city (because it standeth just in the midst of the island, and is therefore most meet for the ambassadors of all parts of the realm) is taken for the chief and head city. The precincts and bounds of the shires be so commodiously appointed out and set forth for the cities, that none of them all hath of any side less than twenty miles of ground, and of some side also much more, as of that part where the cities be of farther distance asunder. None of the cities desire to enlarge the bounds and limits of their shires, for they count themselves rather the good husbands than the owners of their lands.

They have in the country, in all parts of the shire, houses or farms builded, well appointed and furnished with all sorts of instruments and tools belonging to husbandry. These houses be inhabited of the citizens which come thither to dwell by course. No household or farm in the country hath fewer than forty persons, men and women, besides two bondmen which be all under the rule and order of the goodman and the goodwife of the house, being both very sage, discreet, and ancient persons. And every thirty farms or families have one head ruler which is called a Philarch, being as it were a head bailiff. Out of every one of these families or farms cometh every year into the city twenty persons which have continued two years before in the country. In their place so many fresh be sent thither out of the city, who, of them that have been there a year already and be therefore expert and cunning in husbandry, shall be instructed and taught. And they the next year shall teach other. This order is used for fear that either scarceness of victuals or some other like incommodity should chance, through lack of knowledge if they should be altogether new and fresh and unexpert in husbandry. This manner and fashion of yearly changing and renewing the occupiers of husbandry, though it be solemn and customably used to the intent that no man shall be constrained against his will to continue long in that hard and sharp kind of life, yet many of them have such a pleasure and delight in husbandry that they obtain a longer space of years. These husbandmen plow and till the ground, and breed up cattle, and provide and make ready wood which they carry to the city either by land or by water as they may most conveniently.   They bring up a great multitude of pullen, and that by a marvellous policy. For the hens do not sit upon the eggs, but by keeping them in a certain equal heat they bring life into them and hatch them. The chickens, as soon as they be come out of the shell, follow men and women instead of the hens. They bring up very few horses, nor none but very fierce ones; and that for none other use or purpose, but only to exercise their youth in riding and feats of arms, for oxen be put to all the labour of plowing and drawing. Which they grant to be not so good as horses at a sudden brunt and (as we say) at a dead lift, but yet they hold opinion that oxen will abide and suffer much more labour, pain, and hardness than horses will.   And they think that oxen be not in danger and subject unto so many diseases, and that they be kept and maintained with much less cost and charge, and finally that they be good for meat when they be past labour. They sow corn only for bread, for their drink is either wine made of grapes or else of apples or pears, or else it is clear water, and many times mead made of honey or liquorice sodden in water, for thereof they have great store. And though they know certainly (for they know it perfectly indeed) how much victuals the city with the whole country or shire round about it doth spend, yet they sow much more corn and breed up much more cattle than serveth for their own use, parting the overplus among their borderers. Whatsoever necessary things be lacking in the country, all such stuff they fetch out of the city where without any exchange they easily obtain it of the magistrates of the city.   For every month many of them go into the city on the holy day.   When their harvest day draweth near and is at hand, then the Philarchs, which be the head officers and bailiffs of husbandry, send word to the magistrates of the city what number of harvest men is needful to be sent to them out of the city. The which company of harvest men being ready at the day appointed, almost in one fair day dispatcheth all the harvest work.

Of the cities and namely of Amaurote

As for their cities, whoso knoweth one of them knoweth them all, they be all so like one to another as far forth as the nature of the place permitteth. I will describe, therefore, to you one or other of them, for it skilleth not greatly which, but which rather than Amaurote? Of them all this is the worthiest and of most dignity. For the residue knowledge it for the head city because there is the council house. Nor to me any of them all is better beloved, as wherein I lived five whole years together. The city of Amaurote standeth upon the side of a low hill, in fashion almost four-square. For the breadth of it beginneth a little beneath the top of the hill, and still continueth by the space of two miles until it come to the river of Anyder. The length of it, which lieth by the river's side, is somewhat more. The river of Anyder riseth four and twenty miles above Amaurote out of a little spring, but being increased by other small rivers and brooks that run into it, and among other two somewhat big ones, before the city it is half a mile broad, and farther broader. And forty miles beyond the city it falleth into the ocean sea. By all that space that lieth between the sea and the city, and certain miles also above the city, the water ebbeth and floweth six hours together with a swift tide. When the sea floweth in, for the length of thirty miles it filleth all the Anyder with salt water, and driveth back the fresh water of the river. And somewhat farther it changeth the sweetness of the fresh water with saltness. But a little beyond that the river waxeth sweet, and runneth forby the city fresh and pleasant. And when the sea ebbeth and goeth back again, the fresh water followeth it almost even to the very fall into the sea. There goeth a bridge over the river, made not of piles or of timber, but of stonework with gorgeous and substantial arches at that part of the city that is farthest from the sea, to the intent that ships may pass along forby all the side of the city without let. They have also another river which, indeed, is not very great, but it runneth gently and pleasantly. For it riseth even out of the same hill that the city standeth upon, and runneth down a slope through the midst of the city into Anyder. And because it riseth a little without the city, the Amaurotians have enclosed the head spring of it with strong fences and bulwarks, and so have joined it to the city. This is done to the intent that the water should not be stopped nor turned away or poisoned if their enemies should chance to come upon them. From thence the water is derived and conveyed down in channels of brick divers ways into the lower parts of the city. Where that cannot be done, by reason that the place will not suffer it, there they gather the rain water in great cisterns, which doeth them as good service.

The city is compassed about with a high and thick stone wall full of turrets and bulwarks. A dry ditch, but deep and broad and overgrown with bushes, briars, and thorns, goeth about three sides or quarters of the city. To the fourth side the river itself serveth for a ditch. The streets be appointed and set forth very commodious and handsome, both for carriage and also against the winds. The houses be of fair and gorgeous building, and on the street side they stand joined together in a long row through the whole street without any partition or separation. The streets be twenty foot broad. On the back side of the houses, through the whole length of the street, lie large gardens enclosed round about with the back part of the streets. Every house hath two doors, one into the street, and a postern door on the back side into the garden. These doors be made with two leaves never locked nor bolted, so easy to be opened, that they will follow the least drawing of a finger, and shut again alone. Whoso will may go in, for there is nothing within the houses that is private or any man's own. And every tenth year they change their houses by lot.

They set great store by their gardens. In them they have vineyards, all manner of fruit, herbs, and flowers, so pleasant, so well furnished, and so finely kept, that I never saw thing more fruitful nor better trimmed in any place. Their study and diligence herein cometh not only of pleasure, but also of a certain strife and contention that is between street and street concerning the trimming, husbanding, and furnishing of their gardens, every man for his own part. And verily you shall not lightly find in all the city anything that is more commodious, either for the profit of the citizens or for pleasure. And therefore it may seem that the first founder of the city minded nothing so much as these gardens. For they say that King Utopus himself, even at the first beginning, appointed and drew forth the platform of the city into this fashion and figure that it hath now, but the gallant garnishing and the beautiful setting forth of it, whereunto he saw that one man's age would not suffice, that he left to his posterity. For their chronicles, which they keep written with all diligent circumspection, containing the history of 1760 years, even from the first conquest of the island, record and witness that the houses in the beginning were very low and like homely cottages or poor shepherd houses, made, at all adventures, of every rude piece of timber that came first to hand, with mud walls and ridged roofs thatched over with straw. But now the houses be curiously builded after a gorgeous and gallant sort, with three storeys one over another. The outsides of the walls be made either of hard flint or of plaster, or else of brick, and the inner sides be well strengthened with timber work. The roofs be plain and flat, covered with a certain kind of plaster that is of no cost, and yet so tempered that no fire can hurt or perish it, and withstandeth the violence of the weather better than any lead. They keep the wind out of their windows with glass, for it is there much used, and somewhere also with fine linen cloth dipped in oil or amber, and that for two commodities, for by this means more light cometh in, and the wind is better kept out.

Of the Magistrates

Every thirty families or farms choose them yearly an officer which in their old language is called the Syphogrant, and by a newer name the Philarch. Every ten Syphogrants, with all their thirty families, be under an officer which was once called the Tranibore, now the chief Philarch. Moreover, as concerning the election of the prince, all the Syphogrants, which be in number 200, first be sworn to choose him whom they think most meet and expedient. Then by a secret election they name prince one of those four whom the people before named unto them. For out of the four quarters of the city there be four chosen, out of every quarter one, to stand for the election, which be put up to the council. The prince's office continueth all his lifetime, unless he be deposed or put down for suspicion of tyranny. They choose the Tranibores yearly, but lightly they change them not. All the other officers be but for one year. The Tranibores every third day, and sometimes, if need be, oftener, come into the council house with the prince. Their counsel is concerning the commonwealth. If there be any controversies among the commoners, which be very few, they dispatch and end them by and by. They take ever two Syphogrants to them in council, and every day a new couple. And it is provided that nothing touching the commonwealth shall be confirmed and ratified unless it have been reasoned of and debated three days in the council before it be decreed. It is death to have any consultation for the commonwealth out of the council or the place of the common election. This statute, they say, was made to the intent that the prince and Tranibores might not easily conspire together to oppress the people by tyranny, and to change the state of the weal-public. Therefore matters of great weight and importance be brought to the election

house of the Syphogrants, which open the matter to their
families and afterward, when they have consulted among
themselves, they shew their device to the council. Sometimes the matter is brought before the council of the whole
island. Furthermore, this custom also the council useth, to
dispute or reason of no matter the same day that it is first
proposed or put forth, but to defer it to the next sitting of the
council. Because that no man, when he hath rashly there
spoken that cometh to his tongue's end, shall then afterward rather study for reasons wherewith to defend and
maintain his first foolish sentence, than for the commodity
of the commonwealth, as one rather willing the harm or
hindrance of the weal-public than any loss or diminution of
his own existimation, and as one that would be ashamed
(which is a very foolish shame) to be counted anything at the
first overseen in the matter. Who at the first ought to have
spoken rather wisely than hastily or rashly.

Of Sciences, Crafts, and Occupations

Husbandry is a science common to them all in general, both
men and women, wherein they be all expert and cunning. In
this they be all instructed even from their youth, partly in
their schools with traditions and precepts, and partly in the
country nigh the city, brought up, as it were in playing, not
only beholding the use of it, but by occasion of exercising
their bodies practising it also. Besides husbandry, which (as
I said) is common to them all, every one of them learneth one
or other several and particular science as his own proper craft.
That is most commonly either clothworking in wool or flax, or
masonry, or the smith's craft, or the carpenter's science. For
there is none other occupation that any number to speak of
doth use there. For their garments, which throughout all
the island be of one fashion (saving that there is a difference
between the man's garment and the woman's, between the
married and the unmarried), and this one continueth for

evermore unchanged, seemly and comely to the eye, no let to the moving and wielding of the body, also fit both for winter and summer. As for these garments (I say) every family maketh their own. But of the other foresaid crafts every man learneth one, and not only the men, but also the women. But the women, as the weaker sort, be put to the easier crafts, as to work wool and flax; the more laboursome sciences be committed to the men. For the most part every man is brought up in his father's craft, for most commonly they be naturally thereto bent and inclined. But if a man's mind stand to any other, he is by adoption put into a family of that occupation which he doth most fantasy. Whom not only his father but also the magistrates do diligently look to that he be put to a discreet and an honest householder. Yea, and if any person when he hath learned one craft be desirous to learn also another, he is likewise suffered and permitted. When he hath learned both, he occupieth whether he will, unless the city have more need of the one than of the other.

The chief and almost the only office of the Syphogrants is to see and take heed that no man sit idle, but that every one apply his own craft with earnest diligence; and yet for all that, not to be wearied from early in the morning to late in the evening with continual work, like labouring and toiling beasts. For this is worse than the miserable and wretched condition of bondmen, which nevertheless is almost everywhere the life of workmen and artificers, saving in Utopia. For they, dividing the day and the night into twenty-four just hours, appoint and assign only six of those hours to work before noon, upon the which they go straight to dinner. And after dinner, when they have rested two hours, then they work three hours, and upon that they go to supper. About eight of the clock in the evening (counting one of the clock at the first hour after noon) they go to bed; eight hours they give to sleep. All the void time that is between the hours of work, sleep, and meat, that they be suffered to bestow, every man as he liketh best himself. Not to the

intent that they should misspend this time in riot or slothful-
ness, but being then licensed from the labour of their own
occupations, to bestow the time well and thriftily upon some
other science as shall please them. For it is a solemn custom
there, to have lectures daily early in the morning, where to be
present they only be constrained that be namely chosen and
appointed to learning. Howbeit, a great multitude of every
sort of people, both men and women, go to hear lectures, some
one and some another, as every man's nature is inclined. Yet,
this notwithstanding, if any man had rather bestow this time
upon his own occupation (as it chanceth in many whose
minds rise not in the contemplation of any science liberal), he
is not letted nor prohibited, but is also praised and commended as profitable to the commonwealth. After supper
they bestow one hour in play, in summer in their gardens, in
winter in their common halls where they dine and sup.
There they exercise themselves in music, or else in honest and
wholesome communication. Dice-play and such other foolish
and pernicious games they know not; but they use two games
not much unlike the chess. The one is the battle of numbers,
wherein one number stealeth away another. The other is
wherein vices fight with virtues, as it were in battle array or
a set field. In the which game is very properly shewed both
the strife and discord that vices have among themselves, and
again their unity and concord against virtues; and also what
vices be repugnant to what virtues; with what power and
strength they assail them openly; by what wiles and subtlety
they assault them secretly; with what help and aid the virtues
resist and overcome the puissance of the vices; by what craft
they frustrate their purposes; and, finally, by what sleight or
means the one getteth the victory.

But here lest you be deceived, one thing you must look
more narrowly upon. For seeing they bestow but six hours
in work, perchance you may think that the lack of some
necessary things hereof may ensue. But this is nothing so.
For that small time is not only enough but also too much for

the store and abundance of all things that be requisite either
for the necessity or commodity of life. The which thing
you also shall perceive if you weigh and consider with yourselves how great a part of the people in other countries liveth
idle. First, almost all women, which be the half of the whole
number, or else, if the women be somewhere occupied, there
most commonly in their stead the men be idle. Besides
this, how great and how idle a company is there of priests
and religious men, as they call them! Put thereto all rich
men, specially all landed men, which commonly be called
gentlemen and noblemen. Take into this number also their
servants, I mean all that flock of stout bragging rushbucklers;
join to them also sturdy and valiant beggars, cloaking their
idle life under the colour of some disease or sickness, and
truly you shall find them much fewer than you thought, by
whose labour all these things are wrought that in men's affairs
are now daily used and frequented. Now consider with yourself of these few that do work, how few be occupied in
necessary works. For where money beareth all the swing,
there many vain and superfluous occupations must needs be
used, to serve only for riotous superfluity and unhonest
pleasure. For the same multitude that now is occupied in
work, if they were divided into so few occupations as the
necessary use of nature requireth, in so great plenty of things
as then of necessity would ensue doubtless the prices would be
too little for the artificers to maintain their livings. But if all
these that be now busied about unprofitable occupations,
with all the whole flock of them that live idly and slothfully,
which consume and waste every one of them more of these
things that come by other men's labour than two of the workmen themselves do, if all these (I say) were set to profitable
occupations, you easily perceive how little time would be
enough, yea, and too much, to store us with all things that
may be requisite either for necessity or for commodity, yea,
or for pleasure, so that the same pleasure be true and natural.

And this in Utopia the thing itself maketh manifest and

plain. For there, in all the city with the whole country or shire adjoining to it, scarcely 500 persons of all the whole number of men and women that be neither too old nor too weak to work be licensed and discharged from labour. Among them be the Syphogrants, who, though they be by the laws exempt and privileged from labour, yet they exempt not themselves, to the intent that they may the rather by their example provoke others to work. The same vacation from labour do they also enjoy to whom the people, persuaded by the commendation of the priests and secret election of the Syphogrants, have given a perpetual licence from labour to learning. But if any one of them prove not according to the expectation and hope of him conceived, he is forthwith plucked back to the company of artificers. And contrari-wise, often it chanceth that a handicraftsman doth so earnestly bestow his vacant and spare hours in learning, and through diligence so profiteth therein, that he is taken from his handy occupation and promoted to the company of the learned. Out of this order of the learned be chosen ambas-sadors, priests, Tranibores, and finally the prince himself, whom they in their old tongue call Barzanes and, by a newer name, Adamus. The residue of the people being neither idle nor yet occupied about unprofitable exercises, it may be easily judged in how few hours how much good work by them may be done and dispatched towards those things that I have spoken of.

This commodity they have also above other, that in the most part of necessary occupations they need not so much work as other nations do. For, first of all, the building or repairing of houses asketh everywhere so many men's con-tinual labour, because that the unthrifty here suffereth the houses that his father builded in continuance of time to fall in decay. So that which he might have upholden with little cost, his successor is constrained to build it again anew, to his great charge. Yea, many times also the house that stood one man in much money, another is of so nice and so delicate a mind, that he setteth nothing by it; and, it being neglected and therefore shortly falling into ruin, be buildeth up another in another place with no less cost and charge. But among the Utopians, where all things be set in a good order and the commonwealth in a good stay, it very seldom chanceth that they choose a new plot to build an house upon. And they do not only find speedy and quick remedies for present faults, but also prevent them that be like to fall. And by this means their houses continue and last very long with little labour and small reparations; insomuch that this kind of workmen sometimes have almost nothing to do, but that they be commanded to hew timber at home, and to square and trim up stones, to the intent that if any work chance it may the speedlier rise.

Now, sir, in their apparel mark (I pray you) how few workmen they need. First of all, whiles they be at work they be covered homely with leather or skins that will last seven years. When they go forth abroad they cast upon them a cloak which hideth the other homely apparel. These cloaks throughout the whole island be all of one colour, and that is the natural colour of the wool. They therefore do not only spend much less woollen cloth than is spent in other countries, but also the same standeth them in much less cost. But linen cloth is made with less labour, and is therefore had more in use. But in linen cloth only whiteness, in woollen only cleanliness, is regarded. As for the smallness or fineness of the thread, that is nothing passed for. And this is the cause wherefore in other places four or five cloth gowns of divers colours and as many silk coats be not enough for one man. Yea, and if he be of the delicate and nice sort ten be too few, whereas there one garment will serve a man most commonly two years. For why should he desire more, seeing if he had them he should not be the better hapt or covered from cold, neither in his apparel any whit the comelier? Wherefore, seeing they be all exercised in profitable occupations, and that few artificers in the same crafts be sufficient, this is the cause

that, plenty of all things being among them, they do sometimes bring forth an innumerable company of people to
amend the highways if any be broken. Many times also,
when they have no such work to be occupied about, an open
proclamation is made that they shall bestow fewer hours in
work. For the magistrates do not exercise their citizens
against their wills in unneedful labours. For why, in the
institution of that weal-public this end is only and chiefly
pretended and minded, that what time may possibly be
spared from the necessary occupations and affairs of the
commonwealth, all that the citizens should withdraw from
the bodily service to the free liberty of the mind and garnishing of the same. For herein they suppose the felicity of
this life to consist.

Of their Living and Mutual Conversation together

But now will I declare how the citizens use themselves one
towards another, what familiar occupying and entertainment
there is among the people, and what fashion they use in the
distribution of everything. First, the city consisteth of
families; the families most commonly be made of kindreds.
For the women, when they be married at a lawful age, they go
into their husbands' houses, but the male children, with all
the whole male offspring, continue still in their own family
and be governed of the eldest and ancientest father, unless he
dote for age, for then the next to him in age is placed in his
room. But to the intent the prescript number of the citizens
should neither decrease nor above measure increase, it is
ordained that no family, which in every city be six thousand
in the whole besides them of the country, shall at once have
fewer children of the age of fourteen years or thereabout than
ten or more than sixteen, for of children under this age no number can be prescribed or appointed. This measure or number
is easily observed and kept by putting them that in fuller families
be above the number into families of smaller increase. But if

chance be that in the whole city the store increase above the just number, therewith they fill up the lack of other cities. But if so be that the multitude throughout the whole island pass and exceed the due number, then they choose out of every city certain citizens, and build up a town under their own laws in the next land where the inhabitants have much waste and unoccupied ground, receiving also of the same country people to them, if they will join and dwell with them. They thus joining and dwelling together do easily agree in one fashion of living, and that to the great wealth of both the peoples. For they so bring the matter about by their laws, that the ground which before was neither good nor profitable for the one nor for the other is now sufficient and fruitful enough for them both. But if the inhabitants of that land will not dwell with them to be ordered by their laws, then they drive them out of those bounds which they have limited and appointed out for themselves. And if they resist and rebel, then they make war against them. For they count this the most just cause of war, when any people holdeth a piece of ground void and vacant to no good nor profitable use, keeping others from the use and possession of it which notwithstanding by the law of nature ought thereof to be nourished and relieved. If any chance do so much diminish the number of any of their cities that it cannot be filled up again without the diminishing of the just number of the other cities (which they say chanced but twice since the beginning of the land through a great pestilent plague), then they fulfil and make up the number with citizens fetched out of their own foreign towns; for they had rather suffer their foreign towns to decay and perish than any city of their own island to be diminished.

But now again to the conversation of the citizens among themselves. The eldest (as I said) ruleth the family. The wives be ministers to their husbands, the children to their parents, and, to be short, the younger to their elders. Every city is divided into four equal parts or quarters. In the midst of every quarter there is a market-place of all manner of things. Thither the works of every family be brought into certain houses, and every kind of thing is laid up several in barns or storehouses. From hence the father of every family or every householder fetcheth whatsoever he and his have need of, and carrieth it away with him without money, without exchange, without any gage, pawn, or pledge. For why should anything be denied unto him, seeing there is abundance of all things, and that it is not to be feared lest any man will ask more than he needeth? For why should it be thought that that man would ask more than enough which is sure never to lack? Certainly in all kinds of living creatures either fear of lack doth cause covetousness and ravin, or in man only pride, which counteth it a glorious thing to pass and excel other in the superfluous and vain ostentation of things. The which kind of vice among the Utopians can have no place.

Next to the market-places that I spake of stand meat markets, whither be brought not only all sorts of herbs and the fruits of trees, with bread, but also fish, and all manner of four-footed beasts and wild fowl that be man's meat. But first the filthiness and ordure thereof is clean washed away in the running river without the city in places appointed meet for the same purpose. From thence the beasts be brought in, killed, and clean washed by the hands of their bondmen. For they permit not their free citizens to accustom themselves to the killing of beasts, through the use whereof they think clemency, the gentlest affection of our nature, by little and little to decay and perish. Neither they suffer anything that is filthy, loathsome, or uncleanly to be brought into the city, lest the air, by the stench thereof infected and corrupt, should cause pestilent diseases.

Moreover, every street hath certain great large halls set in equal distance one from another, every one known by a several name. In these halls dwell the Syphogrants, and to every one of the same halls be appointed thirty families, on either side fifteen. The stewards of every hall at a certain hour come in to the meat markets, where they receive meat according to the number of their halls. But first and chiefly of all, respect is had to the sick that be cured in the hospitals. For in the circuit of the city, a little without the walls, they have four hospitals, so big, so wide, so ample, and so large, that they may seem four little towns, which were devised of that bigness partly to the intent the sick, be they never so many in number, should not lie too throng or strait, and therefore uneasily and incommodiously; and partly that they which were taken and holden with contagious diseases, such as be wont by infection to creep from one to another, might be laid apart far from the company of the residue. These hospitals be so well appointed, and with all things necessary to health so furnished, and, moreover, so diligent attendance through the continual presence of cunning physicians is given, that though no man be sent thither against his will, yet notwithstanding there is no sick person in all the city that had not rather lie there than at home in his own house. When the steward of the sick hath received such meat as the physicians have prescribed, then the best is equally divided among the halls, according to the company of every one, saving that there is had a respect to the prince, the bishop, the Tranibores, and to ambassadors and all strangers, if there be any, which be very few and seldom. But they also, when they be there, have certain several houses appointed and prepared for them. To these halls at the set hours of dinner and supper cometh all the whole Syphogranty or ward, warned by the noise of a brazen trumpet, except such as be sick in the hospitals, or else in their own houses. Howbeit, no man is prohibited or forbid, after the halls be served, to fetch home meat out of the market to his own house, for they know that no man will do it without a cause reasonable. For though no man be prohibited to dine at home, yet no man doth it willingly because it is counted a point of small honesty. And also it were a folly to take the pain to dress a bad dinner at home, when they may be welcome to good and fine fare so nigh hand at the hall.

In this hall all vile service, all slavery and drudgery, with all laboursome toil and base business, is done by bondmen. But the women of every family, by course, have the office and charge of cookery for seething and dressing the meat and ordering all things thereto belonging. They sit at three tables or more, according to the number of their company. The men sit upon the bench next the wall, and the women against them on the other side of the table, that if any sudden evil should chance to them, as many times happeneth to women with child, they may rise without trouble or disturbance of anybody, and go thence into the nursery.

The nurses sit several alone with their young sucklings in a certain parlour appointed and deputed to the same purpose, never without fire and clean water, nor yet without cradles, that when they will they may lay down the young infants, and at their pleasure take them out of their swathing clothes, and hold them to the fire, and refresh them with play. Every mother is nurse to her own child unless either death or sickness be the let. When that chanceth, the wives of the Syphogrants quickly provide a nurse; and that is not hard to be done, for they that can do it proffer themselves to no service so gladly as to that, because that there this kind of pity is much praised, and the child that is nourished ever after taketh his nurse for his own natural mother. Also among the nurses sit all the children that be under the age of five years. All the other children of both kinds as well boys as girls, that be under the age of marriage, do either serve at the tables or else, if they be too young thereto, yet they stand by with marvellous silence. That which is given to them from the table they eat, and other several dinner time they have none.

The Syphogrant and his wife sit in the midst of the high table, forasmuch as that is counted the honourablest place, and because from thence all the whole company is in their sight. For that table standeth overthwart the over end of the hall. To them be joined two of the ancientest and eldest, for at every table they sit four at a mess. But if there be a church standing in that Syphogranty or ward, then the priest and his wife sitteth with the Syphogrant, as chief in the company. On both sides of them sit young men, and next unto them again old men. And thus throughout all the house equal of age be set together, and yet be mixed and matched with unequal ages. This, they say, was ordained to the intent that the sage gravity and reverence of the elders should keep the youngers from wanton licence of words and behaviour, forasmuch as nothing can be so secretly spoken or done at the table, but either they that sit on the one side or on the other must needs perceive it. The dishes be not set down in order from the first place, but all the old men (whose places be marked with some special token to be known) be first served of their meat, and then the residue equally. The old men divide their dainties as they think best to the younger on each side of them. Thus the elders be not defrauded of their due honour, and nevertheless equal commodity cometh to every one.

They begin every dinner and supper of reading something that pertaineth to good manners and virtue; but it is short, because no man shall be grieved therewith. Hereof the elders take occasion of honest communication, but neither sad nor unpleasant. Howbeit, they do not spend all the whole dinner time themselves with long and tedious talks, but they gladly hear also the young men, yea, and purposely provoke them to talk, to the intent that they may have a proof of every man's wit and towardness or disposition to virtue, which commonly in the liberty of feasting doth shew and utter itself. Their dinners be very short, but their suppers be somewhat longer, because that after dinner followeth labour, after supper sleep and natural rest, which they think to be of more strength and efficacy to wholesome and healthful digestion. No supper is passed without music, nor their banquets lack no conceits nor junkets. They burn sweet gums and spices or perfumes and pleasant smells, and sprinkle about sweet ointments and waters, yea, they leave nothing undone that maketh for the cheering of the company. For they be much inclined to this opinion, to think no kind of pleasure forbidden whereof cometh no harm. Thus, therefore, and after this sort they live together in the city; but in the country they that dwell alone far from any neighbours do dine and sup at home in their own houses. For no family there lacketh any kind of victuals, as from whom cometh all that the citizens eat and live by.

Of their Journeying or Travelling abroad, with divers other Matters cunningly Reasoned and wittily Discussed

But if any be desirous to visit either their friends dwelling in another city or to see the place itself, they easily obtain licence of their Syphogrants and Tranibores, unless there be some profitable let. No man goeth out alone, but a company is sent forth together with their prince's letters, which do testify that they have licence to go that journey and prescribeth also the day of their return. They have a wagon given them with a common bondman which driveth the oxen and taketh charge of them. But unless they have women in their company, they send home the wagon again as an impediment and a let. And though they carry nothing forth with them, yet in all their journey they lack nothing, for wheresoever they come they be at home. If they tarry in a place longer than one day, then there every one of them falleth to his own occupation, and be very gently entertained of the workmen and companies of the same crafts. If any man, of his own head and without leave, walk out of his precinct and bounds, taken without the prince's letters he is brought again for a fugitive or a runaway with great shame and rebuke, and is sharply punished. If he be taken in that fault again, he is punished with bondage. If any be desirous to walk abroad into the fields or into the country that belongeth to the same city that he dwelleth in, obtaining the goodwill of his father and the consent of his wife, he is not prohibited. But into what part of the country soever he cometh he hath no meat given him until he have wrought out his forenoon's task or dispatched so much work as there is wont to be wrought before supper.   Observing this law and condition, he may go whither he will within the bounds of his own city; for he shall be no less profitable to the city than if he were within it. Now you see how little liberty they have to loiter, how they can have no cloak or pretence to idleness.   There be neither wine-taverns, nor ale-houses, nor stews, nor any occasion of vice or wickedness, no lurking corners, no places of wicked councils or unlawful assemblies.   But they be in the present sight and under the eyes of every man.   So that of necessity they must either apply their accustomed labours, or else recreate themselves with honest and laudable pastimes.

This fashion and trade of life being used among the people, it cannot be chosen but that they must of necessity have store and plenty of all things.   And seeing they be all thereof partners equally, therefore can no man there be poor or needy. In the council of Amaurote, whither, as I said, every city sendeth three men apiece yearly, as soon as it is perfectly known of what things there is in every place plenty, and again what things be scant in any place, incontinent the lack of the one is performed and filled up with the abundance of the other.   And this they do freely without any benefit, taking nothing again of them to whom the things is given, but those cities that have given of their store to any other city that lacketh, requiring nothing again of the same city, do take such things as they lack of another city to the which they gave nothing.   So the whole island is as it were one family or household.   But when they have made sufficient provision of store for themselves (which they think not done until they have provided for two years following, because of the uncertainty of the next year's proof), then of those things whereof they have abundance they carry forth into other countries great plenty: as grain, honey, wool, flax, wood, madder, purple-dyed fells, wax, tallow, leather, and living beasts. And the seventh part of all these things they give frankly and freely to the poor of that country. The residue they sell at a reasonable and mean price. By this trade of traffic or merchandise they bring into their own country not only great plenty of gold and silver, but also all such things as they lack at home, which is almost nothing but iron. And by reason they have long used this trade, now they have more abundance of these things than any men will believe.

Now, therefore, they care not whether they sell for ready money, or else upon trust to be paid at a day and to have the most part in debts. But in so doing they never follow the credence of private men, but the assurance or warrantise of the whole city by instruments and writings made in that behalf accordingly. When the day of payment is come and expired, the city gathereth up the debt of the private debtors and putteth it into the common box, and so long hath the use and profit of it until the Utopians, their creditors, demand it. The most part of it they never ask, for that thing which is to them no profit to take it from other to whom it is profitable, they think it no right nor conscience. But if the case so stand that they must lend part of that money to another people, then they require their debt, or when they have war. For the which purpose only they keep at home all the treasure which they have, to be helpen and succoured by it either in extreme jeopardies, or in sudden dangers, but especially and chiefly to hire therewith, and that for unreasonable great wages, strange soldiers. For they had rather put strangers in jeopardy than their own countrymen, knowing that for money enough their enemies themselves many times may be bought or sold, or else through treason be set together by the ears among themselves. For this cause they keep an inestimable treasure, but yet not as a treasure, but so they have it and use it, as in good faith I am ashamed to shew, fearing that my words shall not be believed. And this I have more cause to fear, for that I know how difficult and hardly I myself would have believed another man telling the same, if I had not presently seen it with mine own eyes.

For it must needs be that how far a thing is dissonant and disagreeing from the guise and trade of the hearers, so far shall it be out of their belief. Howbeit, a wise and indifferent esteemer of things will not greatly marvel perchance, seeing all their other laws and customs do so much differ from ours, if the use also of gold and silver among them be applied rather to their own fashions than to ours. I mean, in that they occupy not money themselves, but keep it for that chance which, as it may happen, so it may be that it shall never come to pass. In the meantime gold and silver, whereof money is made, they do so use as none of them doth more esteem it than the very nature of the thing deserveth. And then who doth not plainly see how far it is under iron, as without the which men can no better live than without fire and water? Whereas to gold and silver nature hath given no use that we may not well lack if that the folly of men had not set it in higher estimation for the rareness' sake. But of the contrary part, nature, as a most tender and loving mother, hath placed the best and most necessary things open abroad, as the air, the water, and the earth itself, and hath removed and hid farthest from us vain and unprofitable things. Therefore if these metals among them should be fast locked up in some tower, it might be suspected that the prince and the council (as the people is ever foolishly imagining) intended by some subtlety to deceive the commons and to take some profit of it to themselves. Furthermore, if they should make thereof plate and such other finely and cunningly wrought stuff, if at any time they should have occasion to break it and melt it again, therewith to pay their soldiers' wages, they see and perceive very well that men would be loath to part from those things, that they once began to have pleasure and delight in. To remedy all this they have found out a means which, as it is agreeable to all their other laws and customs, so it is from ours (where gold is so much set by and so diligently kept) very far discrepant and repugnant, and therefore incredible, but only to them that be wise. For whereas they eat and drink in earthen and glass vessels which, indeed, be curiously and properly made and yet be of very small value, of gold and silver they make commonly chamber-pots and other vessels that serve for most vile uses not only in their common halls but in every man's private house. Furthermore, of the same metals they make great chains, fetters, and gyves wherein they tie their bondmen. Finally whosoever for any offence be infamed, by their ears hang rings of gold, upon their fingers they wear rings of gold, and about their necks chains of gold, and, in conclusion, their heads be tied about with gold. Thus by all means possible they procure to have gold and silver among them in reproach and infamy. And these metals, which other nations do as grievously and sorrowfully forgo, as in a manner their own lives, if they should altogether at once be taken from the Utopians, no man there would think that he had lost the worth of one farthing. They gather also pearls by the seaside, and diamonds and carbuncles upon certain rocks; and yet they seek not for them, but by chance finding them, they cut and polish them, and therewith they deck their young infants. Which, like as in the first years of their childhood they make much and be fond and proud of such ornaments, so when they be a little more grown in years and discretion, perceiving that none but children do wear such toys and trifles, they lay them away even of their own shamefastness, without any bidding of their parents, even as our children, when they wax big, do cast away nuts, brooches, and puppets. Therefore these laws and customs, which be so far different from all other nations, how divers fantasies also and minds they do cause, did I never so plainly perceive as in the ambassadors of the Anemolians.

These ambassadors came to Amaurote while I was there. And because they came to entreat of great and weighty matters, those three citizens apiece out of every city were come thither before them. But all the ambassadors of the next countries, which had been there before and knew the fashions and manners of the Utopians, among whom they perceived no honour given to sumptuous apparel, silks to be condemned, gold also to be infamed and reproachful, were wont to come thither in very homely and simple array. But the Anemolians, because they dwell far thence and had very little acquaintance with them, hearing that they were all apparelled alike, and that very rudely and homely, thinking them not to have the things which they did not wear, being therefore more proud than wise, determined in the gorgeousness of their apparel to represent very gods, and with the bright shining and glistering of their gay clothing to dazzle the eyes of the silly poor Utopians. So there came in three ambassadors with an hundred servants all apparelled in changeable colours, the most of them in silks. The ambassadors themselves (for at home in their own country they were noblemen) in cloth of gold, with great chains of gold, with gold hanging at their ears, with gold rings upon their fingers, with brooches and aglets of gold upon their caps which glistered full of pearls and precious stones, to be short, trimmed and adorned with all those things which among the Utopians were either the punishment of bondmen or the reproach of infamed persons or else trifles for young children to play withal.

Therefore it would have done a man good at his heart to have seen how proudly they displayed their peacock's feathers, how much they made of their painted sheaths, and how loftily they set forth and advanced themselves when they compared their gallant apparel with the poor raiment of the Utopians. For all the people were swarmed forth into the streets. And on the other side it was no less pleasure to consider how much they were deceived and how far they missed of their purpose, being contrarywise taken than they thought they should have been. For to the eyes of all the Utopians, except very few which had been in other countries for some reasonable cause, all that gorgeousness of apparel seemed shameful and reproachful. Insomuch that they most reverently saluted the vilest and most abject of them for lords, passing over the ambassadors themselves without any honour, judging them by their wearing of golden chains to be bondmen. Yea, you should have seen children also that had cast away their pearls and precious stones, when they saw the like sticking upon the ambassadors' caps, dig and push their mothers under the sides, saying thus to them: Look, mother, how great a lubber doth yet wear pearls and precious stones as though he were a little child still. But the mother, yea and that also in good earnest, Peace, son, saith she, I think he be some of the ambassadors' fools. Some found fault at their golden chains as to no use nor purpose, being so small and weak that a bondman might easily break them, and again so wide and large, that when it pleased him he might cast them off and run away at liberty whither he would. But when the ambassadors had been there a day or two and saw so great abundance of gold so lightly esteemed, yea, in no less reproach than it was with them in honour, and, besides that, more gold in the chains and gyves of one fugitive bondman than all the costly ornaments of them three was worth, they began to abate their courage, and for very shame laid away all that gorgeous array whereof they were so proud, and specially when they had talked familiarly with the Utopians, and had learned all their fashions and opinions.

For they marvel that any men be so foolish as to have delight and pleasure in the doubtful glistering of a little trifling stone, which may behold any of the stars, or else the sun itself. Or that any man is so mad as to count himself the nobler for the smaller or finer thread of wool, which self-same wool (be it now in never so fine a spun thread) a sheep did once wear, and yet was she all that time no other thing than a sheep. They marvel also that gold, which of its own nature is a thing so unprofitable, is now among all people in so high estimation, that man himself, by whom, yea, and for the use of whom, it is so much set by, is in much less estimation than the gold itself. Insomuch that a lumpish blockheaded

churl, and which hath no more wit than an ass, yea, and as full
of naughtiness as of folly, shall have nevertheless many wise
and good men in subjection and bondage only for this,
because he hath a great heap of gold.   Which if it should be
taken from him by any fortune or by some subtle wile and
cautel of the law (which no less than fortune doth both raise
up the low and pluck down the high) and be given to the most
vile slave and abject drivel of all his household, then shortly
after he shall go into the service of his servant, as an augmen-
tation or overplus beside his money.   But they much more
marvel at and detest the madness of them which to those rich
men, in whose debt and danger they be not, do give almost
divine honours for none other consideration but because they
be rich, and yet knowing them to be such niggish penny-
fathers, that they be sure as long as they live not the worth of
one farthing of that heap of gold shall come to them.

These and suchlike opinions have they conceived, partly by
education, being brought up in that commonwealth whose
laws and customs be far different from these kinds of folly,
and partly by good literature and learning.   For though there
be not many in every city which be exempt and discharged of
all other labours and appointed only to learning (that is to say,
such in whom, even from their very childhood, they have
perceived a singular towardness, a fine wit, and a mind apt to
good learning), yet all in their childhood be instruct in
learning.   And the better part of the people, both men and
women, throughout all their whole life do bestow in learning
those spare hours which we said they have vacant from bodily
labours.   They be taught learning in their own native tongue.
For it is both copious in words and also pleasant to the ear,
and for the utterance of a man's mind very perfect and sure.
The most part of all that side of the world useth the same
language, saving that among the Utopians it is finest and
purest, and according to the diversity of the countries it is
diversely altered.   Of all these philosophers whose names
be here famous in this part of the world to us known, before

our coming thither not as much as the fame of any of them was common among them.   And yet in music, logic, arithmetic, and geometry they have found out in a manner all that our ancient philosophers have taught.

But as they in all things be almost equal to our old ancient clerks, so our new logicians in subtle inventions have far passed and gone beyond them.   For they have not devised one of all those rules of restrictions, amplifications, and suppositions, very wittily invented in the small logicals which here our children in every place do learn.   Furthermore, they were never yet able to find out the second intentions, insomuch that none of them all could ever see man himself in common, as they call him, though he be (as you know) bigger than ever was any giant, yea, and pointed to of us even with our finger.

But they be in the course of the stars and the movings of the heavenly spheres very expert and cunning.   They have also wittily excogitated and devised instruments of divers fashions, wherein is exactly comprehended and contained the movings and situations of the sun, the moon, and of all the other stars which appear in their horizon.   But as for the amities and dissensions of the planets, and all that deceitful divination by the stars, they never as much as dreamed thereof.   Rains, winds, and other courses of tempest they know before by certain tokens which they have learned by long use and observation.   But of the causes of all these things and of the ebbing, flowing, and saltness of the sea, and finally of the original beginning and nature of heaven and of the world, they hold partly the same opinions that our old philosophers hold, and partly, as our philosophers vary among themselves, so they also, while they bring new reasons of things, do disagree from all them, and yet among themselves in all points they do not accord.

In that part of philosophy which entreateth of manners and virtue their reasons and opinions agree with ours.   They dispute of the good qualities of the soul, of the body, and of

fortune, and whether the name of goodness may be applied
to all these or only to the endowments and gifts of the soul.
They reason of virtue and pleasure; but the chief and principal question is in what thing, be it one or more, the felicity
of man consisteth.   But in this point they seem almost too
much given and inclined to the opinion of them which defend
pleasure, wherein they determine either all or the chiefest part
of man's felicity to rest.   And (which is more to be marvelled
at) the defence of this so dainty and delicate an opinion they
fetch even from their grave, sharp, bitter, and rigorous
religion.   For they never dispute of felicity or blessedness
but they join unto the reasons of philosophy certain principles
taken out of religion, without the which to the investigation
of true felicity they think reason of itself weak and unperfect.
Those principles be these and suchlike: That the soul is
immortal, and by the bountiful goodness of God ordained to
felicity.   That to our virtues and good deeds rewards be
appointed after this life, and to our evil deeds punishments.
Though these be pertaining to religion, yet they think it meet
that they should be believed and granted by proofs of reason.
But if these principles were condemned and disannulled, then
without any delay they pronounce no man to be so foolish
which would not do all his diligence and endeavour to obtain
pleasure by right or wrong, only avoiding this inconvenience,
that the less pleasure should not be a let or hindrance to the
bigger, or that he laboured not for that pleasure which would
bring after it displeasure, grief, and sorrow.   For they judge
it extreme madness to follow sharp and painful virtue, and not
only to banish the pleasure of life, but also willingly to suffer
grief, without any hope of profit thereof ensuing.   For what
profit can there be if a man, when he hath passed over all his
life unpleasantly, that is to say, miserably, shall have no
reward after his death?

But now, sir, they think not felicity to rest in all pleasure,
but only in that pleasure that is good and honest, and that
hereto as to perfect blessedness our nature is allured and

drawn even of virtue, whereto only they that be of the contrary opinion do attribute felicity. For they define virtue to be life ordered according to nature, and that we be hereunto ordained of God. And that he doth follow the course of nature, which in desiring and refusing things is ruled by reason. Furthermore, that reason doth chiefly and principally kindle in men the love and veneration of the Divine Majesty of whose goodness it is that we be, and that we be in possibility to attain felicity. And that secondarily it both stirreth and provoketh us to lead our life out of care in joy and mirth, and also moveth us to help and further all other in respect of the society of nature to obtain and enjoy the same.

For there was never man so earnest and painful a follower of virtue and hater of pleasure, that would so enjoin you labours, watchings, and fastings, but he would also exhort you to ease, lighten, and relieve, to your power, the lack and misery of others, praising the same as a deed of humanity and pity. Then, if it be a point of humanity for man to bring health and comfort to man, and specially (which is a virtue most peculiarly belonging to man) to mitigate and assuage the grief of others, and by taking from them the sorrow and heaviness of life to restore them to joy, that is to say, to pleasure, why may it not then be said that nature doth provoke every man to do the same to himself? For a joyful life, that is to say, a pleasant life, is either evil; and if it be so, then thou shouldest not only help no man thereto, but rather, as much as in thee lieth, withdraw all men from it as noisome and hurtful; or else if thou not only mayst, but also of duty art bound, to procure it to other, why not chiefly to thyself to whom thou art bound to shew as much favour and gentleness as to other? For when nature biddeth thee to be good and gentle to other she commandeth thee not to be cruel and ungentle to thyself. Therefore even very nature (say they) prescribeth to us a joyful life, that is to say, pleasure, as the end of all our operations. And they define virtue to be life ordered according to the prescript of nature.

* D 461

But in that that nature doth allure and provoke men one to help another to live merrily (which surely she doth not without a good cause, for no man is so far above the lot of man's state or condition, that nature doth cark and care for him only which equally favoureth all that be comprehended under the communion of one shape, form, and fashion), verily she commandeth thee to use diligent circumspection, that thou do not so seek for thine own commodities, that thou procure others' incommodities. Wherefore their opinion is, that not only covenants and bargains made among private men ought to be well and faithfully fulfilled, observed, and kept, but also common laws, which either a good prince hath justly published, or else the people, neither oppressed with tyranny, neither deceived by fraud and guile, hath by their common consent constituted and ratified concerning the partition of the commodities of life, that is to say, the matter of pleasure. These laws not offended, it is wisdom that thou look to thine own wealth. And to do the same for the commonwealth is no less than thy duty, if thou bearest any reverent love or any natural zeal and affection to thy native country. But to go about to let another man of his pleasure whiles thou procurest thine own, that is open wrong. Contrariwise, to withdraw something from thyself to give to others, that is a point of humanity and gentleness, which never taketh away so much commodity as it bringeth again. For it is recompensed with the return of benefits; and the conscience of the good deed, with the remembrance of the thankful love and benevolence of them to whom thou hast done it, doth bring more pleasure to thy mind than that which thou hast withholden from thyself could have brought to thy body. Finally (which to a godly-disposed and a religious mind is easy to be persuaded), God recompenseth the gift of a short and small pleasure with great and everlasting joy.

Therefore, the matter diligently weighed and considered, thus they think, that all our actions, and in them the virtues themselves, be referred at the last to pleasure as their end and felicity.   Pleasure they call every motion and state of the body or mind wherein man hath naturally delectation. Appetite they join to nature, and that not without a good cause.   For like as not only the senses, but also right reason, coveteth whatsoever is naturally pleasant, so that it may be gotten without wrong or injury, not letting or debarring a greater pleasure nor causing painful labour, even so those things that men by vain imagination do feign against nature to be pleasant (as though it lay in their power to change the things, as they do the names of things), all such pleasures they believe to be of so small help and furtherance to felicity, that they count them a great let and hindrance.   Because that in whom they have once taken place, all his mind they possess with a false opinion of pleasure, so that there is no place left for true and natural delectations.   For there be many things which of their own nature contain no pleasantness, yea, the most part of them much grief and sorrow; and yet, through the perverse and malicious flickering enticements of lewd and unhonest desires, be taken not only for special and sovereign pleasures, but also be counted among the chief causes of life.

In this counterfeit kind of pleasure they put them that I spake of before, which, the better gowns they have on, the better men they think themselves.   In the which thing they do twice err, for they be no less deceived in that they think their gown the better, than they be in that they think themselves the better.   For if you consider the profitable use of the garment, why should wool of a finer-spun thread be thought better than the wool of a coarse-spun thread?   Yet they, as though the one did pass the other by nature and not by their mistaking, advance themselves, and think the price of their own persons thereby greatly increased.   And therefore the honour which in a coarse gown they durst not have looked for, they require, as it were of duty, for their finer gown's sake. And if they be passed by without reverence, they take it displeasantly and disdainfully.   And again, is it not like madness to take a pride in vain and unprofitable honours?

For what natural or true pleasure dost thou take of another man's bare head or bowed knees? Will this ease the pain of thy knees or remedy the frenzy of thy head? In this image of counterfeit pleasure they be of a marvellous madness, which for the opinion of nobility rejoice much in their own conceit, because it was their fortune to come of such ancestors whose stock of long time hath been counted rich (for now nobility is nothing else), specially rich in lands. And though their ancestors left them not one foot of land, or else they themselves have pissed it against the walls, yet they think themselves not the less noble therefore of one hair.

In this number also they count them that take pleasure and delight (as I said) in gems and precious stones, and think themselves almost gods if they chance to get an excellent one, specially of that kind which in that time of their own country-men is had in highest estimation. For one kind of stone keepeth not his price still in all countries and at all times. Nor they buy them not, but taken out of the gold and bare; no nor so neither, until they have made the seller to swear that he will warrant and assure it to be a true stone and no counter-feit gem. Such care they take lest a counterfeit stone should deceive their eyes instead of a right stone. But why shouldest thou not take even as much pleasure in beholding a counterfeit stone, which thine eye cannot discern from a right stone? They should both be of like value to thee, even as to the blind man. What shall I say of them that keep super-fluous riches, to take delectation only in the beholding and not in the use or occupying thereof? Do they take true pleasure, or else be they deceived with false pleasure? Or of them that be in a contrary vice, hiding the gold which they shall never occupy, nor peradventure never see more? And whiles they take care lest they shall lose it, do lose it indeed. For what is it else, when they hide it in the ground, taking it both from their own use and perchance from all other men's also? And yet thou, when thou hast hid thy treasure, as one out of all care hoppest for joy. The which treasure, if it should chance to be stolen, and thou ignorant of the theft shouldst die ten years after, all that ten years' space that thou livest after thy money was stolen, what matter was it to thee whether it had been taken away or else safe as thou leftest it? Truly both ways like profit came to thee.

To these so foolish pleasures they join dicers, whose madness they know by hearsay and not by use. Hunters also, and hawkers. For what pleasure is there (say they) in casting the dice upon a table, which thou hast done so often, that if there were any pleasure in it, yet the oft use might make thee weary thereof? Or what delight can there be, and not rather displeasure, in hearing the barking and howling of dogs? Or what greater pleasure is there to be felt when a dog followeth an hare than when a dog followeth a dog? For one thing is done in both, that is to say, running, if thou hast pleasure therein. But if the hope of slaughter and the expectation of tearing in pieces the beast doth please thee, thou shouldest rather be moved with pity to see a silly innocent hare murdered of a dog: the weak of the stronger, the fearful of the fierce, the innocent of the cruel and unmerciful. Therefore all this exercise of hunting, as a thing unworthy to be used of free men, the Utopians have rejected to their butchers, to the which craft (as we said before) they appoint their bondmen. For they count hunting the lowest, the vilest, and most abject part of butchery, and the other parts of it more profitable and more honest, as bringing much more commodity, in that they kill beasts only for necessity, whereas the hunter seeketh nothing but pleasure of the silly and woeful beast's slaughter and murder. The which pleasure in beholding death they think doth rise in the very beasts, either of a cruel affection of mind, or else to be changed in continuance of time into cruelty by long use of so cruel a pleasure.

These, therefore, and all suchlike, which be innumerable, though the common sort of people doth take them for pleasures, yet they, seeing there is no natural pleasantness in them, do plainly determine them to have no affinity with true

and right pleasure.   For as touching that they do commonly
move the sense with delectation (which seemeth to be a work
of pleasure), this doth nothing diminish their opinion.   For
not the nature of the thing, but their perverse and lewd
custom is the cause hereof, which causeth them to accept
bitter or sour things for sweet things even as women with
child in their vitiate and corrupt taste think pitch and tallow
sweeter than any honey.   Howbeit, no man's judgment
depraved and corrupt, either by sickness or by custom, can
change the nature of pleasure more than it can do the nature
of other things.

They make divers kinds of true pleasures.   For some they
attribute to the soul and some to the body.   To the soul they
give intelligence and that delectation that cometh of the
contemplation of truth.   Hereunto is joined the pleasant
remembrance of the good life past.   The pleasure of the body
they divide into two parts.   The first is when delectation is
sensibly felt and perceived, which many times chanceth by
the renewing and refreshing of those parts which our natural
heat drieth up.   This cometh by meat and drink, and
sometimes whiles those things be expulsed and voided,
whereof is in the body over-great abundance.   This pleasure
is felt when we do our natural easement, or when we be doing
the act of generation, or when the itching of any part is eased
with rubbing or scratching.   Sometimes pleasure riseth
exhibiting to any member nothing that it desireth, nor taking
from it any pain that it feeleth, which nevertheless tickleth
and moveth our senses with a certain secret efficacy, but with
a manifest motion turneth them to it; as is that which
cometh of music.   The second part of bodily pleasure,
they say, is that which consisteth and resteth in the quiet and
upright state of the body.   And that truly is every man's own
proper health, intermingled and disturbed with no grief.
For this, if it be not letted nor assaulted with no grief, is
delectable of itself, though it be moved with no external or
outward pleasure.   For though it be not so plain and mani-

fest to the sense as the greedy lust of eating and drinking, yet, nevertheless, many take it for the chiefest pleasure. All the Utopians grant it to be a right sovereign pleasure and, as you would say, the foundation and ground of all pleasures, as which even alone is able to make the state and condition of life delectable and pleasant; and it being once taken away, there is no place left for any pleasure. For to be without grief not having health, that they call insensibility and not pleasure.

The Utopians have long ago rejected and condemned the opinion of them which said that steadfast and quiet health (for this question also hath been diligently debated among them) ought not therefore to be counted a pleasure, because, they say, it cannot be presently and sensibly perceived and felt by some outward motion. But of the contrary part now they agree almost all in this, that health is a most sovereign pleasure. For seeing that in sickness (say they) is grief, which is a mortal enemy to pleasure, even as sickness is to health, why should not then pleasure be in the quietness of health? For they say it maketh nothing to this matter, whether you say that sickness is a grief, or that in sickness is grief, for all cometh to one purpose. For whether health be a pleasure itself, or a necessary cause of pleasure, as fire is of heat, truly both ways it followeth that they cannot be without pleasure that be in perfect health. Furthermore, whiles we eat (say they), then health, which began to be appaired, fighteth by the help of food against hunger. In the which fight, whiles health by little and little getteth the upper hand, that same proceeding and (as ye would say) that onwardness to the wont strength ministreth that pleasure whereby we be so refreshed. Health, therefore, which in the conflict is joyful, shall it not be merry when it hath gotten the victory? But as soon as it hath recovered the pristinate strength, which thing only in all the fight it coveted, shall it incontinent be astonied? Nor shall it not know nor embrace the own wealth and goodness? For where it is said health cannot be felt, this, they think, is nothing true. For what man waking, say they, feeleth not himself in health, but he that is not? Is there any man so possessed with stonish insensibility or with lethargy, that is to say, the sleeping sickness, that he will not grant health to be acceptable to him, and delectable?

But what other thing is delectation than that which by another name is called pleasure? They embrace chiefly the pleasures of the mind, for them they count the chiefest and most principal of all. The chief part of them they think doth come of the exercise of virtue and conscience of good life. Of these pleasures that the body ministreth, they give the pre-eminence to health. For the delight of eating and drinking, and whatsoever hath any like pleasantness, they determine to be pleasures much to be desired, but no other ways than for health's sake. For such things of their own proper nature be not so pleasant, but in that they resist sickness privily stealing on. Therefore, like as it is a wise man's part rather to avoid sickness than to wish for medicines, and rather to drive away and put to flight careful griefs than to call for comfort, so it is much better not to need this kind of pleasure than thereby to be eased of the contrary grief. The which kind of pleasure if any man take for his felicity, that man must needs grant that then he shall be in most felicity, if he live that life which is led in continual hunger, thirst, itching, eating, drinking, scratching, and rubbing. The which life how not only foul and unhonest, but also how miserable and wretched it is, who perceiveth not? These doubtless be the basest pleasures of all, as unpure and unperfect. For they never come, but accompanied with their contrary griefs, as with the pleasure of eating is joined hunger, and that after no very equal sort. For of these two the grief is both the more vehement and also of longer continuance, for it beginneth before the pleasure, and endeth not until the pleasure die with it.

Wherefore such pleasures they think not greatly to be set by, but in that they be necessary. Howbeit, they have delight also in these, and thankfully knowledge the tender love

of mother nature, which with most pleasant delectation al-
lureth her children to that, to the necessary use whereof they
must from time to time continually be forced and driven.
For how wretched and miserable should our life be, if these
daily griefs of hunger and thirst could not be driven away but
with bitter potions and sour medicines, as the other diseases
be wherewith we be seldomer troubled? But beauty,
strength, nimbleness, these as peculiar and pleasant gifts of
nature they make much of. But those pleasures that be
received by the ears, the eyes, and the nose, which nature
willeth to be proper and peculiar to man (for no other living
creature doth behold the fairness and the beauty of the world
or is moved with any respect of savours, but only for the
diversity of meats, neither perceiveth the concordant and
discordant distances of sounds and tunes), these pleasures, I
say, they accept and allow as certain pleasant rejoicings of
life. But in all things this cautel they use, that a less pleasure
hinder not a bigger, and that the pleasure be no cause of displeasure, which they think to follow of necessity if the pleasure
be unhonest. But yet to despise the comeliness of beauty, to
waste the bodily strength, to turn nimbleness into sluggish-
ness, to consume and make feeble the body with fasting, to do
injury to health, and to reject the pleasant motions of nature
(unless a man neglect these commodities whiles he doth with
a fervent zeal procure the wealth of others or the common
profit, for the which pleasure forborne he is in hope of a
greater pleasure at God's hand), else for a vain shadow of
virtue for the wealth and profit of no man, to punish himself,
or to the intent he may be able courageously to suffer adversity (which perchance shall never come to him), this to do they
think it a point of extreme madness, and a token of a man
cruelly minded towards himself and unkind towards nature,
as one so disdaining to be in her danger, that he renounceth
and refuseth all her benefits.

This is their sentence and opinion of virtue and pleasure,
and they believe that by man's reason none can be found

truer than this, unless any godlier be inspired into man from heaven. Wherein whether they believe well or no, neither the time doth suffer us to discuss, neither it is now necessary. For we have taken upon us to shew and declare their laws and ordinances, and not to defend them. But this thing I believe verily : howsoever these decrees be, that there is in no place of the world neither a more excellent people, neither a more flourishing commonwealth. They be light and quick of body, full of activity and nimbleness, and of more strength than a man would judge them by their stature, which for all that is not too low. And though their soil be not very fruitful, nor their air very wholesome, yet against the air they so defend them with temperate diet, and so order and husband their ground with diligent travail, that in no country is greater increase and plenty of corn and cattle, nor men's bodies of longer life and subject or apt to fewer diseases. There, therefore, a man may see well and diligently exploited and furnished, not only those things which husbandmen do commonly in other countries, as by craft and cunning to remedy the barrenness of the ground, but also a whole wood by the hands of the people plucked up by the roots in one place, and set again in another place. Wherein was had regard and consideration, not of plenty, but of commodious carriage, that wood and timber might be nigher to the sea or the rivers or the cities; for it is less labour and business to carry grain far by land than wood. The people be gentle, merry, quick, and fine witted, delighting in quietness and, when need requireth, able to abide and suffer much bodily labour. Else they be not greatly desirous and fond of it; but in the exercise and study of the mind they be never weary.

When they had heard me speak of the Greek literature or learning (for in Latin there was nothing that I thought they would greatly allow, besides historians and poets) they made wonderful earnest and importunate suit unto me that I would teach and instruct them in that tongue and learning. I began, therefore, to read unto them at the first, truly, more because I would not seem to refuse the labour than that I hoped that they would anything profit therein. But when I had gone forward a little, I perceived incontinent by their diligence that my labour should not be bestowed in vain. For they began so easily to fashion their letters, so plainly to pronounce the words, so quickly to learn by heart, and so surely to rehearse the same, that I marvelled at it, saving that the most part of them were fine and chosen wits, and of ripe age, picked out of the company of the learned men which not only of their own free and voluntary will, but also by the commandment of the council, undertook to learn this language. Therefore in less than three years' space there was nothing in the Greek tongue that they lacked. They were able to read good authors without any stay, if the book were not false. This kind of learning, as I suppose, they took so much the sooner because, it is somewhat alliant to them. For I think that this nation took their beginning of the Greeks, because their speech, which in all other points is not much unlike the Persian tongue, keepeth divers signs and tokens of the Greek language in the names of their cities and of their magistrates.

They have of me (for when I was determined to enter into my fourth voyage, I cast into the ship in the stead of merchandise a pretty fardel of books, because I intended to come again rather never than shortly), they have, I say, of me the most part of Plato's works, more of Aristotle's, also Theophrastus of plants, but in divers places (which I am sorry for) unperfect. For whiles we were a-shipboard a marmoset chanced upon the book as it was negligently laid by, which wantonly playing therewith plucked out certain leaves and tore them in pieces. Of them that have written the grammar, they have only Lascaris, for Theodorus I carried not with me, nor never a dictionary but Hesychius and Dioscorides. They set great store by Plutarch's books, and they be delighted with Lucian's merry conceits and jests. Of the poets they have Aristophanes, Homer, Euripides, and Sophocles in Aldus' small print. Of the historians they have Thucydides, Herodotus, and Herodian. Also, my companion Tricius Apinatus carried with him physic books, certain small works of Hippocrates, and Galen's *Microtechne*. The which book they have in great estimation; for though there be almost no nation under heaven that hath less need of physic than they, yet this notwithstanding, physic is nowhere in greater honour, because they count the knowledge of it among the goodliest and most profitable parts of philosophy. For whiles they by the help of this philosophy search out the secret mysteries of nature, they think themselves to receive thereby not only wonderful great pleasure, but also to obtain great thanks and favour of the Author and Maker thereof. Whom they think, according to the fashion of other artificers, to have set forth the marvellous and gorgeous frame of the world for man with great affection intentively to behold. Whom only He hath made of wit and capacity to consider and understand the excellency of so great a work. And therefore He beareth (say they) more goodwill and love to the curious and diligent beholder and viewer of His work and marveller at the same than He doth to him which, like a very brute beast without wit and reason, or as one without sense or moving, hath no regard to so great and so wonderful a spectacle. The wits, therefore, of the Utopians, inured and exercised in learning, be marvellous quick in the invention of feats helping anything to the advantage and wealth of life. Howbeit, two feats they may thank us for, that is, the science of imprinting and the craft of making paper. And yet not only us, but chiefly and principally themselves.

For when we shewed to them Aldus his print in books of paper, and told them of the stuff whereof paper is made, and of the feat of graving letters, speaking somewhat more than we could plainly declare (for there was none of us that knew perfectly either the one or the other), they forthwith very wittily conjectured the thing. And whereas before they wrote only in skins, in barks of trees, and in reeds, now they have attempted to make paper and to imprint letters. And though at the first it proved not all of the best, yet by often assaying the same they shortly got the feat of both, and have so brought the matter about that if they had copies of Greek authors they could lack no books. But now they have no more than I rehearsed before, saving that by printing of books they have multiplied and increased the same into many thousands of copies. Whosoever cometh thither to see the land, being excellent in any gift of wit, or through much and long journeying well experienced and seen in the knowledge of many countries (for the which cause we were very welcome to them), him they receive and entertain wondrous gently and lovingly. For they have delight to hear what is done in every land, howbeit very few merchant men come thither. For what should they bring thither, unless it were iron, or else gold and silver, which they had rather carry home again? Also such things as are to be carried out of their land, they think it more wisdom to carry that gear forth themselves, than that other should come thither to fetch it, to the intent they may the better know the outlands on every side of them, and keep in use the feat and knowledge of sailing.

Of Bondmen, Sick Persons, Wedlock, and divers other Matters

They neither make bondmen of prisoners taken in battle, unless it be in battle that they fought themselves, nor of bondmen's children, nor, to be short, of any such as they can get out of foreign countries, though he were there a bondman, but either such as among themselves for heinous offences be punished with bondage, or else such as in the cities of other lands for great trespasses be condemned to death. And of this sort of bondmen they have most store.

For many of them they bring home, sometimes paying very little for them, yea, most commonly getting them for gramercy. These sorts of bondmen they keep not only in continual work and labour, but also in bonds. But their own men they handle hardest, whom they judge more desperate, and to have deserved greater punishment, because they being so godly brought up to virtue in so excellent a commonwealth, could not for all that be refrained from misdoing.   Another kind of bondmen they have, when a vile drudge being a poor labourer in another country doth choose of his own free will to be a bondman among them.   These they entreat and order honestly, and entertain almost as gently as their own free citizens, saving that they put them to a little more labour, as thereto accustomed.   If any such be disposed to depart thence (which seldom is seen) they neither hold him against his will, neither send him away with empty hands.

The sick (as I said) they see to with great affection, and let nothing at all pass concerning either physic or good diet, whereby they may be restored again to their health.   Such as be sick of incurable diseases they comfort with sitting by them, with talking with them, and, to be short, with all manner of helps that may be.   But if the disease be not only incurable, but also full of continual pain and anguish, then the priests and the magistrates exhort the man (seeing he is not able to do any duty of life, and by overliving his own death is noisome and irksome to other and grievous to himself), that he will determine with himself no longer to cherish that pestilent and painful disease; and, seeing his life is to him but a torment, that he will not be unwilling to die, but rather take a good hope to him, and either dispatch himself out of that painful life, as out of a prison or a rack of torment, or else suffer himself willingly to be rid out of it by other.   And in so doing they tell him he shall do wisely, seeing by his death he shall lose no commodity, but end his pain.   And because in that act he shall follow the counsel of the priests, that is to say, of the interpreters of God's will and pleasure, they shew him that he shall do like a godly and a virtuous man.   They that be thus persuaded finish their lives willingly, either with hunger, or else die in their sleep without any feeling of death.   But they cause none such to die against his will, nor they use no less diligence and attendance about him, believing this to be an honourable death. Else he that killeth himself before that the priests and the council have allowed the cause of his death, him as unworthy either to be buried or with fire to be consumed, they cast unburied into some stinking marsh.

The woman is not married before she be eighteen years old. The man is four years older before he marry. If either the man or the woman be proved to have actually offended, before their marriage, with another, the party that so hath trespassed is sharply punished, and both the offenders be forbidden ever after in all their life to marry, unless the fault be for-given by the prince's pardon. But both the goodman and the goodwife of the house where that offence was committed, as being slack and negligent in looking to their charge, be in danger of great reproach and infamy. That offence is so sharply punished because they perceive that unless they be diligently kept from the liberty of this vice, few will join together in the love of marriage, wherein all the life must be led with one, and also all the griefs and displeasures coming therewith patiently be taken and borne.

Furthermore, in choosing wives and husbands they observe earnestly and straitly a custom which seemed to us very fond and foolish. For a sad and an honest matron sheweth the woman, be she maid or widow, naked to the wooer. And likewise a sage and discreet man exhibiteth the wooer naked to the woman. At this custom we laughed, and disallowed it as foolish. But they, on the other part, do greatly wonder at the folly of all other nations which, in buying a colt, whereas a little money is in hazard, be so chary and circumspect, that though he be almost all bare, yet they will not buy him unless the saddle and all the harness be taken off, lest under those coverings be hid some gall or sore. And yet in choosing a wife, which shall be either pleasure or displeasure to them all their life after, they be so reckless, that all the residue of the woman's body being covered with clothes, they esteem her scarcely by one handbreadth (for they can see no more but her face), and so to join her to them not without great jeopardy of evil agreeing together, if anything in her body afterward should chance to offend and mislike them. For all men be not so wise as to have respect to the virtuous conditions of the party. And the endowments of the body cause the virtues of the mind more to be esteemed and regarded, yea, even in the marriages of wise men. Verily so foul deformity may be hid under those coverings, that it may quite alienate and take away the man's mind from his wife, when it shall not be lawful for their bodies to be separate again. If such deformity happen by any chance after the marriage is consummate and finished, well, there is no remedy but patience. Every man must take his fortune well a worth. But it were well done that a law were made whereby all such deceits might be eschewed and avoided beforehand.

And this were they constrained more earnestly to look upon, because they only of the nations in that part of the world be content every man with one wife apiece. And matrimony is there never broken but by death, except adultery break the bond, or else the intolerable wayward manners of either party. For if either of them find themself for any such cause grieved, they may by the licence of the council change and take another. But the other party liveth ever after in infamy and out of wedlock. Howbeit, the husband to put away his wife for no other fault but for that some mishap is fallen to her body, this by no means they will suffer. For they judge it a great point of cruelty that anybody in their most need of help and comfort should be cast off and forsaken, and that old age, which both bringeth sickness with it and is a sickness itself, should unkindly and unfaithfully be dealt withal. But now and then it chanceth whereas the man and the woman cannot well agree between themselves, both of them finding other, with whom they hope to live more quietly and merrily, that they by the full consent of them both be divorced asunder and married again to other. But

that not without the authority of the council, which agreeth
to no divorces before they and their wives have diligently tried
and examined the matter.   Yea, and then also they be loath to
consent to it, because they know this to be the next way to
break love between man and wife, to be in easy hope of a new
marriage.

Breakers of wedlock be punished with most grievous
bondage; and if both the offenders were married, then
the parties which in that behalf have suffered wrong, being
divorced from the avoutrers, be married together, if they will,
or else to whom they lust.   But if either of them both do still
continue in love toward so unkind a bedfellow, the use of
wedlock is not to them forbidden, if the party faultless be
disposed to follow in toiling and drudgery the person which
for that offence is condemned to bondage.   And very oft it
chanceth that the repentance of the one and the earnest
diligence of the other doth so move the prince with pity and
compassion, that he restoreth the bond person from servitude
to liberty and freedom again.   But if the same party be taken
eftsoons in that fault, there is no other way but death.   To
other trespasses no prescript punishment is appointed by any
law; but according to the heinousness of the offence, or
contrary, so the punishment is moderated by the discretion
of the council.   The husbands chastise their wives, and the
parents their children, unless they have done any so horrible
an offence, that the open punishment thereof maketh much
for the advancement of honest manners.   But most commonly the most heinous faults be punished with the incommodity of bondage.   For that they suppose to be to the
offenders no less grief, and to the commonwealth more profit,
than if they should hastily put them to death, and so make
them quite out of the way.   For there cometh more profit
of their labour than of their death, and by their example
they fear other the longer from like offences.   But if they,
being thus used, do rebel and kick again, then forsooth they
be slain as desperate and wild beasts, whom neither prison

nor chain could restrain and keep under. But they which take their bondage patiently be not left all hopeless. For after they have been broken and tamed with long miseries, if then they shew such repentance as thereby it may be perceived that they be sorrier for their offence than for their punishment, sometimes by the prince's prerogative, and sometimes by the voice and consent of the people, their bondage either is mitigated or else clean released and forgiven. He that moveth to advoutry is in no less danger and jeopardy than if he had committed advoutry in deed. For in all offences they count the intent and pretenced purpose as evil as the act or deed itself, thinking that no let ought to excuse him that did his best to have no let.

They have singular delight and pleasure in fools. And as it is a great reproach to do any of them hurt or injury, so they prohibit not to take pleasure of foolishness. For that, they think, doth much good to the fools. And if any man be so sad and stern that he cannot laugh neither at their words nor at their deeds, none of them be committed to his tuition, for fear lest he would not entreat them gently and favourably enough: to whom they should bring no delectation (for other goodness in them is none), much less any profit should they yield him. To mock a man for his deformity or for that he lacketh any part or limb of his body is counted great dishonesty and reproach, not to him that is mocked, but to him that mocketh, which unwisely doth embraid any man of that as a vice that was not in his power to eschew.

Also, as they count and reckon very little wit to be in him that regardeth not natural beauty and comeliness, so to help the same with paintings is taken for a vain and a wanton pride, not without great infamy. For they know, even by very experience, that no comeliness of beauty doth so highly commend and advance the wives in the conceit of their husbands as honest conditions and lowliness. For as love is oftentimes won with beauty, so it is not kept, preserved and continued but by virtue and obedience. They do not only fear their

people from doing evil by punishments, but also allure them
to virtue with rewards of honour. Therefore they set up in
the market-place the images of notable men and of such as
have been great and bountiful benefactors to the commonwealth, for the perpetual memory of their good acts, and also
that the glory and renown of the ancestors may stir and provoke their posterity to virtue. He that inordinately and
ambitiously desireth promotions is left all hopeless for ever
attaining any promotion as long as he liveth.

They live together lovingly, for no magistrate is either
haughty or fearful. Fathers they be called, and like fathers
they use themselves. The citizens (as it is their duty) willingly exhibit unto them due honour without any compulsion.
Nor the prince himself is not known from the other by
princely apparel or a robe of state, nor by a crown or diadem
royal or cap of maintenance, but by a little sheaf of corn
carried before him. And so a taper of wax is borne before the
bishop, whereby only he is known.

They have but few laws, for to people so instruct and institute very few do suffice. Yea, this thing they chiefly
reprove among other nations, that innumerable books of laws
and expositions upon the same be not sufficient. But they
think it against all right and justice that men should be bound
to those laws which either be in number more than be able
to be read, or else blinder and darker than that any man can
well understand them. Furthermore, they utterly exclude
and banish all attorneys, proctors, and sergeants at the law,
which craftily handle matters, and subtly dispute of the
laws. For they think it most meet that every man should
plead his own matter, and tell the same tale before the judge
that he would tell to his man of law. So shall there be less
circumstance of words, and the truth shall sooner come to
light, whiles the judge with a discreet judgment doth weigh the
words of him whom no lawyer hath instruct with deceit, and
whiles he helpeth and beareth out simple wits against the
false and malicious circumventions of crafty children. This

is hard to be observed in other countries, in so infinite a
number of blind and intricate laws.   But in Utopia every man
is a cunning lawyer; for (as I said) they have very few laws,
and the plainer and grosser that any interpretation is, that they
allow as most just.   For all laws (say they) be made and
published only to the intent that by them every man should
be put in remembrance of his duty.   But the crafty and subtle
interpretation of them (forasmuch as few can attain thereto)
can put very few in that remembrance, whereas the simple,
the plain, and gross meaning of the laws is open to every man.
Else as touching the vulgar sort of the people, which be both
most in number and have most need to know their duties,
were it not as good for them that no law were made at all, as,
when it is made, to bring so blind an interpretation upon it,
that without great wit and long arguing no man can discuss
it?   To the finding out whereof neither the gross judgment
of the people can attain, neither the whole life of them that
be occupied in working for their livings can suffice thereto.

These virtues of the Utopians have caused their next
neighbours and borderers, which live free and under no
subjection (for the Utopians long ago have delivered many of
them from tyranny), to take magistrates of them, some for a
year and some for five years' space.   Which, when the time
of their office is expired, they bring home again with honour
and praise, and take new again with them into their country.
These nations have undoubtedly very well and wholesomely
provided for their commonwealths.   For seeing that both
the making and marring of the weal-public doth depend
and hang upon the manners of the rulers and magistrates,
what officers could they more wisely have chosen than those
which cannot be led from honesty by bribes (for to them that
shortly after shall depart thence into their own country money
should be unprofitable) nor yet be moved either with favour
or malice towards any man, as being strangers and un-
acquainted with the people?   The which two vices of affection and avarice, where they take place in judgments,

incontinent they break justice, the strongest and surest bond of a commonwealth. These peoples which fetch their officers and rulers from them, the Utopians call their fellows. And others to whom they have been beneficial, they call their friends.

As touching leagues, which in other places between country and country be so oft concluded, broken, and renewed, they never make none with any nation. For to what purpose serve leagues, say they, as though nature had not set sufficient love between man and man? And who so regardeth not nature, think you that he will pass for words? They be brought into this opinion chiefly because that in those parts of the world leagues between princes be wont to be kept and observed very slenderly. For here in Europe, and especially in these parts where the faith and religion of Christ reigneth, the majesty of leagues is everywhere esteemed holy and inviolable, partly through the justice and goodness of princes, and partly at the reverence and motion of the head bishops. Which, like as they make no promise themselves but they do very religiously perform the same, so they exhort all princes in any wise to abide by their promises, and them that refuse or deny so to do, by their pontifical power and authority they compel thereto. And surely they think well that it might seem a very reproachful thing if, in the leagues of them which by a peculiar name be called faithful, faith should have no place. But in that new found part of the world, which is scarcely so far from us beyond the line equinoctial as our life and manners be dissident from theirs, no trust nor confidence is in leagues. But the more and holier ceremonies the league is knit up with, the sooner it is broken by some cavillation found in the words, which many times of purpose be so craftily put in and placed, that the bands can never be so sure nor so strong but they will find some hole open to creep out at, and to break both league and truth. The which crafty dealing, yea, the which fraud and deceit, if they should know it to be practised among private men in their bargains and contracts, they would incontinent cry out at it with an open mouth and a sour countenance, as an offence most detestable, and worthy to be punished with a shameful death, yea, even they that advance themselves authors of like counsel given to princes.   Wherefore it may well be thought, either that all justice is but a base and a low virtue and which avaleth itself far under the high dignity of kings, or, at the least wise, that there be two justices: the one meet for the inferior sort of the people, going afoot and creeping low by the ground, and bound down on every side with many bands because it shall not run at rovers; the other a princely virtue, which like as it is of much higher majesty than the other poor justice, so also it is of much more liberty, as to the which nothing is unlawful that it lusteth after.   These manners of princes (as I said) which be there so evil keepers of leagues, cause the Utopians, as I suppose, to make no leagues at all, which perchance would change their mind if they lived here.   Howbeit, they think that though leagues be never so faithfully observed and kept, yet the custom of making leagues was very evil begun.   For this causeth men (as though nations which be separate asunder by the space of a little hill or a river were coupled together by no society or bond of nature) to think themselves born adversaries and enemies one to another, and that it were lawful for the one to seek the death and destruction of the other if leagues were not; yea, and that after the leagues be accorded, friendship doth not grow and increase, but the licence of robbing and stealing doth still remain, as far forth as, for lack of foresight and advisement in writing the words of the league, any sentence or clause to the contrary is not therein sufficiently comprehended.   But they be of a contrary opinion, that is, that no man ought to be counted an enemy which hath done no injury; and that the fellowship of nature is a strong league, and that men be better and more surely knit together by love and benevolence than by covenants of leagues, by hearty affection of mind than by words.

Of Warfare

War or battle as a thing very beastly, and yet to no kind of beasts in so much use as to man, they do detest and abhor. And, contrary to the custom almost of all other nations, they count nothing so much against glory as glory gotten in war. And therefore, though they do daily practise and exercise themselves in the discipline of war, and not only the men, but also the women upon certain appointed days, lest they should be to seek in the feat of arms if need should require, yet they never go to battle but either in the defence of their own country or to drive out of their friends' land the enemies that have invaded it, or by their power to deliver from the yoke and bondage of tyranny some people that be therewith oppressed. Which thing they do of mere pity and compassion. Howbeit, they send help to their friends, not ever in their defence, but sometimes also to requite and revenge injuries before to them done. But this they do not unless their counsel and advice in the matter be asked, whiles it is yet new and fresh. For if they find the cause probable, and if the contrary part will not restore again such things as be of them justly demanded, then they be the chief authors and makers of the war. Which they do not only as oft as by inroads and invasions of soldiers preys and booties be driven away, but then also much more mortally when their friends' merchants in any land, either under the pretence of unjust laws or else by the wresting and wrong understanding of good laws, do sustain an unjust accusation under the colour of justice.

Neither the battle which the Utopians fought for the Nephelogetes against the Alaopolitans al ittle before our time was made for any other cause, but that the Nephelogete merchantmen, as the Utopians thought, suffered wrong of the Alaopolitans under the pretence of right. But whether it were right or wrong, it was with so cruel and mortal war revenged, the countries round about joining their help and power to the puissance and malice of both parties, that most flourishing and wealthy peoples being some of them shrewdly shaken, and some of them sharply beaten, the mischiefs were not finished nor ended until the Alaopolitans at the last were yielded up as bondmen into the jurisdiction of the Nephelogetes. For the Utopians fought not this war for themselves. And yet the Nephelogetes before the war, when the Alaopolitans flourished in wealth, were nothing to be compared with them.

So eagerly the Utopians prosecute the injuries done to their friends: yea, in money matters, and not their own likewise. For if they by covin or guile be wiped beside their goods, so that no violence be done to their bodies, they wreak their anger by abstaining from occupying with that nation until they have made satisfaction. Not for because they set less store by their own citizens than by their friends, but that they take the loss of their friends' money more heavily than the loss of their own. Because that their friends' merchantmen, forasmuch as that they lose is their own private goods, sustain great damage by the loss. But their own citizens lose nothing but of the common goods, and of that which was at home plentiful and almost superfluous, else had it not been sent forth. Therefore no man feeleth the loss. And for this cause they think it too cruel an act to revenge that loss with the death of many, the incommodity of the which loss no man feeleth neither in his life nor yet in his living. But if it chance that any of their men in any other country be maimed or killed, whether it be done by a common or a private counsel, knowing and trying out the truth of the matter by their ambassadors, unless the offenders be rendered unto them in recompense of the injury, they will not be appeased, but incontinent they proclaim war against them. The offenders yielded, they punish either with death or with bondage. They be not only sorry, but also ashamed to achieve the victory with bloodshed, counting it great folly to buy precious wares too dear.

They rejoice and avaunt themselves, if they vanquish and

oppress their enemies by craft and deceit. And for that act they make a general triumph, and as if the matter were manfully handled, they set up a pillar of stone in the place where they so vanquished their enemies, in token of the victory. For then they glory, then they boast, and crack that they have played the men indeed when they have so overcome, as no other living creature but only man could: that is to say, by the might and puissance of wit. For with bodily strength (say they) bears, lions, boars, wolves, dogs, and other wild beasts do fight. And as the most part of them do pass us in strength and fierce courage, so in wit and reason we be much stronger than they all.

Their chief and principal purpose in war is to obtain that thing, which if they had before obtained, they would not have moved battle. But if that be not possible, they take so cruel vengeance of them which be in the fault, that ever after they be afeard to do the like. This is their chief and principal intent, which they immediately and first of all prosecute and set forward, but yet so that they be more circumspect in avoiding and eschewing jeopardies than they be desirous of praise and renown. Therefore immediately after that war is once solemnly denounced, they procure many proclamations signed with their own common seal to be set up privily at one time in their enemy's land in places most frequented. In these proclamations they promise great rewards to him that will kill their enemy's prince, and somewhat less gifts, but them very great also, for every head of them whose names be in the said proclamations contained. They be those whom they count their chief adversaries, next unto the prince. Whatsoever is prescribed unto him that killeth any of the proclaimed persons, that is doubled to him that bringeth any of the same to them alive; yea, and to the proclaimed persons themselves, if they will change their minds and come in to them, taking their parts, they proffer the same great rewards with pardon and surety of their lives. Therefore it quickly cometh to pass that their enemies have all other men in suspicion, and be unfaithful and mistrusting among themselves one to another, living in great fear and in no less jeopardy. For it is well known, that divers times the most part of them (and specially the prince himself) hath been betrayed of them in whom they put their most hope and trust. So that there is no manner of act nor deed that gifts and rewards do not enforce men unto. And in rewards they keep no measure, but, remembering and considering into how great hazard and jeopardy they call them, endeavour themselves to recompense the greatness of the danger with like great benefits. And therefore they promise not only wonderful great abundance of gold, but also lands of great revenues lying in most safe places among their friends. And their promises they perform faithfully without any fraud or covin.

This custom of buying and selling adversaries among other people is disallowed as a cruel act of a base and a cowardly mind. But they in this behalf think themselves much praiseworthy, as who like wise men by this means dispatch great wars without any battle or skirmish. Yea, they count it also a deed of pity and mercy, because that by the death of a few offenders the lives of a great number of innocents, as well of their own men as also of their enemies, be ransomed and saved, which in fighting should have been slain. For they do no less pity the base and common sort of their enemies' people, than they do their own, knowing that they be driven and enforced to war against their wills by the furious madness of their princes and heads. If by none of these means the matter go forward as they would have it, then they procure occasions of debate, and dissension to be spread among their enemies, as by bringing the prince's brother or some of the noblemen in hope to obtain the kingdom. If this way prevail not, then they raise up the people that be next neighbours and borderers to their enemies, and them they set in their necks under the colour of some old title of right, such as kings do never lack. To them they promise their help and aid in their war; and as for money, they give them abundance. But of their own citizens they send to them few or none, whom they make so much of and love so entirely, that they would not be willing to change any of them for their adversaries' prince. But their gold and silver, because they keep it all for this only purpose, they lay it out frankly and freely, as who should live even as wealthily if they had bestowed it every penny.

Yea, and besides their riches which they keep at home, they have also an infinite treasure abroad, by reason that (as I said before) many nations be in their debt. Therefore they hire soldiers out of all countries and send them to battle, but chiefly of the Zapoletes. This people is 500 miles from Utopia eastward. They be hideous, savage, and fierce, dwelling in wild woods and high mountains where they were bred and brought up. They be of an hard nature, able to abide and sustain heat, cold, and labour, abhorring from all delicate dainties, occupying no husbandry nor tillage of the ground, homely and rude both in building of their houses and in their apparel, given unto no goodness, but only to the breeding and bringing up of cattle. The most part of their living is by hunting and stealing. They be born only to war, which they diligently and earnestly seek for, and when they have gotten it they be wondrous glad thereof. They go forth of their country in great companies together, and whosoever lacketh soldiers, there they proffer their service for small wages. This is only the craft they have to get their living by. They maintain their life by seeking their death. For them whomwith they be in wages they fight hardly, fiercely, and faithfully. But they bind themselves for no certain time; but upon this condition they enter into bonds, that the next day they will take part with the other side for greater wages, and the next day after that they will be ready to come back again for a little more money. There be few wars thereaway, wherein is not a great number of them in both parties. Therefore it daily chanceth that nigh kinsfolk which were hired together on one part, and there very friendly and familiarly used themselves one with another, shortly after being separate in contrary parts, run one against another enviously and fiercely, and, forgetting both kindred and friendship, thrust their swords one in another. And that for none other cause but that they be hired of contrary princes for a little money, which they do so highly regard and esteem, that they will easily be provoked to change parts for a halfpenny more wages by the day, so quickly they have taken a smack in covetousness, which for all that is to them no profit. For that they get by fighting, immediately they spend unthriftily and wretchedly in riot.

This people fighteth for the Utopians against all nations, because they give them greater wages than any other nation will. For the Utopians, like as they seek good men to use well, so they seek these evil and vicious men to abuse, whom, when need requireth, with promises of great rewards they put forth into great jeopardies. From whence the most part of them never cometh again to ask their rewards. But to them that remain alive they pay that which they promised faithfully, that they may be the more willing to put themselves in like danger another time. Nor the Utopians pass not how many of them they bring to destruction, for they believe that they should do a very good deed for all mankind if they could rid out of the world all that foul stinking den of that most wicked and cursed people. Next unto this they use the soldiers of them for whom they fight, and then the help of their other friends, and last of all they join to their own citizens, among whom they give to one of tried virtue and prowess the rule, governance, and conduction of the whole army. Under him they appoint two other which, whiles he is safe, be both private and out of office. But if he be taken or slain, the one of the other two succeedeth him, as it were by inheritance. And if the second miscarry, then the third taketh his room, lest that (as the chance of battle is uncertain and doubtful) the jeopardy or death of the captain should

bring the whole army in hazard.   They choose soldiers out of
every city those which put forth themselves willingly, for they
thrust no man forth into war against his will, because they
believe if any man be fearful and faint-hearted of nature he
will not only do no manful and hardy act himself, but also
be occasion of cowardness to his fellows.   But if any battle be
made against their own country, then they put these cowards
(so that they be strong-bodied) in ships among other bold-
hearted men.   Or else they dispose them upon the walls,
from whence they may not fly.   Thus what for shame that
their enemies be at hand, and what for because they be without hope of running away, they forget all fear.   And many
times extreme necessity turneth cowardness into prowess and
manliness.

But as none of them is thrust forth of his country into war
against his will, so women that be willing to accompany their
husbands in times of war be not prohibited or letted.   Yea,
they provoke and exhort them to it with praises, and in set
field the wives do stand every one by their own husband's side.
Also every man is compassed next about with his own
children, kinsfolk, and alliance, that they whom nature
chiefly moveth to mutual succour, thus standing together,
may help one another.   It is a great reproach and dishonesty
for the husband to come home without his wife, or the wife
without her husband, or the son without his father.   And
therefore if the other part stick so hard by it that the battle
come to their hands, it is fought with great slaughter and
bloodshed, even to the utter destruction of both parts.
For as they make all the means and shifts that may be to keep
themselves from the necessity of fighting or that they may
dispatch the battle by their hired soldiers, so when there is
no remedy, but that they must needs fight themselves, then
they do as courageously fall to it, as before, whiles they might,
they did wisely avoid and refuse it.   Nor they be not most
fierce at the first brunt.   But in continuance by little and
little their fierce courage increaseth with so stubborn and

obstinate minds, that they will rather die than give back an inch. For that surety of living which every man hath at home being joined with no careful anxiety or remembrance how their posterity shall live after them (for this pensiveness oftentimes breaketh and abateth courageous stomachs) maketh them stout and hardy and disdainful to be conquered. Moreover, their knowledge in chivalry and feats of arms putteth them in a good hope. Finally the wholesome and virtuous opinions wherein they were brought up even from their childhood, partly through learning and partly through the good ordinances and laws of their weal-public, augment and increase their manful courage. By reason whereof they neither set so little store by their lives that they will rashly and unadvisedly cast them away, nor they be not so far in lewd and fond love therewith, that they will shamefully covet to keep them when honesty biddeth leave them.

When the battle is hottest and in all places most fierce and fervent, a band of chosen and picked young men, which be sworn to live and die together, take upon them to destroy their adversaries' captain, whom they invade, now with privy wiles, now by open strength. At him they strike both near and far off. He is assailed with a long and a continual assault, fresh men still coming in the wearied men's places. And seldom it chanceth (unless he save himself by flying) that he is not either slain, or else taken prisoner and yielded to his enemies alive. If they win the field they persecute not their enemies with the violent rage of slaughter, for they had rather take them alive than kill them. Neither they do so follow the chase and pursuit of their enemies, but they leave behind them one part of their host in battle array under their standards. Insomuch that if all their whole army be discomfited and overcome, saving the rearward, and that they therewith achieve the victory, then they had rather let all their enemies escape than to follow them out of array. For they remember it hath chanced unto themselves more than once, the whole power and strength of their host being vanquished and put to flight whiles their enemies rejoicing in the victory have persecuted them flying some one way and some another, a small company of their men lying in an ambush, there ready at all occasions, have suddenly risen upon them thus dispersed and scattered out of array and through presumption of safety unadvisedly pursuing the chase, and have incontinent changed the fortune of the whole battle, and spite of their teeth wresting out of their hands the sure and undoubted victory, being a little before conquered, have for their part conquered the conquerors. It is hard to say whether they be craftier in laying an ambush, or wittier in avoiding the same. You would think they intend to fly when they mean nothing less; and contrariwise, when they go about that purpose you would believe it were the least part of their thought. For if they perceive themselves either overmatched in number or closed in too narrow a place, then they remove their camp; either in the night season with silence or by some policy they deceive their enemies, or in the daytime they retire back so softly, that it is no less jeopardy to meddle with them when they give back than when they press on.

They fence and fortify their camp surely with a deep and a broad trench. The earth thereof is cast inward. Nor they do not set drudges and slaves awork about it; it is done by the hands of the soldiers themselves. All the whole army worketh upon it, except them that keep watch and ward in harness before the trench for sudden adventures. Therefore, by the labour of so many a large trench closing in a great compass of ground is made in less time than any man would believe. Their armour or harness which they wear is sure and strong to receive strokes, and handsome for all movings and gestures of the body, insomuch that it is not unwieldy to swim in. For in the discipline of their warfare among other feats they learn to swim in harness. Their weapons be arrows aloof, which they shoot both strongly and surely, not only footmen, but also horsemen. At hand strokes they use not swords but pole-axes, which be mortal as well in sharpness as in weight, both for foins and downstrokes. Engines for war they devise and invent wondrous wittily. Which when they be made they keep very secret, lest, if they should be known before need require, they should be but laughed at and serve to no purpose. But in making them, hereunto they have chief respect, that they be both easy to be carried and handsome to be moved and turned about. Truce taken with their enemies for a short time they do so firmly and faithfully keep, that they will not break it, no. not though they be thereunto provoked. They do not waste nor destroy their enemies' land with foragings, nor they burn not up their corn. Yea, they save it as much as may be from being overrun and trodden down either with men or horses, thinking that it groweth for their own use and profit. They hurt no man that is unarmed, unless he be an espial.

All cities that be yielded unto them they defend; and such as they win by force of assault they neither despoil nor sack, but them that withstood and dissuaded the yielding up of the same they put to death. The other soldiers they punish with bondage. All the weak multitude they leave untouched. If they know that any citizens counselled to yield and render up the city, to them they give part of the condemned men's goods. The residue they distribute and give freely among them whose help they had in the same war, for none of themselves taketh any portion of the prey. But when the battle is finished and ended, they put their friends to never a penny cost of all the charges that they were at, but lay it upon their necks that be conquered. Them they burden with the whole charge of their expenses, which they demand of them partly in money to be kept for like use of battle, and partly in lands of great revenues to be paid unto them yearly for ever. Such revenues they have now in many countries. Which, by little and little rising of divers and sundry causes, be increased above seven hundred thousand ducats by the year. Thither they send forth some of their citizens as lieutenants, to live there sumptuously like men of honour and renown. And yet, this notwithstanding, much money is saved which cometh to the common treasury, unless it so chance that they had rather trust the country with the money. Which many times they do so long until they have need to occupy it; and it seldom happeneth that they demand all. Of these lands they assign part unto them which at their request and exhortation put themselves in such jeopardies as I spake of before. If any prince stir up war against them, intending to invade their land, they meet him incontinent out of their own borders with great power and strength. For they never lightly make war in their own country, nor they be never brought into so extreme necessity as to take help out of foreign lands into their own island.

Of the Religions in Utopia

There be divers kinds of religion not only in sundry parts of the island, but also in divers places of every city. Some worship for god the sun, some the moon, some some other of the planets. There be that give worship to a man that was once of excellent virtue or of famous glory, not only as god, but also as the chiefest and highest god. But the most and the wisest part, rejecting all these, believe that there is a certain godly power unknown, everlasting, incomprehensible, inexplicable, far above the capacity and reach of man's wit, dispersed throughout all the world, not in bigness, but in virtue and power. Him they call the father of all. To him alone they attribute the beginnings, the increasings, the proceedings, the changes, and the ends of all things. Neither they give any divine honours to any other than to him. Yea, all the other also, though they be in divers opinions, yet in this point they agree all together with the wisest sort in believing that there is one chief and principal god, the maker and ruler of the whole world, whom they all commonly in their country language call Mithra. But in this they disagree, that among some he is counted one, and among some another. For every

one of them, whatsoever that is which he taketh for the chief
god, thinketh it to be the very same nature to whose only
divine might and majesty the sum and sovereignty of all
things by the consent of all people is attributed and given.
Howbeit, they all begin by little and little to forsake and fall
from this variety of superstitions, and to agree together in
that religion which seemeth by reason to pass and excel the
residue.   And it is not to be doubted but all the other would
long ago have been abolished, but that whatsoever unpros-
perous thing happened to any of them, as he was minded to
change his religion, the fearfulness of people did take it, not
as a thing coming by chance, but as sent from God out of
heaven, as though the god whose honour he was forsaking
would revenge that wicked purpose against him.

But after they heard us speak of the name of Christ, of His
doctrine, laws, miracles, and of the no less wonderful con-
stancy of so many martyrs, whose blood willingly shed
brought a great number of nations throughout all parts of the
world into their sect, you will not believe with how glad
minds they agreed unto the same, whether it were by the
secret inspiration of God, or else for that they thought it
nighest unto that opinion which among them is counted the
chiefest.   Howbeit, I think this was no small help and furtherance in the matter, that they heard us say that Christ instituted among His all things common, and that the same community doth yet remain amongst the rightest Christian
companies.   Verily, howsoever it came to pass, many of them
consented together in our religion and were washed in the
holy water of baptism.   But because among us four (for
no more of us was left alive, two of our company being dead)
there was no priest, which I am right sorry for, they being
entered and instructed in all other points of our religion, lack
only those sacraments which here none but priests do
minister.   Howbeit, they understand and perceive them and
be very desirous of the same.   Yea, they reason and dispute
the matter earnestly among themselves, whether, without the

sending of a Christian bishop, one chosen out of their own people may receive the order of priesthood. And truly they were minded to choose one, but at my departure from them they had chosen none.

They also which do not agree to Christ's religion fear no man from it nor speak against any man that hath received it, saving that one of our company in my presence was sharply punished. He, as soon as he was baptized, began against our wills, with more earnest affection than wisdom, to reason of Christ's religion, and began to wax so hot in his matter, that he did not only prefer our religion before all other, but also did utterly despise and condemn all other, calling them profane, and the followers of them wicked and devilish and the children of everlasting damnation. When he had thus long reasoned the matter they laid hold on him, accused him, and condemned him into exile, not as a despiser of religion but as a seditious person and a raiser up of dissension among the people. For this is one of the ancientest laws among them, that no man shall be blamed for reasoning in the maintenance of his own religion. For King Utopus, even at the first beginning hearing that the inhabitants of the land were before his coming thither at continual dissension and strife among themselves for their religions, perceiving also that this common dissension (whiles every several sect took several parts in fighting for their country) was the only occasion of his conquest over them all, as soon as he had gotten the victory, first of all he made a decree that it should be lawful for every man to favour and follow what religion he would, and that he might do the best he could to bring other to his opinion, so that he did it peaceably, gently, quietly, and soberly, without hasty and contentious rebuking and inveighing against others. If he could not by fair and gentle speech induce them unto his opinion, yet he should use no kind of violence, and refrain from displeasant and seditious words. To him that would vehemently and fervently in this cause strive and contend was decreed banishment or bondage.

This law did King Utopus make, not only for the maintenance of peace, which he saw through continual contention
and mortal hatred utterly extinguished, but also because he
thought this decree should make for the furtherance of religion.
Whereof he durst define and determine nothing unadvisedly,
as doubting whether God, desiring manifold and diverse sorts
of honour, would inspire sundry men with sundry kinds of
religion. And this surely he thought a very unmeet and
foolish thing, and a point of arrogant presumption, to compel
all other by violence and threatenings to agree to the same
that thou believest to be true. Furthermore, though there be
one religion which alone is true, and all other vain and
superstitious, yet did he well foresee (so that the matter were
handled with reason and sober modesty) that the truth of
its own power would at the last issue out and come to light.
But if contention and debate in that behalf should continually
be used, as the worst men be most obstinate and stubborn
and in their evil opinion most constant, he perceived that
then the best and holiest religion would be trodden underfoot
and destroyed by most vain superstitions, even as good corn
is by thorns and weeds overgrown and choked. Therefore
all this matter he left undiscussed, and gave to every man free
liberty and choice to believe what he would; saving that he
earnestly and straitly charged them that no man should
conceive so vile and base an opinion of the dignity of man's
nature as to think that the souls do die and perish with the
body, or that the world runneth at all aventures, governed by
no divine providence.

And therefore they believe that after this life vices be
extremely punished and virtues bountifully rewarded. Him
that is of a contrary opinion they count not in the number of
men, as one that hath avaled the high nature of his soul to
the vileness of brute beasts' bodies, much less in the number
of their citizens whose laws and ordinances, if it were not for
fear, he would nothing at all esteem. For you may be sure
that he will study either with craft privily to mock, or else

violently to break, the common laws of his country, in whom
remaineth no further fear than of the laws nor no further
hope than of the body.   Wherefore he that is thus minded
is deprived of all honours, excluded from all offices, and reject
from all common administrations in the weal-public.   And
thus he is of all sorts despised as of an unprofitable and of
a base and vile nature.   Howbeit, they put him to no punishment, because they be persuaded that it is in no man's power
to believe what he list.   No nor they constrain him not with
threatenings to dissemble his mind and shew countenance
contrary to his thought; for deceit and falsehood and all
manners of lies, as next unto fraud, they do marvellously
detest and abhor.   But they suffer him not to dispute in his
opinion, and that only among the common people.   For else,
apart among the priests and men of gravity they do not only
suffer but also exhort him to dispute and argue, hoping that
at the last that madness will give place to reason.   There be
also other, and of them no small number, which be not forbidden to speak their minds, as grounding their opinion upon
some reason, being in their living neither evil nor vicious.
Their heresy is much contrary to the other; for they believe
that the souls of brute beasts be immortal and everlasting, but
nothing to be compared with ours in dignity, neither ordained
nor predestinate to like felicity.   For all they believe certainly
and surely that man's bliss shall be so great, that they do
mourn and lament every man's sickness, but no man's death,
unless it be one whom they see depart from his life carefully
and against his will.   For this they take for a very evil token,
as though the soul, being in despair and vexed in conscience
through some privy and secret forefeeling of the punishment
now at hand, were afeard to depart.   And they think he shall
not be welcome to God, which, when he is called, runneth not
to Him gladly but is drawn by force and sore against his will.
They, therefore, that see this kind of death do abhor it, and
them that so die they bury with sorrow and silence.   And
when they have prayed God to be merciful to the soul and

mercifully to pardon the infirmities thereof, they cover the dead corpse with earth.   Contrariwise, all that depart merrily and full of good hope, for them no man mourneth, but followeth the hearse with joyful singing, commending the souls to God with great affection.   And at the last, not with mourning sorrow, but with a great reverence, they burn the bodies; and in the same place they set up a pillar of stone with the dead man's titles therein graved.   When they be come home they rehearse his virtuous manners and his good deeds, but no part of his life is so oft or gladly talked of as his merry death.   They think that this remembrance of the virtue and goodness of the dead doth vehemently provoke and enforce the living to virtue, and that nothing can be more pleasant and acceptable to the dead whom they suppose to be present among them when they talk of them, though to the dull and feeble eyesight of mortal men they be invisible.   For it were an inconvenient thing that the blessed should not be at liberty to go whither they would and it were a point of great unkindness in them to have utterly cast away the desire of visiting and seeing their friends to whom they were in their lifetime joined by mutual love and amity.   Which in good men after their death they count to be rather increased than diminished.   They believe, therefore, that the dead be presently conversant among the quick as beholders and witnesses of all their words and deeds.   Therefore they go more courageously to their business, as having a trust and affiance in such overseers.   And this same belief of the present conversation of their forefathers and ancestors among them feareth them from all secret dishonesty.   They utterly despise and mock soothsayings and divinations of things to come by the flight or voices of birds, and all other divinations of vain superstition, which in other countries be in great observation. But they highly esteem and worship miracles that come by no help of nature, as works and witnesses of the present power of God; and such they say do chance there very often. And sometimes in great and doubtful matters by common intercession and prayers they procure and obtain them with a sure hope and confidence and a steadfast belief.

They think that the contemplation of nature and the praise thereof coming is to God a very acceptable honour. Yet there be many so earnestly bent and affectioned to religion, that they pass nothing for learning, nor give their minds to any knowledge of things. But idleness they utterly forsake and eschew, thinking felicity after this life to be gotten and obtained by busy labours and good exercises. Some, therefore, of them attend upon the sick, some amend highways, cleanse ditches, repair bridges, dig turfs, gravel, and stones, fell and cleave wood, bring wood, corn, and other things into the cities in carts, and serve not only in common works, but also in private labours as servants, yea, more than bondmen. For whatsoever unpleasant, hard, and vile work is anywhere from the which labour, loathsomeness, and desperation doth fray other, all that they take upon them willingly and gladly, procuring quiet and rest to other, remaining in continual work and labour themselves, not embraiding others therewith. They neither reprove other men's lives nor glory in their own. These men, the more serviceable they behave themselves, the more they be honoured of all men. Yet they be divided into two sects. The one is of them that live single and chaste, abstaining not only from the company of women but also from eating of flesh, and some of them from all manner of beasts. Which, utterly rejecting the pleasures of this present life as hurtful, be all wholly set upon the desire of the life to come by watching and sweating, hoping shortly to obtain it, being in the mean season merry and lusty.

The other sect is no less desirous of labour; but they embrace matrimony, not despising the solace thereof, thinking that they cannot be discharged of their bounden duties towards nature without labour and toil nor towards their native country without procreation of children. They abstain from no pleasure that doth nothing hinder them from labour. They love the flesh of four-footed beasts because they believe that by that meat they be made hardier and stronger to work. The Utopians count this sect the wiser, but the other the holier. Which in that they prefer single life before matrimony and that sharp life before an easier life, if herein they grounded upon reason they would mock them. But now forasmuch as they say they be led to it by religion, they honour and worship them. And these be they whom in their language by a peculiar name they call Buthrescas, the which word by interpretation signifieth to us men of religion or religious men.

They have priests of exceeding holiness and therefore very few, for there be but thirteen in every city according to the number of their churches, saving when they go forth to battle. For then seven of them go forth with the army, in whose steads so many new be made at home. But the other at their return home again re-enter every one into his own place. They that be above the number, until such time as they succeed into the places of the other at their dying, be in the mean season continually in company with the bishop, for he is the chief head of them all. They be chosen of the people, as the other magistrates be, by secret voices for the avoiding of strife. After their election they be consecrate of their own company. They be overseers of all divine matters, orderers of religions, and, as it were, judges and masters of manners. And it is a great dishonesty and shame to be rebuked or spoken to by any of them for dissolute and incontinent living. But as it is their office to give good exhortations and counsel, so is it the duty of the prince and the other magistrates to correct and punish offenders, saving that the priests whom they find exceeding vicious livers, them they excommunicate from having any interest in divine matters. And there is almost no punishment among them more feared; for they run in very great infamy and be inwardly tormented with a secret fear of religion, and shall not long scape free with their bodies. For unless they by quick repentance approve the amendment of their lives to the priests, they be taken and punished of the council as wicked and irreligious.

Both childhood and youth is instructed and taught of them. Nor they be not more diligent to instruct them in learning than in virtue and good manners; for they use with very great endeavour and diligence to put into the heads of their children, whiles they be yet tender and pliant, good opinions and profitable for the conservation of their weal-public. Which, when they be once rooted in children, do remain with them all their life after and be wondrous profitable for the defence and maintenance of the state of the commonwealth, which never decayeth but through vices rising of evil opinions.

The priests, unless they be women (for that kind is not excluded from priesthood, howbeit few be chosen, and none but widows and old women), the men priests, I say, take to their wives the chiefest women in all their country; for to no office among the Utopians is more honour and pre-eminence given. Insomuch that if they commit any offence they be under no common judgment, but be left only to God and themselves. For they think it not lawful to touch him with man's hand, be he never so vicious, which after so singular a sort was dedicate and consecrate to God as a holy offering. This manner may they easily observe because they have so few priests, and do choose them with such circumspection. For it scarcely ever chanceth that the most virtuous among virtuous, which in respect only of his virtue is advanced to so high a dignity, can fall to vice and wickedness. And if it should chance indeed (as man's nature is mutable and frail), yet by reason they be so few and promoted to no might nor power, but only to honour, it were not to be feared that any great damage by them should happen and ensue to the commonwealth. They have so rare and few priests, lest if the honour were communicated to many, the dignity of the order, which among them now is so highly esteemed, should run in contempt; specially because they think it hard to find many so good as to be meet for that dignity, to the execution and discharge whereof it is not sufficient to be endued with mean virtues.

Furthermore, these priests be not more esteemed of their own countrymen than they be of foreign and strange countries. Which thing may hereby plainly appear, and I think also that this is the cause of it. For whiles the armies be fighting together in open field they a little beside, not far off, kneel upon their knees in their hallowed vestments, holding up their hands to heaven, praying first of all for peace, next for victory of their own part, but to neither part a bloody victory. If their host get the upper hand, they run into the main battle and restrain their own men from slaying and cruelly pursuing their vanquished enemies. Which enemies, if they do but see them and speak to them, it is enough for the safeguard of their lives. And the touching of their clothes defendeth and saveth all their goods from ravin and spoil. This thing hath avanced them to so great worship and true majesty among all nations, that many times they have as well preserved their own citizens from the cruel force of their enemies as they have their enemies from the furious rage of their own men. For it is well known that when their own army hath reculed, and in despair turned back and run away, their enemies fiercely pursuing with slaughter and spoil, then the priests coming between have stayed the murder and parted both the hosts, so that peace hath been made and concluded between both parts upon equal and indifferent conditions. For there was never any nation so fierce, so cruel, and rude but they had them in such reverence, that they counted their bodies hallowed and sanctified, and therefore not to be violently and unreverently touched.

They keep holy the first and the last day of every month and year, dividing the year into months which they measure by the course of the moon, as they do the year by the course of the sun. The first days they call in their language Cynemernes, and the last Trapemernes, the which words may be interpreted primifest and finifest, or else, in our speech, first

feast and last feast.   Their churches be very gorgeous, and
not only of fine and curious workmanship, but also (which in
the fewness of them was necessary) very wide and large, and
able to receive a great company of people.   But they be all
somewhat dark.   Howbeit, that was not done through
ignorance in building, but, as they say, by the counsel of the
priests, because they thought that overmuch light doth dis-
perse men's cogitations, whereas in dim and doubtful light
they be gathered together, and more earnestly fixed upon
religion and devotion.   Which because it is not there of one
sort among all men, and yet all the kinds and fashions of it
(though they be sundry and manifold) agree together in the
honour of the divine nature, as going divers ways to one end,
therefore nothing is seen nor heard in the churches, but that
seemeth to agree indifferently with them all.

If there be a distinct kind of sacrifice peculiar to any several
sect, that they execute at home in their own houses.   The
common sacrifices be so ordered that they be no derogation
nor prejudice to any of the private sacrifices and religions.
Therefore no image of any god is seen in the church, to the
intent it may be free for every man to conceive God by their
religion after what likeness and similitude they will.   They
call upon no peculiar name of God but only Mithra, in the
which word they all agree together in one nature of the divine
majesty whatsoever it be.   No prayers be used but such as
every man may boldly pronounce without the offending of
any sect.   They come, therefore, to the church the last day of
every month and year, in the evening yet fasting, there to give
thanks to God for that they have prosperously passed over
the year or month whereof that holy day is the last day.   The
next day they come to the church early in the morning to pray
to God that they may have good fortune and success all the
new year or month which they do begin of that same holy day.

But in the holy days that be the last days of the months and
years, before they come to the church the wives fall down
prostrate before their husbands' feet at home, and the children

before the feet of their parents, confessing and acknowledging themselves offenders either by some actual deed or by omission of their duty, and desire pardon for their offence. Thus if any cloud of privy displeasure was risen at home, by this satisfaction it is overblown, that they may be present at the sacrifices with pure and charitable minds. For they be afeard to come there with troubled consciences. Therefore if they know themselves to bear any hatred or grudge towards any man, they presume not to come to the sacrifices before they have reconciled themselves and purged their consciences, for fear of great vengeance and punishment for their offence. When they come thither the men go into the right side of the church and the women into the left side. There they place themselves in such order, that all they which be of the male kind in every household sit before the goodman of the house, and they of the female kind before the goodwife. Thus it is foreseen that all their gestures and behaviours be marked and observed abroad of them by whose authority and discipline they be governed at home. This also they diligently see unto, that the younger evermore be coupled with his elder, lest, children being joined together, they should pass over that time in childish wantonness, wherein they ought principally to conceive a religious and devout fear towards God, which is the chief and almost the only incitation to virtue.

They kill no living beast in sacrifice, nor they think not that the merciful clemency of God hath delight in blood and slaughter, which hath given life to beasts to the intent they should live. They burn frankincense and other sweet savours, and light also a great number of wax candles and tapers, not supposing this gear to be anything available to the divine nature, as neither the prayers of men; but this un-hurtful and harmless kind of worship pleaseth them. And by these sweet savours and lights and other such ceremonies men feel themselves secretly lifted up and encouraged to devotion with more willing and fervent hearts. The people weareth in the church white apparel.

The priest is clothed in changeable colours, which in workmanship be excellent, but in stuff not very precious. For their vestments be neither embroidered with gold nor set with precious stones, but they be wrought so finely and cunningly with divers feathers of fowls, that the estimation of no costly stuff is able to countervail the price of the work. Furthermore, in these birds' feathers and in the due order of them which is observed in their setting, they say, is contained certain divine mysteries, the interpretation whereof known, which is diligently taught by the priests, they be put in remembrance of the bountiful benefits of God toward them, and of the love and honour which of their behalf is due to God, and also of their duties one toward another. When the priest first cometh out of the vestry thus apparelled, they fall down incontinent every one reverently to the ground with so still silence on every part, that the very fashion of the thing striketh into them a certain fear of God, as though He were there personally present. When they have lain a little space on the ground, the priest giveth them a sign for to rise. Then they sing praises unto God, which they intermix with instruments of music, for the most part of other fashions than these that we use in this part of the world. And like as some of ours be much sweeter than theirs, so some of theirs do far pass ours. But in one thing doubtless they go exceeding far beyond us. For all their music, both that they play upon instruments and that they sing with man's voice, doth so resemble and express natural affections, the sound and tune is so applied and made agreeable to the thing, that whether it be a prayer or else a ditty of gladness, of patience, of trouble, of mourning, or of anger, the fashion of the melody doth so represent the meaning of the thing, that it doth wonderfully move, stir, pierce, and inflame the hearers' minds. At the last the people and the priest together rehearse solemn prayers in words expressly pronounced, so made that every man may privately apply to himself that which is commonly spoken of all. In these prayers every man recognizeth and knowledgeth God to be his maker, his governor, and the principal cause of all other goodness, thanking Him for so many benefits received at His hand. But namely that through the favour of God he hath chanced into that public weal which is most happy and wealthy, and hath chosen that religion which he hopeth to be most true. In the which thing if he do anything err, or if there be any other better than either of them is, being more acceptable to God, he desireth Him that He will of His goodness let him have knowledge thereof, as one that is ready to follow what way soever He will lead him. But if this form and fashion of a commonwealth be best, and his own religion most true and perfect, then he desireth God to give him a constant steadfastness in the same, and to bring all other people to the same order of living and to the same opinion of God, unless there be anything that in this diversity of religions doth delight His unsearchable pleasure. To be short, he prayeth Him that after his death he may come to Him; but how soon or late, that he dare not assign or determine. Howbeit, if it might stand with His Majesty's pleasure, he would be much gladder to die a painful death and so to go to God, than by long living in worldly prosperity to be away from Him. When this prayer is said they fall down to the ground again, and a little after they rise up and go to dinner. And the residue of the day they pass over in plays and exercise of chivalry.

Now I have declared and described unto you as truly as I could the form and order of that commonwealth, which verily in my judgment is not only the best, but also that which alone of good right may claim and take upon it the name of a commonwealth or public weal. For in other places they speak still of the commonwealth, but every man procureth his own private gain. Here, where nothing is private, the common affairs be earnestly looked upon. And truly on both parts they have good cause so to do as they do; for in other countries who knoweth not that he shall starve for hunger, unless he make some several provision for himself, though the commonwealth flourish never so much in riches? And therefore he is compelled even of very necessity to have regard to himself rather than to the people, that is to say, to other. Contrariwise, there where all things be common to every man, it is not to be doubted that any man shall lack any thing necessary for his private uses, so that the common store, houses and barns, be sufficiently stored. For there nothing is distributed after a niggish sort, neither there is any poor man or beggar; and though no man have anything, yet every man is rich. For what can be more rich than to live joyfully and merrily, without all grief and pensiveness, not caring for his own living, nor vexed or troubled with his wife's importunate complaints, nor dreading poverty to his son, nor sorrowing for his daughter's dowry? Yea, they take no care at all for the living and wealth of themselves and all theirs, of their wives, their children, their nephews, their children's children, and all the succession that ever shall follow in their posterity. And yet, besides this, there is no less provision for them that were once labourers and be now weak and impotent, than for them that do now labour and take pain.

Here now would I see if any man dare be so bold as to compare with this equity the justice of other nations, among whom I forsake God if I can find any sign or token of equity and justice. For what justice is this, that a rich goldsmith or an usurer or, to be short, any of them which either do nothing at all, or else that which they do is such that it is not very necessary to the commonwealth, should have a pleasant and a wealthy living, either by idleness or by unnecessary business, when in the meantime poor labourers, carters, ironsmiths, carpenters, and plowmen (by so great and continual toil, as drawing and bearing beasts be scant able to sustain, and again so necessary toil, that without it no commonwealth were able to continue and endure one year), should yet get so hard and poor a living and live so wretched and miserable a life, that the state and condition of the labouring beasts may seem much better and wealthier? For they be not put to so continual labour, nor their living is not much worse, yea, to them much pleasanter, taking no thought in the mean season for the time to come. But these silly poor wretches be presently tormented with barren and unfruitful labour, and the remembrance of their poor, indigent, and beggarly old age killeth them up. For their daily wages is so little that it will not suffice for the same day, much less it yieldeth any overplus that may daily be laid up for the relief of old age.

Is not this an unjust and an unkind public weal, which giveth great fees and rewards to gentlemen, as they call them, and to goldsmiths and to such other, which be either idle persons, or else only flatterers and devisers of vain pleasures, and of the contrary part maketh no gentle provision for poor plowmen, colliers, labourers, carters, ironsmiths, and carpenters, without whom no commonwealth can continue? But after it hath abused the labours of their lusty and flowering age, at the last, when they be oppressed with old age and sickness, being needy, poor, and indigent of all things, then, forgetting their so many painful watchings, not remembering their so many and so great benefits, recompenseth and acquiteth them most unkindly with miserable death. And yet besides this the rich men, not only by private fraud but also by common laws, do every day pluck and snatch away from the poor some part of their daily living. So whereas it seemed before unjust to recompense with unkindness their pains that have been beneficial to the public weal, now they have to this their wrong and unjust dealing (which is yet a much worse point) given the name of justice, yea, and that by force of a law.

Therefore, when I consider and weigh in my mind all these commonwealths which nowadays anywhere do flourish, so God help me, I can perceive nothing but a certain conspiracy of rich men procuring their own commodities under the name and title of the commonwealth. They invent and devise all means and crafts, first how to keep safely, without fear of

losing, that they have unjustly gathered together, and next
how to hire and abuse the work and labour of the poor for as
little money as may be.   These devices, when the rich men
have decreed to be kept and observed under colour of the
commonalty, that is to say, also of the poor people, then they
be made laws.   But these most wicked and vicious men, when
they have by their unsatiable covetousness divided among
themselves all those things which would have sufficed all
men, yet how far be they from the wealth and felicity of the
Utopian commonwealth!   Out of the which, in that all the
desire of money with the use thereof is utterly secluded and
banished, how great a heap of cares is cut away!   How great
an occasion of wickedness and mischief is plucked up by the
roots!   For who knoweth not that fraud, theft, ravin,
brawling, quarrelling, brabbling, strife, chiding, contention,
murder, treason, poisoning, which by daily punishments are
rather revenged than refrained, do die when money dieth?
And also that fear, grief, care, labours, and watchings do
perish even the very same moment that money perisheth?
Yea, poverty itself, which only seemed to lack money if
money were gone, it also would decrease and vanish
away.

   And that you may perceive this more plainly, consider with
yourselves some barren and unfruitful year wherein many
thousands of people have starved for hunger.   I dare be bold
to say that in the end of that penury so much corn or grain
might have been found in the rich men's barns, if they had
been searched, as, being divided among them whom famine
and pestilence then consumed, no man at all should have felt
that plague and penury.   So easily might men get their
living, if that same worthy princess Lady Money did not alone
stop up the way between us and our living, which, a God's
name, was very excellently devised and invented, that by her
the way thereto should be opened.   I am sure the rich men
perceive this, nor they be not ignorant how much better it
were to lack no necessary thing than to abound with overmuch

superfluity, to be rid out of innumerable cares and troubles, than to be besieged and encumbered with great riches.

And I doubt not that either the respect of every man's private commodity, or else the authority of our Saviour Christ (which for His great wisdom could not but know what were best, and for His inestimable goodness could not but counsel to that which He knew to be best) would have brought all the world long ago into the laws of this weal-public, if it were not that one only beast, the princess and mother of all mischief, Pride, doth withstand and let it. She measureth not wealth and prosperity by her own commodities, but by the misery and incommodities of other. She would not by her goodwill be made a goddess if there were no wretches left over whom she might, like a scornful lady, rule and triumph, over whose miseries her felicities might shine, whose poverty she might vex, torment, and increase by gorgeously setting forth her riches. This hellhound creepeth into men's hearts and plucketh them back from entering the right path of life, and is so deeply rooted in men's breasts, that she cannot be plucked out.

This form and fashion of a weal-public, which I would gladly wish unto all nations, I am glad yet that it hath chanced to the Utopians, which have followed those institutions of life whereby they have laid such foundations of their commonwealth as shall continue and last not only wealthily, but also, as far as man's wit may judge and conjecture, shall endure for ever. For, seeing the chief causes of ambition and sedition with other vices be plucked up by the roots and abandoned at home, there can be no jeopardy of domestical dissension, which alone hath cast under foot and brought to naught the well fortified and strongly defenced wealth and riches of many cities. But forasmuch as perfect concord remaineth, and wholesome laws be executed at home, the envy of all foreign princes be not able to shake or move the empire, though they have many times long ago gone about to do it, being evermore driven back.

Thus when Raphael had made an end of his tale, though many things came to my mind which in the manners and laws of that people seemed to be instituted and founded of no good reason, not only in the fashion of their chivalry and in their sacrifices and religions and in other of their laws, but also, yea, and chiefly, in that which is the principal foundation of all their ordinances, that is to say, in the community of their life and living without any occupying of money (by the which thing only all nobility, magnificence, worship, honour, and majesty, the true ornaments and honours, as the common opinion is, of a commonwealth, utterly be overthrown and destroyed), yet because I knew that he was weary of talking, and was not sure whether he could abide that anything should be said against his mind (specially remembering that he had reprehended this fault in other, which be afeard lest they should seem not to be wise enough, unless they could find some fault in other men's inventions), therefore I, praising both their institutions and his communication, took him by the hand and led him in to supper, saying that we would choose another time to weigh and examine the same matters and to talk with him more at large therein.   Which would God it might once come to pass.   In the mean time, as I cannot agree and consent to all things that he said, being else without doubt a man singularly well learned and also in all worldly matters exactly and profoundly experienced, so must I needs confess and grant that many things be in the Utopian weal-public which in our cities I may rather wish for than hope for.

THUS ENDETH THE AFTERNOON'S TALK OF RAPHAEL HYTHLO-
DAY CONCERNING THE LAWS AND INSTITUTIONS OF THE ISLAND
OF UTOPIA.

TO THE RIGHT HONOURABLE
HIEROME BUSLIDE

PROVOST OF ARIENN AND COUNSELLOR TO THE CATHOLIC KING CHARLES,

PETER GILES, CITIZEN OF ANTWERP, WISHETH HEALTH AND FELICITY

THOMAS MORE, the singular ornament of this our age, as you yourself (right honourable Buslide) can witness, to whom he is perfectly well known, sent unto me this other day the *Island of Utopia*, to very few as yet known, but most worthy. Which, as far excelling Plato's *Commonwealth*, all people should be willing to know: specially of a man most eloquent, so finely set forth, so cunningly painted out, and so evidently subject to the eye, that as oft as I read it, methinketh that I see somewhat more than when I heard Raphael Hythloday himself (for I was present at that talk as well as Master More) uttering and pronouncing his own words. Yea, though the same man according to his pure eloquence did so open and declare the matter, that he might plainly enough appear to report not things which he had learned of others only by hearsay, but which he had with his own eyes presently seen and thoroughly viewed, and wherein he had no small time been conversant and abiding: a man, truly, in mine opinion, as touching the knowledge of regions, peoples, and worldly experience, much passing, yea, even the very famous and renowned traveller Ulysses; and indeed such a one, as for the space of these 800 years past I think nature into the world brought not forth his like, in comparison of whom Vespucci may be thought to have seen nothing. Moreover, whereas we be wont more effectually and pithily to declare and express things that we have seen than which we have but only heard, there was besides that in this man a certain peculiar grace and singular dexterity to describe and set forth a matter withal.

136

Yet the selfsame things as oft as I behold and consider them drawn and painted out with Master More's pencil, I am therewith so moved, so delighted, so inflamed, and so rapt, that sometime methink I am presently conversant, even in the island of Utopia. And I promise you, I can scant believe that Raphael himself, by all that five years' space that he was in Utopia abiding, saw there so much as here in Master More's description is to be seen and perceived. Which description with so many wonders and miraculous things is replenished, that I stand in great doubt whereat first and chiefly to muse or marvel: whether at the excellency of his perfect and sure memory, which could wellnigh word by word rehearse so many things once only heard, or else at his singular prudence, who so well and wittily marked and bare away all the original causes and fountains (to the vulgar people commonly most unknown) whereof both issueth and springeth the mortal confusion and utter decay of a commonwealth and also the avancement and wealthy state of the same may rise and grow, or else at the efficacy and pith of his words which in so fine a Latin style, with such force of eloquence, hath couched together and comprised so many and divers matters, specially being a man continually encumbered with so many busy and troublesome cares, both public and private, as he is. Howbeit, all these things cause you little to marvel (right honourable Buslide) for that you are familiarly and thoroughly acquainted with the notable, yea, almost divine wit of the man.

But now to proceed to other matters, I surely know nothing needful or requisite to be adjoined unto his writings, only a metre of four verses written in the Utopian tongue, which after Master More's departure Hythloday by chance shewed me, that have I caused to be added thereto, with the alphabet of the same nation, and have also garnished the margin of the book with certain notes. For, as touching the situation of the island, that is to say, in what part of the world Utopia standeth, the ignorance and lack whereof not a little troubleth and grieveth Master More, indeed Raphael left not that unspoken of. Howbeit, with very few words he lightly touched it, incidentally by the way passing it over, as meaning of likelihood to keep and reserve that to another place. And the same, I wot not how, by a certain evil and unlucky chance escaped us both. For when Raphael was speaking thereof, one of Master More's servants came to him and whispered in his ear. Wherefore, I being then of purpose more earnestly addict to hear, one of the company, by reason of cold taken, I think, a-shipboard, coughed out so loud, that he took from my hearing certain of his words. But I will never stint nor rest until I have got the full and exact knowledge hereof, insomuch that I will be able perfectly to instruct you, not only in the longitude or true meridian of the island, but also in the just latitude thereof, that is to say, in the sublevation or height of the pole in that region, if our friend Hythloday be in safety and alive. For we hear very uncertain news of him. Some report that he died in his journey homeward. Some again affirm that he returned into his country; but partly for that he could not away with the fashions of his country folk, and partly for that his mind and affection was altogether set and fixed upon Utopia, they say that he hath taken his voyage thitherward again. Now as touching this, that the name of this island is nowhere found among the old and ancient cosmographers, this doubt Hythloday himself very well dissolved. For why, it is possible enough, quoth he, that the name which it had in old time was afterward changed, or else that they never had knowledge of this island, forasmuch as now in our time divers lands be found which to the old geographers were unknown. Howbeit, what needeth it in this behalf to fortify the matter with arguments, seeing Master More is author hereof sufficient? But whereas he doubteth of the edition or imprinting of the book, indeed herein I both commend and also knowledge the man's modesty. Howbeit, unto me it seemeth a work most unworthy to be long suppressed and most worthy to go

abroad into the hands of men; yea, and under the title of your
name to be published to the world, either because the singular
endowments and qualities of Master More be to no man better
known than to you, or else because no man is more fit and
meet than you with good counsels to further and advance the
commonwealth, wherein you have many years already continued and travailed with great glory and commendation,
both of wisdom and knowledge, and also of integrity and
uprightness.   Thus, O liberal supporter of good learning, and
flower of this our time, I bid you most heartily well to fare.
At Antwerp 1516, the first day of November.

A METRE OF FOUR VERSES IN THE UTOPIAN TONGUE,

Briefly touching as well the strange beginning, as also the happy and wealthy continuance of the same commonwealth

Utopos ha Boccas peu la chama polta chamaan.
Bargol he maglomi baccan soma gymnosophaon.
Agrama gymnosophon labarem bacha bodamilomin.
Volvala barchin heman la lavolvala dramme pagloni.

Which verses the translator, according to his simple knowledge and mean understanding in the Utopian tongue, hath thus rudely englished.

My king and conqueror Utopos by name,
A prince of much renown and immortal fame,
Hath made me an isle that erst no island was,
Full fraught with worldly wealth, with pleasure and solace.
I one of all other without philosophy
Have shaped for man a philosophical city.
As mine I am nothing dangerous to impart,
So better to receive I am ready with all my heart.

A short metre of Utopia, written by Anemolius poet laureate and nephew to Hythloday by his sister

Me Utopie cleped Antiquity,
Void of haunt and herborough,
Now am I like to Plato's city,
Whose fame flieth the world thorough;
Yea, like, or rather more likely
Plato's plat to excel and pass.
For what Plato's pen hath platted briefly
In naked words, as in a glass,
The same have I performed fully,
With laws, with men, and treasure fitly.
Wherefore not Utopie, but rather rightly
My name is Eutopie: a place of felicity.

140

Gerard Noviomage of Utopia

Doth pleasure please?   Then place thee here, and well thee
   rest;
Most pleasant pleasures thou shalt find here.
Doth profit ease?   Then here arrive, this isle is best.
For passing profits do here appear.
Doth both thee tempt, and wouldst thou grip both gain and
   pleasure?
This isle is fraught with both bounteously.
To still thy greedy intent, reap here incomparable treasure
Both mind and tongue to garnish richly.
The hid wells and fountains both of vice and virtue
Thou hast them here subject unto thine eye.
Be thankful now, and thanks where thanks be due:
Give to Thomas More London's immortal glory.

Cornelius Graphey to the Reader

Wilt thou know what wonders strange be in the land that
   late was found?
Wilt thou learn thy life to lead by divers ways that godly be?
Wilt thou of virtue and of vice understand the very ground?
Wilt thou see this wretched world, how full it is of vanity?
Then read and mark and bear in mind for thy behoof, as thou
   may best,
All things that in this present work, that worthy clerk Sir
   Thomas More,
With wit divine full learnedly unto the world hath plain
   exprest,
In whom London well glory may, for wisdom and for godly
   lore.

THE PRINTER TO THE READER

THE Utopian alphabet, good reader, which in the above written epistle is promised, hereunto I have not now adjoined, because I have not as yet the true characters or forms of the Utopian letters. And no marvel, seeing it is a tongue to us much stranger than the Indian, the Persian, the Syrian, the Arabic, the Egyptian, the Macedonian, the Sclavonian, the Cyprian, the Scythian, etc. Which tongues, though they be nothing so strange among us as the Utopian is, yet their characters we have not. But I trust, God willing, at the next impression hereof, to perform that which now I cannot: that is to say, to exhibit perfectly unto thee the Utopian alphabet. In the meantime accept my goodwill. And so farewell.

A DIALOGUE OF COMFORT

AGAINST TRIBULATION MADE IN THE YEAR OF OUR LORD 1534
BY SIR THOMAS MORE, KNIGHT, WHILE HE WAS PRISONER IN
THE TOWER OF LONDON, WHICH HE ENTITLED THUS AS
FOLLOWETH:

A DIALOGUE OF COMFORT
AGAINST TRIBULATION,

MADE BY AN HUNGARIAN IN LATIN, AND TRANSLATED OUT OF
LATIN INTO FRENCH, AND OUT OF FRENCH INTO ENGLISH

Anthony and Vincent

Vincent. Who would have weened, O my good uncle, afore a
few years passed, that such as in this country would visit their
friends lying in disease and sickness should come (as I do now)
to seek and fetch comfort of them, or in giving comfort to
them use the way that I may well use to you? For albeit
that the priests and friars be wont to call upon sick men to
remember death, yet we worldly friends, for fear of discom-
forting them, have ever had a guise in Hungary to lift up
their hearts, and put them in good hope of life. But now,
my good uncle, the world is here waxen such, and so great
perils appear here to fall at hand, that methinketh the greatest
comfort that a man can have is when he may see that he shall
soon be gone; and we that are likely long to live here in
wretchedness have need of some comfortable counsel against
tribulation, to be given us by such as you be, good uncle,
that have so long lived virtuously and are so learned in the
law of God as very few be better in this country here, and
have had of such things as we do now fear good experience
and assay in yourself, as he that hath been taken prisoner in
Turkey two times in your days, and now likely to depart

hence ere long.   But that may be your great comfort, good
uncle, sith you depart to God: but us here shall you leave of
your kindred a sort of sorry comfortless orphans, to all whom
your good help, comfort, and counsel hath long been a great
stay, not as an uncle unto some and to some as one farther of
kin, but as though that unto us all you had been a natural
father.

Anthony.   Mine own good cousin, I cannot much say nay
but that there is indeed, not here in Hungary only, but almost
also in all places of Christendom, such a customable manner
of unchristian comforting, which albeit that in any sick man it
doth more harm than good with drawing him in time of sickness with looking and longing for life from the meditation of
death, judgment, heaven, and hell (whereof he should beset
much part of his time, even all his whole life in his best
health), yet is that manner in my mind more than mad, where
such kind of comfort is used to a man of mine age.   For as we
well wot that a young man may die soon, so be we very sure
that an old man cannot live long.   And yet sith there is (as
Tully saith) no man for all that so old but that he hopeth yet
that he may live one year more, and of a frail folly delighteth
to think thereon, and comforting himself therewith (other
men's words of like manner comfort adding more sticks to
that fire), shall in a manner burn up quite the pleasant
moisture that most should refresh him, the wholesome dew, I
mean, of God's grace, by which he should wish with God's
will to be hence, and long to be with Him in heaven.   Now
where you take my departing from you so heavily, as of him of
whom you recognize of your goodness to have had here before
help and comfort, would God I had to you and to other more
done half so much as myself reckoneth had been my duty to
do.   But whensoever God take me hence, to reckon yourselves then comfortless, as though your chief comfort stood in
me, therein make you, methinketh, a reckoning very much
like as though you would cast away a strong staff, and lean
upon a rotten reed.   For God is and must be your comfort,

and not I. And He is a sure comforter that, as He said unto
His disciples, never leaveth His servants in case of comfortless
orphans; not even when He departed from His disciples by
death, but both, as He promised, sent them a comforter, the
Holy Spirit of His Father and Himself, and made them also
sure that to the world's end He would ever dwell with them
Himself. And therefore if you be part of His flock and
believe His promise, how can you be comfortless in any
tribulation, when Christ and His Holy Spirit, and with them
their inseparable Father (if you put full trust and confidence
in them), be never neither one finger breadth of space nor one
minute of time from you?

Vincent. O my good uncle, even these selfsame words,
wherewith you well prove that because of God's own gracious
presence we cannot be left comfortless, make me now feel
and perceive what a miss of much comfort we shall have
when you be gone. For albeit, good uncle, that while you
do tell me this I cannot but grant it for true, yet if I now had
not heard it of you I had not remembered it, nor it had not
fallen in my mind. And over that, like as our tribulations
shall in weight and number increase, so shall we need not
only one such good word or twain, but a great heap thereof, to
stable and strength the walls of our hearts against the great
surges of this tempestuous sea.

Anthony. Good cousin, trust well in God and He shall
provide you teachers abroad convenient in every time, or
else shall Himself sufficiently teach you within.

Vincent. Very well, good uncle; but yet if we would leave
the seeking of outward learning, where we may have it, and
look to be inwardly taught only by God, then should we
thereby tempt God, and displease Him. And sith that I
now see the likelihood that when you be gone we shall be sore
destitute of any such other like, therefore thinketh me that
God of duty bindeth me to sue to you now, good uncle, in
this short time that we have you, that it may like you against
these great storms of tribulation with which both I and all

mine are sore beaten already, and now upon the coming of
this cruel Turk fear to fall in far more, I may learn of you such
plenty of good counsel and comfort, that I may, with the same
laid up in remembrance, govern and stay the ship of our
kindred, and keep it afloat from peril of spiritual drowning.
You be not ignorant, good uncle, what heaps of heaviness
hath of late fallen among us already, with which some of our
poor family be fallen into such dumps, that scantily can any
such comfort as my poor wit can give them anything assuage
their sorrow. And now sith these tidings have come hither
so brim of the great Turk's enterprise into these parts here,
we can almost neither talk nor think of any other thing else
than of his might and our mischief. There falleth so continually before the eyes of our heart a fearful imagination of
this terrible thing, his mighty strength and power, his high
malice and hatred, and his incomparable cruelty, with
robbing, spoiling, burning, and laying waste all the way that
his army cometh; then killing or carrying away the people
far thence from home, and there sever the couples and the
kindred asunder, every one far from other: some kept in
thraldom, and some kept in prison, and some for a triumph
tormented and killed in his presence; then sending his people
hither, and his false faith therewith, so that such as are here
and remain still shall either both lose all and be lost too, or
forced to forsake the faith of our Saviour Christ, and fall to
the false sect of Mahomet. And yet (which we more fear
than all the remnant), no small part of our own folk that
dwell even here about us are, as we fear, falling to him or
already confedered with him; which, if it so be, shall haply
keep his quarter from the Turk's incursion. But then shall
they that turn to his law leave all their neighbours nothing,
but shall have our good given them, and our bodies both,
but if we turn as they do, and forsake our Saviour too. And
then (for there is no born Turk so cruel to Christian folk as is
the false Christian that falleth from the faith) we shall stand in
peril (if we persevere in the truth) to be more hardly handled,

and die more cruel death by our own countrymen at home, than if we were taken hence and carried into Turkey. These fearful heaps of peril lie so heavy at our hearts while we wot not into which we shall fortune to fall, and therefore fear all the worst, that, as our Saviour prophesied of the people of Jerusalem, many wish among us already, before the peril come, that the mountains would overwhelm them, or the valleys open and swallow them up and cover them. Therefore, good uncle, against these horrible fears of these terrible tribulations, of which some, ye wot well, our house already hath and the remnant stand in dread of, give us while God lendeth you us such plenty of your comfortable counsel as I may write and keep with us, to stay us when God shall call you hence.

Anthony. Ah, my good cousin, this is an heavy hearing, and likewise as we that dwell here in this part fear that thing sore now which, few years past, feared it not at all. So doubt I not that ere it long be, they shall fear it as much that think themself now very sure because they dwell farther off. Greece feared not the Turk when that I was born; and within a while after that whole empire was his. The great sultan of Syria thought himself more than his match; and long since you were born hath he that empire too. Then hath he taken Belgrade, the fortress of this realm, and since hath he destroyed our noble young goodly king. And now strive there twain for us. Our Lord send the grace that the third dog carry not away the bone from them both. What should I speak of the noble strong city of the Rhodes, the winning whereof he counted as a victory against the whole corps of Christendom, sith all Christendom was not able to defend that strong town against him. Howbeit, if the princes of Christendom everywhere about would, whereas need was, have set to their hands in time, the Turk had never taken any one place of all those places. But partly dissensions fallen among our self, partly that no man careth what harm other folk feel, but each part suffereth other to shift for itself, the Turk is in few years wonderfully increased, and Christendom on the other side very sore decayed: and all this worketh our wickedness, with which God is not content. But now, whereas you desire of me some plenty of comfortable things, which ye may put in remembrance and comfort therewith your company, verily, in the rehearsing and heaping of your manifold fears, myself began to feel that there should much need against so many troubles many comfortable counsels. For surely a little before your coming, as I devised with myself upon the Turk's coming, it happed my mind to fall suddenly from that into the devising upon my own departing. Wherein, albeit that I fully put my trust and hope, to be a saved soul by the great mercy of God, yet sith no man is here so sure, that without revelation may clean stand out of dread, I bethought me also upon the pain of hell. And after, I bethought me then upon the Turk again. And first methought his terror nothing when I compared with it the joyful hope of heaven. Then compared I it on the other side with the fearful dread of hell; and therein casting in my mind those terrible devilish tormentors with the deep consideration of that furious endless fire, methought that if the Turk with his whole host and all trumpets and his timbrels too, were to kill me in my bed come to my chamber door, in respect of the other reckoning I regard him not a rush. And yet when I now heard your lamentable words, laying forth as it were present before my face that heap of heavy sorrowful tribulations that, beside those that are already fallen, are in short space like to follow, I waxed therewith myself suddenly somewhat afflight. And therefore I will allow your request in this behalf, that would have store of comfort aforehand ready by you to resort to and to lay up in your heart as a triacle against the poison of all desperate dread that might rise of occasion of sore tribulation. And herein shall I be glad, as my poor wit will serve me, to call to mind with you such things as I before have read, heard, or thought upon, that may conveniently serve us to this purpose.

*That the comfort devised by the old paynim philosophers
were insufficient, and the cause wherefore*

THE FIRST CHAPTER

FIRST shall you, good cousin, understand this, that the natural
wise men of this world, the old moral philosophers, laboured
much in this matter, and many natural reasons have they
written, whereby they might encourage men to set little by
such goods or such hurts either, the going or the coming
whereof are the matter and the cause of tribulation, as are the
goods of fortune, riches, favour, friends, fame, worldly worship, and such other things; or of the body, as beauty, strength,
agility, quickness, and health. These things (ye wot well)
coming to us, are matter of worldly wealth, and taken from
us by fortune or by force or the fear of the losing, be matter
of adversity and tribulation. For tribulation seemeth
generally to signify nothing else but some kind of grief, either
pain of the body or heaviness of the mind. Now the body
not to feel that it feeleth, all the wit in the world cannot bring
about. But that the mind should not be grieved neither
with the pain that the body feeleth, nor with occasions of
heaviness offered and given unto the soul itself, this thing
laboured the philosophers very much about; and many
goodly sayings have they toward the strength and comfort
against tribulation, exciting men to the full contempt of all
worldly loss and despising of sickness, and all bodily grief,
painful death, and all. Howbeit, in very deed, for anything
that ever I read in them, I never could yet find that ever those
natural reasons were able to give sufficient comfort of themself; for they never stretch so far but that they leave untouched, for lack of necessary knowledge, that special
point which is not only the chief comfort of all, but without
which also all other comforts are nothing, that is to wit, the
referring the final end of their comfort unto God, and to

repute and take for the special cause of comfort, that by the patient sufferance of their tribulation they shall attain his favour, and for their pain, receiveth reward at His hand in heaven. And for lack of knowledge of this end they did (as they needs must) leave untouched also the very special mean, without which we can never attain to this comfort, that is to wit, the gracious aid and help of God to move, stir, and guide us forward, in the referring all our ghostly comfort, yea, and our worldly comfort too, all unto that heavenly end. And therefore, as I say, for the lack of these things, all their comfortable counsels are very far insufficient.

Howbeit, though they be far unable to cure our disease of themself, and therefore are not sufficient to be taken for our physicians, some good drugs have they yet in their shops for which they may be suffered to dwell among our poticaries, if their medicines be made not of their own brains, but after the bills made by the great physician God, prescribing the medicines Himself, and correcting the faults of their erroneous receipts. For without this way taken with them, they shall not fail to do as many bold blind poticaries do, which, either for lucre or of a foolish pride, give sick folk medicines of their own devising, and therewith kill up in corners many such simple folk as they find so foolish to put their lives in such lewd and unlearned blind Bayards' hands. We shall therefore neither fully receive these philosophers' reasons in this matter, nor yet utterly refuse them; but, using them in such order as shall beseem them, the principal and the effectual medicines against these diseases of tribulation shall we fetch from that high, great, and excellent physician without whom we could never be healed of our very deadly disease of damnation. For our necessity wherein, the Spirit of God spiritually speaketh of Himself to us, and biddeth us of all our health give Him the honour, and therein thus saith unto us: *Honora medicum propter necessitatem, etenim ordinavit eum altissimus :* Honour thou the physician, for him hath the high God ordained for thy necessity. Therefore let us require that high physician, our Blessed Saviour Christ, whose holy manhood God ordained for our necessity, to cure our deadly wounds with the medicine made of the most wholesome blood of His own blessed body; that likewise as He cured by the incomparable medicine our mortal malady, it may like Him to send us and put in our minds such medicines at this time, as against the sickness and sorrows of tribulations may so comfort and strength us in His grace, as our deadly enemy the devil may never have the power by his poisoned dart of murmur, grudge, and impatience to turn our short sickness of worldly tribulation into the endless everlasting death of infernal damnation.

That for a foundation men must needs begin with faith

THE SECOND CHAPTER

SITH all our principal comfort must come of God, we must first presuppose in him to whom we shall with any ghostly counsel give any effectual comfort one ground to begin withal, whereupon all that we shall build must be supported and stand; that is to wit, the ground and foundation of faith, without which had ready before, all the spiritual comfort that any man may speak of can never avail a fly. For likewise as it were utterly vain to lay natural reasons of comfort to him that hath no wit, so were it undoubtedly frustrate to lay spiritual causes of comfort to him that hath no faith. For except a man first believe that Holy Scripture is the word of God, and that the word of God is true, how can a man take any comfort of that that the Scripture telleth him therein? Needs must the man take little fruit of the Scripture, if he either believe not that it were the word of God, or else ween that though it were, it might yet be for all that untrue. This faith as it is more faint or more strong, so shall the comfortable words of Holy Scripture stand the man in more stead or less.

This virtue of faith can neither any man give himself nor yet any one man another; but though men may with preaching be ministers unto God therein, and the man with his own free will obeying freely the inward inspiration of God be a weak worker with Almighty God therein, yet is the faith indeed the gracious gift of God himself. For as Saint James saith: *Omne datum optimum et omne donum perfectum de sursum est descendens a patre luminum :* Every good gift and every perfect gift is given from above, descending from the Father of Lights.   Therefore, feeling our faith by many tokens very faint, let us pray to Him that giveth it that it may please Him to help and increase it.   And let us first say with him in the Gospel: *Credo Domine, adiuva incredulitatem meam :* I believe, good Lord, but help Thou the lack of my belief. And after let us pray with the apostles: *Domine, adauge nobis fidem :* Lord, increase our faith.   And finally, let us consider by Christ's saying unto them, that if we would not suffer the strength and fervour of our faith to wax lukewarm, or rather key-cold, and in manner loose his vigour by scattering our minds abroad about so many trifling things, that of the matters of our faith we very seldom think but that we would withdraw our thought from the respect and regard of all worldly fantasies, and so gather our faith together into a little narrow room.   And like the little grain of mustard seed, which is of nature hot, set it in the garden of our soul, all weeds pulled out for the better feeding of our faith, then shall it grow, and so spread up in height, that the birds, that is to wit the holy angels of heaven, shall breed in our soul, and bring forth virtues in the branches of our faith; and then with the faithful trust, that through the true belief of God's word we shall put in His promise, we shall be well able to command a great mountain of tribulation to void from the place where he stood in our heart, whereas with a very feeble faith and a faint we shall be scant able to remove a little hillock.   And therefore, as for the first conclusion, as we must of necessity before any spiritual comfort presuppose the foundation of faith, so sith no man can give us faith but only God, let us never cease to call upon God therefore.

Vincent. Forsooth, good uncle, methinketh that this foundation of faith, which, as you say, must be laid first, is so necessarily requisite, that without it all spiritual comfort were utterly given in vain. And therefore now shall we pray God for a full and a fast faith. And I pray you, good uncle, proceed you farther in the process of your matter of spiritual comfort against tribulation.

Anthony. That shall I, cousin, with goodwill.

The first comfort in tribulation may a man take in this: When he feeleth in himself a desire and longing to be comforted by God.

THE THIRD CHAPTER

I WILL in my poor mind assign for the first comfort the desire and longing to be by God comforted, and not without some reason call I this the first cause of comfort. For like as the cure of that person is in a manner desperate that hath no will to be cured, so is the discomfort of that person desperate that desireth not his own comfort.

And here shall I note you two kinds of folk that are in tribulation and heaviness: one sort that will seek for no comfort, another sort that will. And yet of those that will not are there also two sorts. For first one sort there are that are so drowned in sorrow, that they fall into a careless deadly dullness, regarding nothing, thinking almost of nothing, no more than if they lay in a lethargy, with which it may so fall that wit and remembrance will wear away, and fall even fair from them. And this comfortless kind of heaviness in tribulation is the highest kind of the deadly sin of sloth. Another sort are there that will seek for no comfort, nor yet none receive, but are in their tribulation (be it loss or sickness) so testy, so fumish, and so far out of all patience, that it booteth no man to speak to them; and these are in a manner with impatience as furious as though they were in half a frenzy, and may with a custom of such fashioned behaviour fall in thereto full and whole.   And this kind of heaviness in tribulation is even a mischievous high branch of the mortal sin of ire.

Then is there, as I told you, another kind of folk which fain would be comforted, and yet are they of two sorts too. One sort are those that in their sorrow seek for worldly comfort; and of them shall we now speak the less, for the divers occasions that we shall after have to touch them in more places than one.   But this will I here say, that I learned of Saint Bernard: he that in tribulation turneth himself into worldly vanities, to get help and comfort by them, fareth like a man that in peril of drowning catcheth whatsoever cometh next to hand, and that holdeth he fast be it never so simple a stick, but then that helpeth him not.   For that stick he draweth down under the water with him, and there lie they drowned both together.

So surely if we custom ourself to put our trust of comfort in the delight of these peevish worldly things, God shall for that foul fault suffer our tribulation to grow so great, that all the pleasures of this world shall never bear us up, but all our peevish pleasure shall in the depth of tribulation drown with us.

The other sort is, I say, of those that long and desire to be comforted of God.   And as I told you before, they have an undoubted great cause of comfort, even in that point alone that they consider themself to desire and long to be by Almighty God comforted.   This mind of theirs may well be cause of great comfort unto them for two great considerations. The token is that they see themself seek for their comfort where they cannot fail to find it; for God both can give them comfort, and will.   He can, for He is almighty.   He will, for He is all good, and hath Himself promised *Petite et accipietis :* Ask and ye shall have.   He that hath faith (as he must needs have that shall take comfort) cannot doubt but that God will surely keep His promise. And therefore hath he a great cause to be of good comfort, as I say, in that he considereth that he longeth to be comforted by Him, which his faith maketh him sure will not fail to comfort him.

But here consider this, that I speak here of him that in tribulation longeth to be comforted by God; and it is he that referreth the manner of his comforting to God, holding himself content, whether it be by the taking away or the minishment of the tribulation itself, or by the giving him patience and spiritual consolation therein. For him that only longeth to have God take his trouble from him, we cannot so well warrant that mind for a cause of so great comfort. For both may he desire that that never mindeth to be the better, and may miss also the effect of his desire, because his request is haply not good for himself. And of this kind of longing and requiring we shall have occasion farther to speak hereafter. But he which, referring the manner of his comfort unto God, desireth of God to be comforted, asketh a thing so lawful and so pleasant unto God, that he cannot fail to speed; and therefore hath he, as I say, great cause to take comfort in the very desire itself.

Another cause hath he to take of that desire a very great occasion of comfort. For sith his desire is good and declareth unto himself that he hath in God a good faith, it is a good token unto him that he is not an abject, cast out of God's gracious favour, while he perceiveth that God hath put such a virtuous well-ordered appetite in his mind. For as every evil mind cometh of the world and ourself and the devil, so is every such good mind, either immediately or by the mean of our good angel or other gracious occasion, inspired into man's heart by the goodness of God Himself. And what a comfort, then, may this be unto us, when we by that desire perceive a sure undoubted token that toward our final salvation our Saviour is Himself so graciously busy about us!

That tribulation is a mean to draw men to that good mind,
to desire and long for the comfort of God

THE FOURTH CHAPTER

Vincent. Forsooth, good uncle, this good mind of longing for
God's comfort is a good cause of great comfort indeed. Our
Lord in tribulation send it us. But by this I see well that woe
may they be which in tribulation lack that mind and that
desire, not to be comforted by God, but are either of sloth or
impatience discomfortless, or of folly seek for their chief ease
and comfort anywhere else.

Anthony. That is, good cousin, very true, as long as they
stand in that state. But then must you consider that tribulation is yet a mean to drive him from that state. And that is
one of the causes for which God sendeth it unto man. For
albeit that pain was ordained of God for the punishment of
sins (for which they that never can now but sin can never be
but ever punished in hell), yet in this world, in which His
high mercy giveth men space to be better, the punishment by
tribulation that He sendeth serveth ordinarily for a mean of
amendment. Saint Paul was himself sore against Christ, till
Christ gave him a great fall and threw him to the ground, and
strake him stark blind; and with that tribulation he turned
to him at the first word, and God was his physician, and
healed him soon after both in body and soul by His minister
Ananias, and made him His blessed apostle. Some are in
the beginning of tribulation very stubborn and stiff against
God, and yet at length tribulation bringeth them home. The
proud king Pharaoh did abide and endure two or three of the
first plagues, and would not once stoop at them. But then
God laid on a sorer lash that made him cry to Him for help;
and then sent he for Moses and Aaron, and confessed himself
a sinner and God for good and righteous, and prayed them to

pray for him, and to withdraw that plague, and he would let them go. But when his tribulation was withdrawn, then was he naught again. So was his tribulation occasion of his profit, and his help again cause of his harm. For his tribulation made him call to God, and his help made hard his heart again. Many a man that in an easy tribulation falleth to seek his ease in the pastime of worldly fantasies, findeth in a greater pain all those comforts so feeble, that he is fain to fall to the seeking of God's help; and therefore is, I say, the very tribulation itself many times a mean to bring the man to the taking of the afore-remembered comfort therein, that is to wit, to the desire of comfort given by God, which desire of God's comfort is, as I have proved you, great cause of comfort itself.

The special means to get this first comfort in tribulation

THE FIFTH CHAPTER

HOWBEIT, though the tribulation itself be a mean oftentimes to get man this first comfort in it, yet itself some time alone bringeth not a man to it; and therefore, sith without this comfort first had there can in tribulation none other good comfort come forth, we must labour the means that this first comfort may come. And thereunto seemeth me, that if the man of sloth or impatience or hope of worldly comfort have no mind to desire and seek for comfort of God, those that are his friends that come to visit and comfort him must afore all thing put that point in his mind, and not spend the time (as they commonly do) in trying and turning him to the fantasies of the world. They must also move him to pray God to put this desire in his mind, which when he getteth once, he then hath the first comfort, and without doubt (if it be well considered) a comfort marvellous great. His friends also that thus counsel him must unto the attaining thereof help to pray for him themself, and cause him to desire good folk to help him to pray therefore.   And then if these ways be taken for the getting, I nothing doubt but the goodness of God shall give it.

It sufficeth not that a man have a desire to be comforted by God only by the taking away of the tribulation

THE SIXTH CHAPTER

Vincent.   Verily methinketh, good uncle, that this counsel is very good.   For except the person have first a desire to be comforted by God, else can I not see what it can avail to give him any further counsel of any spiritual comfort.   Howbeit, what if the man have this desire of God's comfort, that is to wit, that it may please God to comfort him in his tribulation by taking that tribulation from him?   Is not this a good desire of God's comfort and a desire sufficient for him that is in tribulation?

Anthony.   No, cousin, that is it not.   I touched before a word of this point and passed it over, because I thought it would fall in our way again, and so wot I well it will ofter than once.   And now am I glad that you move it me here yourself. A man may many times well and without sin desire of God the tribulation to be taken from him; but neither may we desire that in every case, nor yet very well in no case (except very few) but under a certain condition, either expressed or implied.   For tribulations are, ye wot well, of many sundry kinds: some by loss of goods or possessions, some by the sickness of ourself, and some by the loss of friends or by some other pain put unto our bodies, some by the dread of the losing these things that we fain would save, under which fear fall all the same things that we have spoken before.   For we may fear loss of goods or possessions or the loss of our friends, their

grief and trouble or our own, by sickness, imprisonment, or
other bodily pain.   We may be troubled with the dread of
death; and many a good man is troubled most of all with the
fear of that thing which he that most need hath feareth lest of
all, that is to wit, the fear of losing through deadly sin the life
of his silly soul.   And this last kind of tribulation, as the sorest
tribulation of all, though we touch here and there some pieces
thereof before, yet the chief part and the principal point will I
reserve to treat apart effectually that matter in the last end.
But now, as I said, where the kinds of tribulation are so divers,
some of these tribulations a man may pray God take from him,
and take some comfort in the trust that God will so do; and
therefore against hunger, sickness, and bodily hurt, and
against the loss of either body or soul, men may lawfully many
times pray to the goodness of God either for themself or their
friend.   And toward this purpose are expressly prayed many
devout orisons in the common service of our Mother Holy
Church.   And toward our help in some of these things serve
some of the petitions in the *Pater noster*, wherein we pray
daily for our daily food and to be preserved from the fall in
temptation and to be delivered from evil.   But yet may we
not alway pray for the taking away from us of every kind of
temptation.   For if a man should in every sickness pray for
his health again, when should he shew himself content to die
and to depart unto God?   And that mind must a man have,
ye wot well, or else it will not be well.   One tribulation is it
to good men to feel in themself the conflict of the flesh against
the soul, the rebellion of sensuality against the rule and
governance of reason, the relics that remain in mankind of
old original sin, of which Saint Paul so sore complaineth in
his Epistle to the Romans.

And yet may we not pray, while we stand in this life, to
have this kind of tribulation utterly taken from us; for it
is left us by God's ordinance to strive against it, and fight
withal, and by reason and grace to master it, and use it for
the matter of our merit.   For the salvation of our soul may

we boldly pray.   For grace may we boldly pray, for faith, for hope and for charity, and for every such virtue as shall serve us to heavenward.   But as for all other things before remembered, in which is contained the matter of every kind of tribulation, we may never well make prayers so precisely, but that we must express or imply a condition therein, that is to wit, that if God see the contrary better for us, we refer it whole to His will, and instead of our grief taking away, pray that God may send us of His goodness either spiritual comfort to take it gladly, or strength at the least wise to bear it patiently.   For if we determine with ourself that we will take no comfort in nothing but in the taking of our tribulation from us, then either prescribe we to God that we will He shall no better turn do us, though He would, than we will ourself appoint him; or else do we declare that what thing is best for us ourself can better tell than He.   And therefore, I say, let us in tribulation desire His help and comfort, and let us remit the manner of that comfort unto His own high pleasure; which when we do, let us nothing doubt but that like as His high wisdom better seeth what is best for us than we can see ourself, so shall His high sovereign goodness give us that thing that shall indeed be best.   For else, if we will presume to stand to our own choice (except it so be that God offer us the choice Himself, as He did to David in the choice of his own punishment after his high pride conceived in the numbering of his people), we may foolishly choose the worst; and by the prescribing unto God ourself so precisely what we will that He shall do for us (except that of His gracious favour He reject our folly), He shall for indignation grant us our own request, and after shall we well find that it shall turn us to harm.   How many men attain health of body that were better for their soul's health their bodies were sick still?   How many get out of prison that hap on such harm abroad as the prison should have kept them from?   How many that have been loath to lose their worldly goods have in keeping of their goods soon after lost their life?

So blind is our mortality and so unware what will fall, so unsure also what manner mind we will ourself have tomorrow, that God could not lightly do man a more vengeance than in this world to grant him his own foolish wishes. What wit have we poor fools, to wit what will serve us, when the blessed apostle himself, in his sore tribulation praying thrice unto God to take it away from him, was answered again by God, in a manner that he was but a fool in asking that request, but that the help of God's grace in that tribulation to strength him was far better for him than to take that tribulation from him. And therefore, by experience perceiving well the truth of the lesson, he giveth us good warning not to be too bold of our minds when we require aught of God, nor to be precise in our asking, but refer the choice to God at His own pleasure. For His own Holy Spirit so sore desireth our weal, that as men might say, He groaneth for us in such wise as no tongue can tell. *Nos autem*, saith Saint Paul, *quid oremus ut oportet, nescimus, sed ipse Spiritus postulat pro nobis gemitibus inenarrabilibus:* We, what we may pray for that were behovable for us cannot ourself tell, but the Spirit Himself desireth for us with unspeakable groanings. And therefore I say for conclusion of this point, let us never ask of God precisely our own ease by delivery from our tribulation, but pray for His aid and comfort by which ways Himself shall best like, and then may we take comfort even of our such request. For both be we sure that this mind cometh of God, and also be we very sure that as He beginneth to work with us, so (but if ourself flit from Him) He will not fail to tarry with us; and then, He dwelling with us, what trouble can do us harm? *Si Deus nobiscum, quis contra nos?* If God be with us, saith Saint Paul, who can stand against us?

A great comfort it may be in tribulation, that every tribulation is (if we ourself will) a thing either medicinable, or else more than medicinable.

THE SEVENTH CHAPTER

Vincent. You have, good uncle, well opened and declared the question that I demanded you, that is to wit, what manner comfort a man might pray for in tribulation. And now proceed forth, good uncle, and shew us yet farther some other spiritual comfort in tribulation.

Anthony. This may be, thinketh me, good cousin, great comfort in tribulation, that every tribulation which any time falleth unto us is either sent to be medicinable if men will so take it, or may become medicinable if men will so make it, or is better than medicinable, but if we will forsake it.

Vincent. Surely this is very comfortable if we may well perceive it.

Anthony. These three things that I tell you, we shall consider thus. Every tribulation that we fall in cometh either by our own known deserving deed, bringing us thereunto, as the sickness that followeth our intemperate surfeit, or the prisonment or other punishment put upon a man for his heinous crime; or else is it sent us by God without any certain deserving cause open and known unto ourself, either for punishment of some sins past (certainly we know not for which), or for preserving us from sin in which we were else like to fall, or finally for no respect of the man's sin at all, but for the proof of his patience and increase of his merit. In all the former cases tribulation is (if we will) medicinable. In this last case of all it is better than medicinable.

The declaration larger concerning them that fall in tribulation by their own well-known fault, and that yet such tribulation is medicinable.

THE EIGHTH CHAPTER

Vincent. This seemeth me very good, good uncle, saving that it seemeth somewhat brief and short, and thereby, methinketh, somewhat obscure and dark.

Anthony. We shall, therefore, to give it light withal, touch every member somewhat more at large. One member is, you wot well, of them that fall in tribulation through their own certain well-deserving deed open and known unto themself, as where we fall in a sickness following upon our own gluttonous feasting, or a man that is punished for his own open fault. These tribulations, lo, and such other like, albeit that they may seem discomfortable in that a man may be sorry to think himself the cause of his own harm, yet hath he good cause of comfort in them if he consider that he may make them medicinable for himself, if he himself will. For whereas there was due to that sin, except it were purged here, a far greater punishment after this world in another place, this worldly tribulation of pain and punishment, by God's good provision for him put upon him here in this world before, shall by the mean of Christ's passion (if the man will in true faith and good hope, by meek and patient sufferance of his tribulation so make it) serve him for a sure medicine to cure him, and clearly discharge him of all the sickness and disease of those pains that else he should suffer after. For such is the great goodness of Almighty God, that He punisheth not one thing twice. And albeit so that this punishment is put unto the man, not of his own election and free choice, but so by force as he would fain avoid it, and falleth in it against his will, and therefore seemeth worthy no thank, yet so far passeth the great goodness of Almighty God the poor unperfect goodness of man, that though men make their reckoning one here with another such, God yet of His high bounty in man's account toward Him alloweth it far otherwise. For though that otherwise a man fall in his pain by his own fault, and also first against his will, yet as soon as he confesseth his fault and applieth his will to be content to suffer that pain and punishment for the same, and waxeth sorry, not for that only that he shall sustain such punishment, but for that also that he hath offended God and thereby deserved much more, our Lord from that time count-eth it not for pain taken against His will, but it shall be a marvellous good medicine and work, as a willingly taken pain, the purgation and cleansing of his soul with gracious remission of his sin, and of the far greater pain that else had been pre-pared therefore peradventure for ever in hell. For many there are undoubtedly that would else drive forth and die in their deadly sin, which yet in such tribulation, feeling their own frailty so effectually, and the false flattering world failing them so fully, turn goodly to God and call for mercy, and by grace make virtue of necessity and make a medicine of their malady, taking their trouble meekly, and make a right godly end.

Consider well the story of Achan that committed sacrilege at the great city of Jericho, whereupon God took a great ven-geance upon the children of Israel, and after told them the cause and bade them to seek the fault and try it out by lots. When the lot fell upon the very man that did it, being tried by the falling first upon his tribe, and then upon his family, and then upon his house, and finally upon his person, he might well see that he was deprehended and taken against his will. But yet at the good exhortation of Joshua saying unto him: *Fili mi, da gloriam Deo Israel, et confitere et indica mihi quid feceris et ne abscondas* (Mine own son, give glory to the God of Israel, and confess and shew me what thou hast done, and hide it not), he confessed humbly the theft, and meekly took his death therefore, and had, I doubt not, both strength and comfort in his pain, and died a very good man, which, if he had never come in tribulation, had been in peril never haply to have had just remorse thereof in all his whole life, but might have died wretchedly and gone to the devil eternally; and thus made this thief a good medicine of his well-deserved pain and tribulation. Consider the well-converted thief that hung on Christ's right hand. Did not he, by his meek sufferance and humble knowledge of his fault, asking forgiveness of God and yet content to suffer for his sin, make of his just punishment and well-deserved tribulation a very good special medicine to cure him of all pain in the other world and win him eternal salvation? And thus I say that this kind of tribulation, though it seem the most base and the least comfortable, is yet, if the man will so make it, a very marvellous wholesome medicine, and may therefore be to the man that will so consider it a great cause of comfort and spiritual consolation.

The second point, that is to wit, that tribulation that is sent us by God without any open certain deserving cause known to ourself: and that this kind of tribulation is medicinable if men will so take it, and therefore great occasion of comfort.

THE NINTH CHAPTER

Vincent. Verily, mine uncle, this first kind of tribulation have you to my mind opened sufficiently, and therefore I pray you resort now to the second.

Anthony. The second kind was, you wot well, of such tribulation as is so sent us by God, that we know no certain cause deserving that present trouble as we certainly know that upon such a surfeit we fell in such a sickness or as the thief knoweth that for such a certain theft he is fallen into such a certain punishment. But yet, sith we seldom lack faults against God worthy and well deserving great punishment, indeed we may well think (and wisdom it is so to do), that with sin we have deserved it, and that God for some sin sent it, though we certainly know not ourself for which.   And therefore as yet thus farforth is this kind of tribulation somewhat in effect in comfort to be taken like unto the other.   For this, as you see, if we thus will take it, well reckoning it to be sent for sin, and suffering it meekly therefore, is medicinable against the pain in the other world to come, for our sins in this world passed, which is, as I shewed you, a cause of right great comfort.   But yet may, then, this kind of tribulation be to some men of more sober living and thereby of the more clear conscience, somewhat a little more comfortable; for though they may none otherwise reckon themself than sinners (for, as Saint Paul saith: *Nullius mihi conscius sum, sed non in hoc iustificatus sum* (My conscience grudgeth me not of anything, but yet am I not thereby justified); and as Saint John saith: *Si dixerimus quia peccatum non habemus ipsi nos seducimus, et veritas in nobis non est* (if we say that we have no sin in us, we beguile ourself and truth is there not in us)), yet forasmuch as the cause is to them not so certain as it is to the other afore-remembered in the first kind, and that it is also certain that God sometime sendeth tribulation for keeping and preserving a man from such sin as he should else fall in, and sometime also for exercise of their patience and increase of merit, great cause of increase in comfort have those folk of the clearer conscience in the fervour of their tribulation, in that they may take the comfort of a double medicine, and of that thing also that is of the kind which we shall finally speak of, that I call better than medicinable.

But as I have before spoken of this kind of tribulation, how it is medicinable in that it cureth the sin passed and purchaseth remission of the pain due therefore, so let us somewhat consider how this tribulation sent us by God is medicinable, in that it preserveth us from the sins into which we were else like to fall.   If that thing be a good medicine that restoreth us our health when we lose it, as good a medicine must this needs be that preserveth our health while we have it, and suffereth us not to fall into that painful sickness that must after drive us to a painful plaster. Now seeth God sometime that worldly wealth is with one that is yet good, coming upon him so fast that, foreseeing how much weight of worldly wealth the man may bear and how much will overcharge him and enhance his heart up so high, that grace should fall from him low, God of His goodness, I say, preventeth his fall, and sendeth him tribulation betime, while he is yet good, to gar him ken his Maker, and, by less liking the false flattering world, set a cross upon the ship of his heart and bear a low sail thereon, that the boisterous blast of pride blow him not under the water.

Some young lovely lady, lo, that is yet good enough, God seeth a storm come toward her, that would, if her health and her fat feeding should a little longer last, strike her into some lecherous love, and instead of her old-acquainted knight lay her abed with a new-acquainted knave. But God, loving her more tenderly than to suffer her fall into such shameful beastly sin, sendeth her in season a goodly fair fervent fever that maketh her bones to rattle; and wasteth away her wanton flesh; and beautifieth her fair fell with the colour of a kite's claw; and maketh her look so lovely that her lover would have little lust to look upon her; and maketh her also so lusty that if her lover lay in her lap, she should so sore long to break unto him the very bottom of her stomach, that she should not be able to restrain it from him, but suddenly lay it all in his neck.

Did not, as I before shewed you, the blessed apostle himself confess that the high revelations that God had given him might have enhanced him into so high pride that he might have caught a foul fall had not the provident goodness of God provided for his remedy? And what was his remedy, but a painful tribulation, so sore, that he was fain thrice to call to God to take the tribulation from him: and yet would not God grant his request, but let him lie so long therein, till Himself that saw more in Saint Paul than Saint Paul saw in himself, wist well the time was come, in which He might well without his harm take it from him.   And thus you see, good cousin, that tribulation is double medicine, both a cure of the sin passed, and a preservative from the sin that is to come.   And therefore in this kind of tribulation is there good occasion of a double comfort; but that is, I say, diversely to sundry divers folks, as their own conscience is with sin cumbered or clear. Howbeit, I will advise no man to be so bold as to think that their tribulation is sent them to keep them from the pride of their holiness.   Let men leave that kind of comfort hardly to Saint Paul till their living be like, but of the remnant may men well take great comfort and good beside.

Of the third kind of tribulation, which is not sent a man for his sin, but for exercise of his patience and increase of his merit, which is better than medicinable.

THE TENTH CHAPTER

Vincent.   The third kind, uncle, yet remaineth now behind, that is to wit, which is sent a man by God, and not for his sin, neither committed nor which would else come, and therefore is not medicinable, but sent for exercise of our patience and increase of our merit; and therefore better than medicinable, though it be, as you say, and as indeed it is, better for the man than any of the other two kinds in another world, where the reward shall be received.   Yet can I not see by what reason a man may in this world, where the tribulation is suffered, take any more comfort therein than in any of the other twain that are sent a man for his sin, sith he cannot here know whether it be sent him for sin before committed, or sin that else should fall, or for increase of merit and reward after to come; namely, sith every man hath cause enough to fear and think that his sin already passed hath deserved it, and that it is not without peril a man to think otherwise.

Anthony.   This that you say, cousin, hath place of truth

in far the most part of men, and therefore must they not envy nor disdain (sith they may take in their tribulation consolation for their part sufficient) that some other that more be worthy take yet a great deal more. For as I told you, cousin, though the best must confess himself a sinner, yet be there many men (though to the multitude few) that for the kind of their living, and thereby the clearness of their conscience, may well and without sin have a good hope that God sendeth them some great grief for exercise of their patience and for increase of their merit, as it appeareth not only by Saint Paul, in the place before remembered, but also by the holy man Job, which in sundry places of his dispicions with his burdenous comforters letted not to say that the clearness of his own conscience declared and shewed to himself that he deserved not that sore tribulation that he then had. Howbeit, as I told you before, I will not advise every man at adventure to be bold upon this manner of comfort. But yet some men know I such, as I durst (for their more ease and comfort in their great and grievous pains) put them in right good hope that God sendeth it unto them not so much for their punishment as for exercise of their patience. And some tribulations are there also that grow upon such causes, that in those cases I would never let but alway would without any doubt give that counsel and comfort to any man.

Vincent. What causes, good uncle, be those?

Anthony. Marry, cousin, wheresoever a man falleth in tribulation for the maintenance of justice, or for the defence of God's cause. For if I should hap to find a man that had long lived a very virtuous life, and had at last happed to fall into the Turk's hands, and there did abide by the truth of his faith, and with the suffering of all kind of torments taken upon his body still did teach and testify the truth; if I should in his passion give him spiritual comfort, might I be bold to tell him no farther but that he should take patience in his pain, and that God sendeth it him for his sin, and that he is well worthy to have it although it were yet much more? He might then well answer me, and such other comforters, as Job answered his: *Onerosi consolatores estis vos:* Burdenous and heavy comforters be you. Nay, I would not fail to bid him boldly, while I should see him in his passion, cast sin and hell and purgatory and all upon the devil's pate, and doubt not but, like as if he gave over his hold all his merit were lost, and he turned to misery, so if he stand and persevere still in the confession of his faith, all his whole pain shall turn all into glory.

Yea, more shall I yet say than this: that if there were a Christian man that had among those infidels committed a very deadly crime, such as were worthy death not by their laws only, but by Christ's too, as manslaughter or adultery or such other thing like, if when he were taken he were offered pardon of his life upon condition that he should forsake the faith of Christ; if this man would now rather suffer death than so do, should I comfort him in his pain but as I would a malefactor? Nay, this man, though he should have died for his sin, dieth now for Christ's sake, while he might live still if he would forsake Him. The bare patient taking of his death should have served for the satisfaction of his sin, through the merit of Christ's Passion I mean, without help of which no pain of our own could be satisfactory. But now shall Christ for his forsaking of his own life in the honour of his faith forgive the pain of all his sins, of His mere liberality, and accept all the pain of his death for merit of reward in heaven, and shall assign no part thereof to the payment of his debt in purgatory, but shall take it all as an offering, and requite it all with glory. And this man among Christian men, all had he been before a devil, nothing after would I doubt to take him for a martyr.

Vincent. Verily, good uncle, methinketh this is said marvellous well, and it specially delighteth and comforteth me to hear it, because of our principal fear that I first spake of, the Turk's cruel incursion into this country of ours.

Anthony. Cousin, as for the matter of that fear, I purpose to touch last of all; nor I meant not here to speak thereof, had it not been that the vehemency of your objection brought it in my way. But rather would I else have put some example for this place of such as suffer tribulation for maintenance of right and justice, and that rather choose to take harm than do wrong in any manner of matter. For surely if a man may (as indeed he may) have great comfort in the clearness of his conscience, that hath a false crime put upon him and by false witness proved upon him and he falsely punished and put to worldly shame and pain therefore, an hundred times more comfort may he have in his heart that where white is called black and right is called wrong abideth by the truth and is persecuted for justice.

Vincent. Then if a man sue me wrongfully for my own land in which myself have good right, it is a comfort yet to defend it well, sith God shall give me thank therefore.

Anthony. Nay, nay, cousin, nay, there walk you somewhat wide. For there you defend your own right for your temporal avail. And sith Saint Paul counselleth: *Non vosmet defendentes charissimi* (Defend not yourself, my most dear friends); and our Saviour counselleth: *Si quis vult tecum iudicio contendere et tunicam tuam tollere, demitte ei et pallium* (If a man will strive with thee at the law and take away thy coat, leave him thy gown too), the defence, therefore, of our own right asketh no reward. Say you speed well if you get leave, look hardly for no thank; but on the other side if you do as Saint Paul biddeth: *Quærentes non quæ sua sunt sed quæ aliorum* (Seek not for your own profit but for other folk's), but defend, therefore, of pity a poor widow or a poor fatherless child, and rather suffer sorrow by some strong extortioner than suffer them take wrong, or if you be a judge and will have such zeal to justice that you will rather abide tribulation by the malice of some mighty man than judge wrong for his favour, such tribulations, lo, be those that are better than only medicinable, and every man upon whom they fall may be bold so to reckon them, and in his deep trouble may well say to himself the words that Christ hath taught him for his comfort: *Beati misericordes quoniam misericordiam consequentur*: Blessed be the merciful men, for they shall have mercy given them. *Beati qui persecutione patiuntur propter iustitiam, quoniam ipsorum est regnum cœlorum*: Blessed be they that suffer persecution for justice, for theirs is the kingdom of heaven. Here is an high comfort, lo, for them that are in the case. And in this case their own conscience can shew it them and so may fulfil their hearts with spiritual joy, that the pleasure may far surmount the heaviness and the grief of all their temporal trouble. But God's nearer cause of faith against the Turks hath yet a far passing comfort that by many degrees far excelleth this which, as I have said, I purpose to treat last. And for this time this sufficeth concerning the special comfort that men may take in this third kind of tribulation.

Another kind of comfort yet in the base kind of tribulation sent for our sin

THE ELEVENTH CHAPTER

Vincent. Of truth, good uncle, albeit that every of these kinds of tribulations have cause of comfort in them, as you have well declared, if men will so consider them, yet hath this third kind above all a special prerogative therein.

Anthony. That is undoubtedly true; but yet is there not, good cousin, the most base kind of them all but that it hath more causes of comfort than I have spoken of yet. For I have, you wot well, in that kind that is sent us for our sin spoken of none other comfort yet but twain: that is to wit, one that it refraineth us from sin that else we would fall in, and in that serveth us through the merit of Christ's Passion as a mean by which God keepeth us from hell, and serveth for the satisfaction of such pain as else we should endure in purgatory.

Howbeit, there is therein another great cause of joy besides this; for surely those pains here sent us for our sin, in whatsoever wise they happen unto us, be our sin never so sore nor never so open and evident unto ourself and all the world too, yet if we pray for grace to take it meekly and patiently, and confessing to God that it is far over too little for our fault, beseech Him yet, nevertheless, that sith we shall come hence so void of all good works whereof we should have any reward in heaven, to be not only so merciful to us as to take that our present tribulation in relief of our pains in purgatory, but also so gracious unto us as to take our patience therein for a matter of merit and reward in heaven. I verily trust, and nothing doubt it, but God shall of His high bounty grant us our boon. For likewise as in hell pain only serveth for punishment without any manner of purging, because all possibility of purging is passed, and in purgatory punishment serveth for only purging, because the place of deserving is passed. So while we be yet in this world in which is our place and our time of merit and well deserving, the tribulation that is sent us for our sin here shall (if we faithfully so desire), beside the cleansing and purging of our pain, serve us also for increase of reward. And so shall I suppose and trust in God's goodness all such penance and good works as a man willingly performeth enjoined by his ghostly father in confession, or which he willingly farther doth of his own devotion beside. For though man's penance with all the good works that he can do be not able to satisfy of themself for the least sin that we do, yet the liberal goodness of God through the merit of Christ's bitter Passion, without which all our works could neither satisfy nor deserve (nor yet do not indeed neither merit nor satisfy so much as a spoonful to a great vessel full in comparison of the merit and satisfaction that Christ hath merited and satisfied for us Himself), this liberal goodness of God, I say, shall yet at our faithful instance and request cause our penance and tribulation patiently taken in this world to serve us in the other world both for release and reward, tempered after such rate as His high goodness and wisdom shall see convenient for us, whereof our blind mortality cannot here imagine nor devise the stint.   And thus hath yet even the first kind of tribulation and the most base, though not fully so great as the second and very far less than the third, far greater cause of comfort yet than I spake of before.

A certain objection against the things aforesaid

THE TWELFTH CHAPTER

Vincent.   Verily, good uncle, this liketh me very well; but yet is there, ye wot well, some of these things now brought in question.   For as for any pain due for our sin to be minished in purgatory by the patient sufferance of our tribulation here, there are, ye wot well, many that utterly deny that, and affirm for a sure truth that there is no purgatory at all.   And then is, if they say true, the cause of the comfort gone, if the comfort that we should take be but in vain and need not.   They say, ye wot well also, that men merit nothing at all, but God giveth all for faith alone, and that it were sin and sacrilege to look for reward in heaven, either for our patience and glad suffering for God's sake, or for any other good deed; and then is there gone, if this be thus, the other cause of our farther comfort too.

Anthony.   Cousin, if some things were as they be not, then should some things be as they shall not.   I cannot indeed say nay, but that some men have of late brought up some such opinions and many more than these besides, and have spread them abroad.   And albeit that is a right heavy thing to see such variances in our belief rise and grow among ourself to the great encouraging of the common enemies of us all, whereby they have our faith in derision and catch hope to overwhelm us all, yet do there three things not a little comfort my mind.

The first is, that in some communications had of late together, hath appeared good likelihood of some good agreement to grow together in one accord of our faith.

The second, that in the meanwhile, till this may come to pass, contentions, dispicions, with uncharitable behaviour, is prohibited and forbidden in effect upon all parts: all such parts, I mean, as fell before to fight for it.

The third is, that all Germany, for all their divers opinions, yet as they agree together in profession of Christ's name, so agree they now together in preparation of a common power in defence of Christendom against our common enemy the Turk. And I trust in God that this shall not only help us here to strength us in this war, but also that as God hath caused them to agree together in the defence of His name, so shall He graciously bring them to agree together in the truth of His faith. Therefore will I let God work and leave off contention; and nothing shall I now say, but that with which they that are themself of the contrary mind shall in reason have no cause to be discontented.

For first, as for purgatory, though they think there be none, yet sith they deny not that all the corps of Christendom by so many hundred years have believed the contrary (and among them all the old interpreters of Scripture from the apostles' days down to our time, of whom they deny not many for holy saints), that I dare not now believe these men against all those. These men must of their courtesy hold my poor fear excused; and I beseech our Lord heartily for them, that when they depart out of this wretched world they find no purgatory at all, so God keep them from hell.

As for the merit of man in his good works, neither are they that deny it full agreed among themself, nor any man is there almost of them all that sith they began to write hath not somewhat changed and varied from himself. And far the more part are thus far agreed with us, that like as we grant them that no good work is aught worth to heavenward without faith, and that no good work of man is rewardable in heaven of its own nature, but through the mere goodness of God that

lust to set so high a price upon so poor a thing, and that this
price God setteth through Christ's Passion, and for that also
that they be His own works with us (for good works to Godward worketh no man without God work with him); and as
we grant them also that no man may be proud of his works for
his own unperfect working, and for that in all that man may do
he can do God no good, but is a servant unprofitable and doth
but his bare duty; as we, I say, grant unto them these things,
so this one thing or twain do they grant us again, that men are
bound to work good works if they have time and power, and
that whoso worketh in true faith most, shall be most rewarded.
But then set they thereto, that all his reward shall be given
him for his faith alone, and nothing for his works at all,
because his faith is the thing, they say, that forceth him to
work well.   Strive will I not with them for this matter now,
but yet this I trust to the great goodness of God, that if the
question hang on that narrow point, while Christ saith in the
Scripture in so many places that men shall in heaven be
rewarded for their works, He shall never suffer our souls that
are but mean-witted men, and can understand His words but
as Himself hath set them, and as old holy saints have construed them before, and as all Christian people this thousand
year have believed, to be damned for lack of perceiving such a
sharp subtle thing; specially sith some men that have right
good wits and are, beside that, right well learned too, can in no
wise perceive for what cause or why these folk that from good
works take away the reward and give that reward all whole to
faith alone, give the reward to faith rather than to charity.
For this grant they themself, that faith serveth of nothing but
if she be companied with her sister charity.   And then saith
the Scripture too: *Fides, spes, charitas, tria hæc, maior autem
horum est charitas:* Of these three virtues, faith, hope, and
charity, of all these three, the greatest is charity, and therefore
as worthy to have the thank as faith.   Howbeit, as I said, I
will not strive therefore; nor, indeed, as our matter standeth,
I shall not greatly need.   For if they say that he which

suffereth tribulation or martyrdom for the faith shall have high reward, not for his work but for his well working faith, yet sith that they grant that have it, he shall, the cause of high comfort in the third kind of tribulation standeth, and that is, you wot well, the effect of all my purpose.

Vincent. Verily, good uncle, this is truly driven and tried unto the uttermost as it seemeth me. And therefore I pray you proceed at your pleasure.

That a man ought to be comfortable to himself and have good hope and be joyful also in tribulation, appeareth well by this, that a man hath great cause of fear and heaviness that continueth alway still in wealth, discontinued with no tribulation.

THE THIRTEENTH CHAPTER

Anthony. Cousin, it were a long work to peruse every comfort that a man may well take of tribulation. For as many comforts, you wot well, may a man take thereof as there be good commodities therein, and that be there surely so many that it would be very long to rehearse and treat of them. But meseemeth we cannot lightly better perceive what profit and commodity, and thereby what comfort, they may take of it that have it, than if we well consider what harm the lack is, and thereby what discomfort the lack thereof should be to them that never have it. So is it now that all holy men agree, and all the Scripture is full, and our own experience proveth at our eye, that we be not come into this wretched world to dwell here, nor have not, as Saint Paul saith, our dwelling city here, but we be seeking for the city that is to come; and therefore Saint Paul sheweth us that we do seek for it, because he would put us in mind that we should seek for it as they that are good folk and fain would come thither too. For surely whoso setteth so little thereby that he listeth not to seek therefore, it will, I fear me, be long ere he come thereat, and marvellous great grace if ever he come thither. *Sic currite*, saith Saint Paul, *ut comprehendatis:* Run so that you may get it. If it must then be gotten with running, when shall he come at it that lift not one step towards it?

Now because that this world is, as I tell you, not our eternal dwelling but our little-while wandering, God would that we should in such wise use it as folk that were weary of it, and that we should in this vale of labour, toil, tears, and misery, not look for rest and ease, game, pleasure, wealth, and felicity. For they that so do fare like a fond fellow that, going towards his own house where he should be wealthy, would for a tapster's pleasure become an hostler by the way, and die in a stable, and never come at home. And would God that those that drown themself in the desire of this world's wretched wealth were not yet more fools than so. But alas! their folly as far passeth the foolishness of that other fond fellow as there is difference between the height of heaven and the very depth of hell. For our Saviour saith: *Væ vobis qui ridetis nunc, quia lugebitis et flebitis:* Wo may you be that laugh now, for you shall wail and weep. *Est tempus flendi*, saith the Scripture, *et est tempus ridendi:* There is time of weeping and there is time of laughing. But, as you see, he setteth the weeping time before; for that is the time of this wretched world, and the laughing time shall come after in heaven. There is also a time of sowing and a time of reaping too. Now must we in this world sow that we may in the other world reap; and in this short sowing time of this weeping world must we water our seed with the showers of our tears, and then shall we have in heaven a merry laughing harvest for ever. *Euntes ibant et flebant*, saith the prophet, *mittentes semina sua:* They went forth and sowed their seeds weeping. But what saith he shall follow thereof? *Venientes autem venient cum exultatione portantes manipulos suos:* They shall come again more than laughing, with great joy and exultation, with their handfuls of corn in their hands. Lo, they that in their going home towards heaven sow their seeds with weeping shall at the day of judgment come to their bodies again with everlasting plentiful laughing.

And for to prove that this life is no laughing time, but rather the time of weeping, we find that our Saviour Himself wept twice or thrice, but never find we that He laughed so much as once. I will not swear that He never did, but at the least wise He left us no ensample of it. But on the other side He left us ensample of weeping. Of weeping have we matter enough, both for our own sins and for other folks' too; for surely so should we do, bewail their wretched sins and not be glad to detract them nor envy them neither. Alas, silly souls, what cause is there to envy them that are ever wealthy in this world and ever out of tribulation, which, as Job saith, *ducunt in bonis dies suos, et in puncto ad inferna descendunt,* lead all their days in wealth, and in a moment of an hour descend into their graves and be painfully buried in hell? Saint Paul saith unto the Hebrews that God those that He loveth He chastiseth. *Et flagellat onnem filium quem recipit:* And he scourgeth every son of his that he receiveth. Saint Paul saith also: *Per multas tribulationes oportet nos introire in regnum Dei:* By many tribulations must we go into the kingdom of God. And no marvel, for our Saviour Christ said of Himself unto His two disciples that were going into the castle of Emmaus: *An nesciebatis quia oportebat Christum pati et sic introire in regnum suum?* Know you not that Christ must suffer and so go into His kingdom? And would we that are servants look for more privilege in our Master's house than our Master Himself? Would we get into His kingdom with ease when He Himself got not into His own but by pain? His kingdom hath He ordained for His disciples, and He saith unto us all: *Qui vult esse meus discipulus, tollat crucem suam et sequatur me:* If any man will be My disciple, let him learn at Me to do as I have done, take his cross of tribulation upon his back and follow Me. He saith not here Lo, let him laugh and make merry.

Now if heaven serve but for Christ's disciples, and they be

those that take their cross of tribulation, when shall these folk come there that never have tribulation? And if it be true that Saint Paul saith that God chastiseth all them that He loveth, and scourgeth every child whom He receiveth, and to heaven shall none come but such as He loveth and receiveth, when shall they then come thither whom He never chastiseth nor never doth vouchsafe to file His hands upon them nor give them so much as one lash? And if we cannot (as Saint Paul saith we cannot) come to heaven but by many tribulations, how shall they come thither then that never have none at all? Thus see we well by the very Scripture itself how true the words are of old holy saints, that with one voice in a manner say all one thing, that is to wit, that we shall not have both continual wealth in this world and in the other too. And therefore, sith they that in this world without any tribulation enjoy their long continual course of never interrupted prosperity have a great cause of fear and of discomfort lest they be far fallen out of God's favour and stand deep in His indignation and displeasure while He never sendeth them tribulation (which He is ever wont to send them whom He loveth), they therefore, I say, that are in tribulation have on the other side a great cause to take in their grief great inward comfort and spiritual consolation.

A certain objection and the answer thereto

THE FOURTEENTH CHAPTER

Vincent. Verily, good uncle, this seemeth so indeed. Howbeit yet, methink that you say very sore in something concerning such persons as are in continual prosperity, and they be, you wot well, not a few, and those are they also that have the rule and authority of this world in their hand. And I wot well that when they talk with such great cunning men as can I trow tell the truth, and when they ask them whether, while they make merry here in earth all their life, they may not yet for all that have heaven after too, they do tell them yes, yes, well enough. For I have heard them tell them so myself.

Anthony. I suppose, good cousin, that no very wise man, and specially none that very good is therewith, will tell any man fully of that fashion; but surely such as so say to them, I fear me that they flatter them either for lucre or fear. Some of them think peradventure thus: This man maketh much of me now, and giveth me money also to fast and watch and pray for him; but so, I fear me, would he do no more if I should go tell him now that all that I do for him will not serve him but if he go fast and watch and pray for himself too. For if I should set thereto and say farther that my diligent intercession for him should, I trust, be the mean that God should the sooner give him grace to amend and fast and watch and pray and take affliction in his own body for the bettering of his sinful soul, he would be wondrous wroth with that. For he would be loath to have any such grace at all as should make him go leave of any of his mirth, and so sit and mourn for his sin. Such mind as this, lo, have there some of those that are not unlearned and have worldly wit at will; which tell great men such tales as perilously beguile them, rather than the flatterer that so telleth them would with a true tale jeopard to lose his lucre.

Some are there also that such tales tell them for consideration of another fear. For seeing the man so sore set on his pleasure that they despair any amendment of him whatsoever they should shew him, and then seeing also beside that the man doth no great harm, but of a gentle nature doth some good men some good, they pray God themself to send him grace, and so they let him lie lame still in his fleshly lusts, *ad probaticam piscinam expectantes aquæ motum*, at the pool that the Gospel speaketh of beside the temple wherein they washed the sheep for the sacrifice; and they tarry to see the water stirred, and when his good angel coming from God shall once begin to stir the water of his heart and move him to

* G 461

the lowly meekness of a simple sheep, then if he call them to him they will tell him another tale, and help to bear him and plunge him into the pool of penance over head and ears. But in the meanwhile, for fear lest when he would wax never the better, he would wax much the worse, and from gentle, smooth, sweet, and courteous, wax angry, rough, froward, and sour, and thereupon be troublous and tedious to the world, to make fair weather withal, they give him fair words for the while, and put him in good comfort, and let him for the rem- nant stand at his own adventure. And in such wise deal they with him as the mother doth sometime with her child, which, when the little boy will not rise in time for her but lie still abed and slug, and when he is up weepeth because he hath lien so long, fearing to be beaten at school for his late coming thither, she telleth him then that it is but early days, and he shall come time enough, and biddeth him: Go, good son, I warrant thee, I have sent to thy master myself; take thy bread and butter with thee, thou shalt not be beaten at all. And thus, so she may send him merry forth at the door that he weep not in her sight at home, she studieth not much upon the matter though he be taken tardy and beaten when he cometh to school. Surely thus, I fear me, fare there many friars and state's chaplains too, in comfort giving to great men when they be loath to displease them. I cannot commend their thus doing, but surely I fear me thus they do.

Other objections

THE FIFTEENTH CHAPTER

Vincent. But yet, good uncle, though that some do thus, this answereth not the full matter; for we see that the whole Church in the common service use divers collects in which all men pray specially for the princes and the prelates, and generally every man for other and for himself too, that God would vouchsafe to send them all perpetual health and prosperity. And I can see no good man pray God send another sorrow, nor no such prayers are there put in the priest's portas, as far as I can hear. And yet if it were as you say, good uncle, that perpetual prosperity were to the soul so perilous and tribulation thereto so fruitful, then were, as meseemeth, every man bounden of charity not only to pray God send their neighbour sorrow, but also to help thereto themself; and when folk are sick, not pray God send them health, but when they come to comfort them they should say: I am glad, good gossip, that you be so sick, I pray God keep you long therein. And neither should any man give any medicine to another, nor take any medicine himself neither, for by the minishing of the tribulation he taketh away part of the profit from his soul, which can with no bodily profit be sufficiently recompensed.

And also this, wot you well, good uncle, that we read in Holy Scripture of men that were wealthy and rich, and yet were good withal. Solomon was, you wot well, the richest and the most wealthy king that any man could in his time tell of, and yet was he well beloved with God. Job was also no beggar, pardy, nor no wretch otherwise, nor lost his riches and his wealth; for that God would not that His friend should have wealth but for the shew of his patience to the increase of his merit and confusion of the devil, and for proof that prosperity may stand with God's favour: *Reddidit Deus Iob omnia duplicia:* God restored him double of all that ever he lost, and gave him after long life to take his pleasure long. Abraham was eke, you wot well, a man of great substance, and so continued all his life in honour and in wealth; yea, and when he died too, he went unto such wealth that Lazarus which died in tribulation and poverty, the best place that he came to was that rich man's bosom. Finally, good uncle, this we find at our eye, and every day we prove it by plain experience, that many a man is right wealthy and yet therewith right good, and many a miserable wretch as evil as he is wretched. And therefore it seemeth hard, good uncle, that between prosperity and tribulation the matter should go thus, that tribulation should be given alway by God to those that He loveth, for a sign of salvation, and prosperity sent for displeasure, as a token of eternal damnation.

The answer to the objections

THE SIXTEENTH CHAPTER

Anthony. Either I said not, cousin, or else meant I not to say, that for an undoubted rule worldly prosperity were always displeasant to God, or tribulation evermore wholesome to every man. For well wot I that our Lord giveth in this world unto either sort of folk either sort of fortune, *et facit solem suum oriri super bonos et malos, et pluit super iustos et iniustos :* He maketh His sun to shine both upon the good and the bad, and His rain both on the just and on the unjust. And on the other side, *Flagellat omnem filium quem recipit :* He scourgeth every son that He receiveth. And yet He beateth not only good folk that he loveth, but *multa flagella peccatoris* too, there are many scourges for sinners also. He giveth evil folk good fortune in this world, both to call them by kindness, and if they thereby come not, the more is their unkindness; and yet where wealth will not bring them, He giveth them some-time sorrow. And some that in prosperity cannot to God creep forward, in tribulation toward Him they run apace. *Multiplicatæ sunt infirmitates eorum postea acceleraverunt :* Their infirmities were multiplied, saith the prophet, and after that they made haste. To some that are good men God sendeth wealth here also, and they give Him great thank for His gift, and He rewardeth them for that thank too. To some good folk He sendeth sorrow, and they thank Him thereof too. If God should give the goods of this world only to evil folk, then would men ween that God were not the Lord thereof. If God would give the goods only to good men, then would folk take occasion to serve Him but for them. Some will in wealth fall into folly. *Homo cum in honore esset non intellexit, comparatus est iumentis insipientibus, et similis factus est illis:* When man was in honour his understanding failed him, then was he compared with beasts and made like unto them. Some man with tribulation will fall into sin, and therefore saith the prophet, *non relinquet Dominus virgam peccatorum super sortem iustorum, ut non extendant iusti ad iniquitatem manus suas:* God will not leave the rod of wicked men upon the lot of righteous men, lest the righteous peradventure hap to extend and stretch out their hands to iniquity. So say I not nay, but that in either state, wealth or tribulation, may be matter of virtue and matter of vice also. But this is the point, lo, that standeth here in question between you and me: not whether every prosperity be a perilous token, but whether continual wealth in this world without any tribulation be a fearful sign of God's indignation. And therefore this mark that we must shoot at, set up well in our sight, we shall now mete for the shoot and consider how near toward, or how far off, your arrows are from the prick.

Vincent. Some of my bolts, uncle, will I now take up myself, and prettily put them under my belt again. For some of them, I see well, be not worth the meting, and no great marvel, though I shoot wide while I somewhat mistake the mark.

Anthony. Those that make toward the mark and light far too short, when the shot is met shall I take up for you.

To prove that perpetual wealth should be no evil token, you say first that for princes and prelates and every man for other we pray all for perpetual prosperity, and that in the common prayers of the Church too.

Then say you secondly that if prosperity were so perilous and tribulation so profitable, every man ought then to pray God to send other sorrow.

Thirdly you furnish your objections with ensamples of Solomon, Job, and Abraham.

And fourthly, in the end of all, you prove by experience of our own time daily before our face that some wealthy folk are good and some needy very naught. That last bolt I think so, that sith I say the same myself, you be content to take up, it lieth so far wide.

Vincent. That will I with a good will, uncle.

Anthony. Well, do so then, cousin, and we shall mete for the remnant. First must you, cousin, be sure that you look well to the mark, and that can you not but if you know what thing tribulation is. For sith that is one of the things that we principally speak of, but if you consider well what that is, you may miss the mark again. I suppose now that you will agree that tribulation is every such thing as troubleth and grieveth a man either in body or mind, and is, as it were, the prick of a thorn, a bramble, or a briar thrust into his flesh or into his mind; and surely, cousin, the prick that very sore pricketh the mind as far almost passeth in pain the grief that paineth the body as doth a thorn sticking in the heart pass and exceed in pain the thorn that is thrust in the heel.

Now, cousin, if tribulation be this that I call it, then shall you soon consider this, that there be more kinds of tribulation than peradventure you thought on before. And thereupon it followeth also that sith every kind of tribulation is an interruption of wealth, and prosperity (which is but of wealth another name) may be discontinued by more ways than you would before have weened, then say I thus unto you, cousin, that sith tribulation is not only such pangs as pain the body, but every trouble also that grieveth the mind, many good men have many tribulations that every man marketh not, and consequently their wealth interrupted therewith when other men are not ware. For trow you, cousin, that the temptations of the devil, the world, and the flesh, soliciting the mind of a good man unto sin, is not a great inward trouble and secret grief to his heart? To such wretches as care not for their conscience, but like unreasonable beasts follow their foul affections, many of these temptations be no trouble at all, but

matter of their bodily pleasure.   But unto him, cousin, that
standeth in dread of God, the tribulation of temptation is so
painful, that to be rid thereof or sure of the victory therein
(be his substance never so great) he would gladly give more
than half.   Now, if he that careth not for God think this
trouble but a trifle, and with such tribulation prosperity not
interrupted, let him cast in his mind if himself hap upon a
fervent longing for the thing which get he cannot (and as a
good man will not), as percase his pleasure of some certain
good woman that will not be caught; and then let him tell me
whether the ruffle of his desire shall so torment his mind as all
the pleasures that he can take beside shall for lack of that one
not please him of a pin.   And I dare be bold to warrant him
that the pain in resisting, and the great fear of falling that
many a good man hath in his temptation, is an anguish and a
grief every deal as great as his.

Now say I farther, cousin, that if this be true (as in very
deed true it is) that such trouble is tribulation and thereby
consequently an interruption of prosperous wealth, no man
precisely meaneth to pray for other to keep him in continual
prosperity without any manner of discontinuance or change in
this world; for that prayer, without other condition added or
employed, were inordinate and were very childish.   For it
were to pray that either they should never have temptation, or
else that, if they had, they might follow it and fulfil their
affection.   Who dare, good cousin, for shame or for sin, or
himself or any man else, make this manner kind of prayer?
Besides this, cousin, the Church, ye wot well, adviseth every
man to fast, to watch, and pray, both for taming of his fleshly
lusts, and also to mourn and lament his sin before committed
and to bewail his offence done against God, and as they did at
the city of Nineveh, and as the prophet David did for their sin,
put affliction to their flesh; and when a man so doth, cousin,
is this no tribulation to him because he doth it himself?   For
I wot well you would agree that it were if another man did it
against his will.   Then is tribulation, you wot well, tribulation

still, though it be taken well in worth; yea, and though it be taken too with very right goodwill, yet is pain, you wot well, pain; and therefore so is it though a man do it himself. Then sith the Church adviseth every man to take tribulation for his sin, whatsoever words you find in any prayer, they never mean (you may be fast and sure) to pray God to keep every good man nor every bad man neither from every manner kind of tribulation.

Now, he that is not in some kind of tribulation, as peradventure in sickness or in loss of goods, is not yet out of tribulation if he have his ease of body or of mind inquieted and thereby his wealth interrupted with another kind of tribulation, as is either temptation to a good man, or voluntary affliction either of body by penance or of mind by contrition and heaviness for his sin and offence against God. And thus I say that for precise perpetual wealth and prosperity in this world, that is to say, for the perpetual lack of all trouble and all tribulation, there is no wise man that either prayeth for himself or for any man else, and thus answer I your first objection.

Now before I meddle with your second, your third will I join to this. For upon this answer will the solution of your ensamples conveniently depend. As for Solomon was, as you say, all his days a marvellous wealthy king and much was he beloved with God, I wot well, in the beginning of his reign; but that the favour of God persevered him, as his prosperity did, that can I not tell. And therefore will I not warrant it, but surely we see that his continual wealth made him fall first into such wanton folly, in multiplying wives to an horrible number, contrary to the commandment of God given in the law of Moses, and secondly taking to wife among other such as were infidels, contrary to another commandment of God's written law also, that finally, by the mean of his miscreant wife, he fell into maintenance of idolatry himself. And of this find we no amendment or repentance, as we find of his father. And therefore, though he were buried where his father was, yet whether he went to the rest that his father did through some secret sorrow for his sin at last, that is to say, by some kind of tribulation, I cannot tell, and am content, therefore, to trust well and pray God he did so. But surely we be not sure; and therefore the ensample of Solomon can very little serve you, for you might as well lay it for a proof that God favoureth idolatry as that He favoureth prosperity, for Solomon was, you wot well, in both.

As for Job, sith our question hangeth upon prosperity perpetual, the wealth of Job that was with so great adversity so sore interrupted can, as yourself seeth, serve you for no ensample. And that God gave him here in this world all thing double that he lost, little toucheth my matter, which denieth not prosperity to be God's gift and given to some good men too, namely such as have tribulation too.

But in Abraham, cousin, I suppose is all your chief hold, because that you not only shew riches and prosperity perpetual in him, through the course of all his whole life in this world, but that after his death also. Lazarus, that poor man that lived in tribulation and died for pure hunger and thirst, had after his death his place of comfort and rest in Abraham that wealthy rich man's bosom. But here must you consider that Abraham had not such continual prosperity, but that it was discontinued with divers tribulations.

1. Was it nothing to him, trow you, to leave his own country, and at God's sending to go into a strange land which God promised him and his seed for ever? But in all his whole life he gave himself never a foot.

2. Was it no trouble, that his cousin Lot and himself were fain to part company because their servants could not agree together?

3. Though he recovered Lot again from the three kings, was his taking no trouble to him, trow you, in the meanwhile?

4. Was the destruction of the five cities no heaviness to his heart? A man would ween yes that readeth in the story what labour he made to save them.

5. His heart was, I dare say, in no little sorrow when he was fain to let Abimelech the king have his wife, whom though God provided to keep undefiled and turned all to wealth, yet was it no little woe to him in the mean time.

6. What continual grief was it to his heart many a long day that he had no child of his own body begotten? He that doubteth thereof shall find it in Genesis of his own moan made to God.

7. No man doubteth but Ishmael was great comfort unto him at his birth, and was it no grief, then, when he must cast out the mother and the child both?

8. Isaac that was the child of promission: although God kept his life that was unlooked for, yet while the loving father bound him and went about to behead him and offer him up in sacrifice, who but himself can conceive what heaviness his heart had then? I would ween in my mind (because you speak of Lazarus) that Lazarus's own death panged him not so sore. Then as Lazarus's pain was patiently born, so was Abraham's taken not only patiently but, which is a thing much more meritorious, of obedience willingly. And therefore, though Abraham had not, as he did indeed, far excelled Lazarus in merit of reward for many other things beside, and specially for that he was a special patriarch of the faith, yet had he far passed him, even by the merit of tribulation well taken here for God's sake too. And so serveth for your purpose no man less than Abraham. But now, good cousin, let us look a little longer here upon the rich Abraham and Lazarus the poor, and as we shall see Lazarus set in wealth somewhat under the rich Abraham, so shall we see another rich man lie full low beneath Lazarus crying and calling out of his fiery couch, that Lazarus might with a drop of water falling from his finger's end a little cool and refresh the tip of his burning tongue. Consider well now what Abraham answered to the rich wretch: *Fili, recordare quia recepisti bona in vita tua et Lazarus similiter mala, nunc autem hic consolatur, tu vero cruciaris:* Son, remember that thou hast in thy life received wealth and

Lazarus in likewise pain; but now receiveth he comfort and
thou sorrow, pain, and torment.   Christ describeth his wealth
and his prosperity, gay and soft apparel with royal delicate
fare, continually day by day.   *Epulabatur*, saith our Saviour,
quotidie splendide: He did fare royally every day, his wealth
was continual; lo, no time of tribulation between.   And
Abraham telleth him the same tale, that he had taken his
wealth in this world and Lazarus likewise his pain, and that
they had now changed each to the clean contrary: poor
Lazarus from tribulation into wealth, and the rich man from
his continual prosperity into perpetual pain.   Here was laid
expressly to Lazarus no very great virtue by name, nor to this
rich glutton no great heinous crime, but the taking of his
continual ease and pleasure without any tribulation or grief,
whereof grew sloth and negligence to think upon the poor
man's pain.   For that ever himself saw Lazarus and wist him
die for hunger at his door, that laid neither Christ nor
Abraham to his charge.   And therefore, cousin, this story, lo,
of which by occasion of Abraham and Lazarus you put me in
remembrance, well declareth what peril is in continual worldly
wealth and contrariwise what comfort cometh of tribulation.
And thus as your other ensamples of Solomon and Job
nothing for the matter further you, so your ensample of rich
Abraham and poor Lazarus have not a little hindered you.

An answer to the second objection

THE SEVENTEENTH CHAPTER

Vincent.   Surely, uncle, you have shaken mine ensamples
sore, and have in your meting of your shot removed me these
arrows, methinketh, farther off from the prick than methought
they stack when I shot them; and I shall therefore now be
content to take them up again.   But yet meseemeth surely
that my second shot may stand.   For of truth, if every kind of

tribulation be so profitable that it be good to have it as you say it is I cannot see wherefore any man should either wish or pray or any manner of thing do to have any kind of tribulation withdrawn, either from himself or any friend of his.

Anthony. I think in very deed tribulation so good and profitable that I should haply doubt as you do wherefore a man might labour or pray to be delivered of it, saving that God which teacheth us the one teacheth us also the other. And as He biddeth us take our pain patiently and exhort our neighbours to do also the same, so biddeth He us also not let to do our devoir to remove the pain from us both.   And then when it is God that teacheth both, I shall not need to break my brain in devising wherefore He would bid us to do both, the one seeming to resist the other.   If He send the scourge of scarcity and of great famine, He will we shall bear it patiently; but yet will He that we shall eat our meat when we can hap to get it.   If He send us the plague of pestilence, He will we shall patiently take it; but yet will He that we let us blood, and lay plasters to draw it, and ripe it, and lance it, and get it away.   Both these points teacheth God in Scripture in more than many places.   Fasting is better than eating, and more thank hath of God; and yet will God that we shall eat.   Praying is better than drinking, and much more pleasant to God; and yet will God that we shall drink.   Waking in good business is much more acceptable to God than sleeping; and yet will God that we shall sleep.   God hath given us our bodies here to keep, and will that we maintain them to do Him service with, till He send for us hence.   Now can we not tell surely how much tribulation may mar it, or peradventure hurt the soul also; wherefore the apostle, after that he had commanded the Corinthians to deliver to the devil the abominable fornicator that forbare not the bed of his own father's wife, yet after that he had been a while accursed and punished for his sin the apostle commanded them charitably to receive him again and give him consolation, *ut non a magnitudine doloris absorbeatur*, that the greatness of his sorrow

should not swallow him up. And therefore when God
sendeth the tempest, He will that the shipmen shall get them
to their tackling and do the best they can for themself, that
the sea eat them not up. For help ourselves as well as we
can, He can make His plague as sore and as long lasting as
Himself lust.

And as He will that we do for ourself, so will He that we do
for our neighbour too, and that we shall in this world be each
to other piteous and not *sine affectione*, for which the apostle
rebuketh them that lack their tender affections here, so that of
charity sorry should we be for their pain too upon whom
for cause necessary we be driven ourself to put it. And
whoso saith that for pity of his neighbour's soul he will have
none of his body, let him be sure that, as Saint John saith, he
that loveth not his neighbour whom he seeth, loveth God but
a little whom he seeth not. So he that hath no pity on the
pain that he seeth his neighbour feel afore him, pitieth little
(whatsoever he say) the pain of his soul that he seeth not yet.

God sendeth us also such tribulation sometime because His
pleasure is to have we pray unto Him for help. And therefore, when Saint Peter was in prison the Scripture sheweth
that the whole Church without intermission prayed inces-
santly for him, and at their fervent prayer God by miracle
delivered him. When the disciples in the tempest stood in
fear of drowning they prayed unto Christ and said: *Salva nos
Domine, perimus:* Save us, Lord, we perish. And then at
their prayer He shortly ceased the tempest. And now see
we proved often that in sore weather or sickness by general
processions God giveth gracious help; and many a man in his
great pain and sickness by calling upon God is marvellously
made whole. This is God's goodness that, because in wealth
we remember Him not but forget to pray to Him, sendeth us
sorrow and sickness to force us to draw toward Him, and
compelleth us to call upon Him and pray for release of our
pain, whereby when we learn to know Him and to seek to
Him we take a good occasion to fall after into farther grace.

Of them that in tribulation seek not unto God, but some to the flesh, and some to the world, and some to the devil himself

THE EIGHTEENTH CHAPTER

Vincent.   Verily, good uncle, with this good answer I am well content.

Anthony.   Yea, cousin, but many men are there with whom God is not content, which abuse this great high goodness of His, whom neither fair treating nor hard handling can cause to remember their Maker, but in wealth they be wanton and forget God and follow their lust.   And when God with tribulation draweth them toward Him, then ware they wood and draw back all that ever they may, and rather run and seek help at any other hand than to go set it at his.   Some for comfort seek to the flesh, some to the world, and some to the devil himself.   Some man that in worldly prosperity is very dull, and hath deep stepped into many a sore sin (which sins, when he did them, he counted for part of his pleasure), God, willing of His goodness to call the man to grace, casteth a remorse into his mind among after his first sleep, and maketh him lie a little while and bethink him.   Then beginneth he to remember his life, and from that he falleth to think upon his death, and how he must leave all this worldly wealth within a while behind here in this world and walk hence alone.   He wotteth not whither, nor how soon, he shall take his journey thither, nor can tell what company he shall meet there, and then beginneth he to think that it were good to make sure and to be merry, so that he be wise therewith, lest there hap to be such black bugs indeed as folk call devils, whose torments he was wont to take for poets' tales.   Those thoughts, if they sink deep, are a sore tribulation; and surely if he take hold of the grace that God therein offereth him, his tribulation is wholesome, and shall be full comfortable to remember, that God by this tribulation calleth him and biddeth him come home out of the country of sin that he was bred and brought up so long in, and come into the land of behest that floweth milk and honey. And then if he follow this calling (as many one full well doeth) joyful shall his sorrow be, and glad shall he be to change his life, leave his wanton lusts, and do penance for his sins, bestowing his time upon better business.

But some men now, when this calling of God causeth them to be sad, they be loath to leave their sinful lusts that hang in their hearts, and specially if they have any such kind of living as they must needs leave off or fall deeper in sin, or if they have done so many great wrongs that they have many mends to make that must (if they follow God) minish much their money. Then are these folks, alas, woefully bewrapped; for God pricketh upon them of His great goodness still, and the grief of this great pang pincheth them at the heart, and of wickedness they wry away, and from this tribulation they turn to their flesh for help and labour to shake off this thought; and then they mend their pillow and lay their head softer, and assay to sleep, and when that will not be then they find a talk a while with them that lie by them. If that cannot be neither, then they lie and long for day, and then get them forth about their worldly wretchedness, the matter of their prosperity, the selfsame sinful things with which they displease God most; and at length, with many times using this manner, God utterly casteth them off. And then they set naught neither by God nor devil. *Peccator cum in profundum venerit, contemnit:* When the sinner cometh even into the depth, then he contemneth and setteth naught by nothing, saving worldly fear that may fall by chance or that needs must (they wot well) fall once by death? But, alas, when death cometh, then cometh again their sorrow; then will no soft bed serve, nor no company make him merry; then must he leave his outward worship and comfort of his glory, and lie panting in his bed as it were on a pine bank; then cometh his fear of his evil life and of his dreadful death. Then cometh the torment, his cumbered conscience and fear of his heavy judgment. Then the devil draweth him to despair with imagination of hell, and suffereth him not then to take it for a fable. And yet if he do, then findeth it the wretch no fable. Ah, woe worth the while that folk think not of this in time!

God sendeth to some man great trouble in his mind and great tribulation about his worldly goods because He would of His goodness take his delight and his confidence from them. And yet the man withdraweth no part of his fond fantasies, but falleth more fervently to them than before, and setteth his whole heart like a fool more upon them. And then he taketh him all to the devices of his worldly counsellors, and, without any counsel of God or any trust put in Him, maketh many wise ways (as he weeneth) and all turn at length unto folly, and one subtle drift driveth another to naught. Some have I seen even in their last sickness, set up in their death-bed underpropped with pillows, take their playfellows to them and comfort themself with cards; and this, they said, did ease them well to put fantasies out of their heads. And what fantasies, trow you? Such as I told you right now, of their own lewd life and peril of their soul, of heaven and of hell that irked them to think of, and therefore cast it out with cards-play as long as ever they might till the pure pangs of death pulled their heart from their play and put them in the case they could not reckon their game. And then left them their gameners and slyly slunk away, and long was it not ere they galped up the ghost; and what game they came then to, that God knoweth and not I. I prayed God it were good, but I fear it very sore.

Some men are there also that do (as did King Saul) in their tribulation go seek unto the devil. This king had commanded all such to be destroyed as use the false abominable superstition of this ungracious witchcraft and necromancy; and yet fell he to such folly afterward himself that ere he went to battle he sought unto a witch, and besought her to raise up a dead man to tell him how he should speed. Now had God shewed him by Samuel before that he should come to naught, and he went about none amendment, but waxed worse and worse, so that God lust not to look to him; and when he sought by the prophet to have answer of God, there came none answer to him. Which thing he thought strange, and because he was not with God heard at his pleasure, he made suit to the devil, desiring a woman by witchcraft to raise up dead Samuel. But speed had he such thereof as commonly they have all that in their business meddle with such matters; for an evil answer had he, and an evil speed thereafter, his army discomfited, and himself slain. And, as it is rehearsed in Paralipomenon, the tenth chapter of the first book, one cause of his fall was for lack of trust in God, for which he left to take counsel of God, and fell to seek counsel of the witch against God's prohibition in the law, and against his own good deed, by which he punished and put out all witches so late afore.

Such speed let them look for that play the same part as I see many do, that in a great loss send to seek a conjurer to get their gear again; and marvellous things there they see sometime, but never great of their good. And many fond fools are there that when they lie sick will meddle with no physic in no manner wise, nor send his water to no cunning man, but send his cap or his hose to a wise woman, otherwise called a witch. Then sendeth she word again that she hath spied in his hose where, when he took no heed, he was taken with a sprite between two doors as he went in the twilight. But the sprite would not let him feel it in five days after, and it hath all the while festered in his body, and it is the grief that paineth him so sore, but let him go to no leechcraft, nor any manner physic, other than good meat and strong drink, for syrups should souse him up. But he shall have five leaves of valerian that she enchanted with a charm, and gathered with her left hand. Let him lay those five leaves to his right thumb, not bind it fast to, but let it hang loose thereat by a green thread; he shall never need to change it, look it fall not away, but let it hang till he be whole and he shall need no more. In such wise witches, and in such mad medicines have there many fools more faith a great deal than in God. And thus, cousin, as I tell you, all these kind of folk that in their tribulation call not upon God, but seek for their ease and help otherwhere, to the flesh and the world and to the flinging fiend, the tribulation that God's goodness sendeth them for good themself by their folly turn into their harm; and they that on the other side seek unto God therein, both comfort and profit they greatly take thereby.

Another objection with the answer thereunto

THE NINETEENTH CHAPTER

Vincent. I like well, good uncle, all your answers herein; but one doubt yet remaineth there in my mind which riseth upon this answer that you make, and that doubt solved, I will as for this time, mine own good uncle, encumber you no farther. For methink I do you very much wrong to give you occasion to labour yourself so much in matter of some study, with long talking at once. I will therefore at this time move you but one thing, and seek some other time at your more ease for the remnant. My doubt, good uncle, is this. I perceive well by your answers gathered and considered together that you will well agree that a man may both have worldly wealth and yet well go to God. And that on the other side a man may be miserable and live in tribulation and yet go to the devil. And as a man may please God by patience in adversity, so may he please God by thanks given in prosperity. Now sith you grant these things to be such that either of them both may be matter of virtue or else matter of sin, matter of damnation or matter of salvation, they seem neither good nor bad of their own nature, but things of themself equal and indifferent, turning to good or the contrary after as they be taken. And then, if this be thus, I can perceive no cause why you should give the pre-eminence unto tribulation, or wherefore you

should reckon more cause of comfort therein than you should
reckon to stand in prosperity, but rather a great deal less, by
in a manner half.   Sith that in prosperity the man is well at
ease and may also, by giving thank to God, get good unto his
soul, whereas in tribulation, though he may merit by patience
(as in abundance of worldly wealth the other may by thank),
yet lacketh he much comfort that the wealthy man hath, in
that he sore is grieved with heaviness and pain.   Besides this
also, that a wealthy man well at ease may pray to God quietly
and merrily with alacrity and great quietness of mind, whereas
he that lieth groaning in his grief cannot endure to pray nor
think almost upon nothing but upon his pain.

   Anthony.   To begin, cousin, where you leave, the prayers
of him that is in wealth and him that is in woe, if the men be
both naught, their prayers be both like.   For neither hath
the one lust to pray nor the other neither.   And as that one is
let with his pain, so is the other with his pleasure, saving that
the pain stirreth him sometime to call upon God in his grief,
though that man be right bad, where the pleasure pulleth his
mind another way, though the man be meetly good.   And this
point I think there are few that can (if they say true) say that
they find it otherwise.   For in tribulation (which cometh, you
wot well, in many sundry kinds), any man that is not a dull
beast or a desperate wretch calleth upon God, not hourly but
right heartily, and setteth his heart full whole upon his
request, so sore he longeth for ease and help of his heaviness.
But when men are wealthy and well at their ease, while our
tongue pattereth upon our prayers apace, good God, how
many mad ways our mind wandereth the while!   Yet wot I
well that in some tribulation such sore sickness there is or
other grievous bodily pain, that hard it were for a man to say
a long pair of Matins; and yet some that lie a-dying say full
devoutly the Seven Psalms and other prayers with the priest
at their aneling.   But those that for the grief of their pain
cannot endure to do it, or that be more tender and lack that
strong heart and stomach that some other have, God requireth

no such long prayers of them, but the lifting up of their heart alone without any word at all is more acceptable to Him of one in such case than long service so said as folk use to say it in health.

The martyrs in their agony made no long prayers aloud, but one inch of such a prayer so prayed in that pain was worth a whole ell and more, even of their own prayers prayed at some other time.   Great learned men say that Christ, albeit He was very God, and as God was in eternal equal bliss with His Father, yet as man merited not for us only, but for Himself too. For proof whereof they lay in these words the authority of Saint Paul: *Christus humiliavit semetipsum factus obediens usque ad mortem, mortem autem crucis.   Propter quod et Deus exaltavit illum et donavit illi nomen quod est super omne nomen, ut in nomine Iesu omne genuflectatur cœlestium, terrestrium, et infernorum, et omnis lingua confiteatur quia Dominus Iesus Christus in gloria est Dei Patris:* Christ hath humbled Himself, and became obedient unto the death, and that unto the death of the cross, for which thing God hath also exalted Him, and given Him a name which is above all names: that in the name of Jesus every knee be bowed, both of the celestial creatures and the terrestrial, and of the infernal too, and that every tongue shall confess that our Lord Jesus Christ is in the glory of God His Father.   Now, if it so be, as these great learned men upon such authorities of Holy Scripture say, that our Saviour so merited as man, and as man deserved reward, not for us only but for Himself also, then were there in His deeds, as it seemeth, sundry degrees and differences of deserving, and not His maundy-like merit as His Passion, nor His sleep-like merit as His watch and His prayer, no, nor His prayers peradventure all of like merit neither.   But though there none was, nor none could be, in His most blessed person but excellent and incomparably passing the prayer of any pure creature, yet His own not all alike, but some one far above some other.

And then if it thus be, of all His holy prayers the chief

seemeth me those that He made in His great agony and pain of His bitter Passion. The first, when He thrice fell prostrate in His agony, when the heaviness of His heart with fear of death at hand, so painful and so cruel as He well beheld it, made such a fervent commotion in His blessed body, that the bloody sweat of His holy flesh dropped down on the ground. The other were the painful prayers that He made upon the cross, where for all the torment that He hanged in of beating, nailing, and stretching out all His limbs, with the wresting of His sinews and breaking of His tender veins, and the sharp crown of thorn so pricking Him into the head, that His blessed blood streamed down all His face. In all these hideous pains, in all their cruel despites, yet two very devout and fervent prayers He made, the one for their pardon that so dispiteously put Him to His pain, and the other about His own deliverance, commending His own soul unto His Holy Father in heaven. These prayers of His, among all that ever He made, made in His most pain, reckon I for the chief. And these prayers of our Saviour at His bitter Passion, and of His holy martyrs in the fervour of their torment, shall serve us to see that there is no prayer made at pleasure so strong and effectual, as in tribulation.

Now come I to the touching of the reason you make, where you tell me that I grant you that both in wealth and in woe some man may be naught and offend God, the one by impatience, the other by fleshly lust. And on the other side, both in tribulation and prosperity too, some man may also do very well and deserve thank of God by thanks given to God, as well of His gift of riches, worship, and wealth, as of need and penury, prisonment, sickness, and pain, and that therefore you cannot see for what cause I should give any pre-eminence in comfort unto tribulation, but rather allow prosperity for the thing more comfortable, and that not a little, but in manner by double, sith therein hath the soul comfort and the body both, the soul by thank given unto God for His gift, and then the body by being well at ease, where the person pained in tribulation taketh no comfort but in his soul alone.   First as for your double comfort, cousin, you may cut off the one. For a man in prosperity, though he be bound to thank God of His gift wherein he feeleth ease, and may be glad also that he giveth thank to God, yet for that he taketh his ease here hath he little cause of comfort, except that the sensual feeling of bodily pleasure you lust for to call by the name of comfort. Nor I say not nay, but that sometime men use so to take it when they say: This good drink comforteth well mine heart. But comfort, cousin, is properly taken by them that take it right rather for the consolation of good hope that men take in their heart of some good growing toward them than for a present pleasure with which the body is delighted and tickled for the while.

Now, though a man without patience can have no reward for his pain, yet when his pain is patiently taken for God's sake and his will conformed to God's pleasure therein, God rewardeth the sufferer after the rate of his pain; and this thing appeareth by many a place in Scripture, of which some have I shewed you and yet shall I shew you more.   But never found I any place in Scripture that I remember in which though the wealthy man thank God for His gift, our Lord promised any reward in heaven because the man took his ease and his pleasure here.   And therefore, sith I speak but of such comfort as is very comfort indeed (by which a man hath hope of God's favour and remission of his sins with minishing of his pain in purgatory or reward else in heaven), and such comfort cometh of tribulation, and for tribulation well taken, but not for pleasure, though it be well taken; therefore of your comfort that you double by prosperity you may, as I told you, cut very well away the half.

Now why I give prerogative in comfort unto tribulation far above prosperity, though a man may do well in both, of this thing will I shew you causes two or three.   First, as I before have at length shewed you out of all question, continual wealth interrupted with no tribulation is a very discomfortable token of everlasting damnation; whereupon it followeth that tribulation is one cause of comfort unto a man's heart, in that it dischargeth him of the discomfort that he might of reason take of overlong lasting wealth.   Another is that the Scripture much commendeth tribulation as occasion of more profit than wealth and prosperity, not to them only that are therein, but to them too that resort unto them, and therefore saith Ecclesiastes: *Melius est ire ad domum luctus quam ad domum convivii; in illa enim finis cunctorum admonetur hominum, et vivens cogitat quid futurum sit:* Better is it to go to the house of weeping and wailing for some man's death than to the house of a feast; for in that house of heaviness is a man put in remembrance of the end of every man, and while he yet liveth he thinketh what shall come after.   And after yet he farther saith: *Cor sapientium ubi tristitia est, et cor stultorum ubi lætitia:* The heart of wise men is there as heaviness is, and the heart of fools is there as is mirth and gladness.   And verily, there as you shall hear worldly mirth seem to be commended in Scripture, it is either commonly spoken, as in the person of some worldly disposed people, or understanden of rejoicing spiritual, or meant of some small moderate refreshing of the mind against an heavy discomfortable dullness.

Now, whereas prosperity was to the children of Israel promised in the old law as a special gift of God, that was for their imperfection at that time to draw them to God with gay things and pleasant, as men to make children learn give them cake, bread, and butter.   For, as the Scripture maketh mention, that people were much after the manner of children in lack of wit and in waywardness.   And therefore was their master Moses called *Pedagogus*, that is, a teacher of children or, as they call such one in the grammar schools, an usher or a master of the petits.   For as Saint Paul saith: *Nihil ad perfectum duxit lex:* The old law brought nothing unto perfection.   And God also threateneth folk with tribulation in this world for sin, not for that worldly tribulation is evil, but for that we should be well ware of the sickness of sin for fear of that thing to follow, which though it be indeed a very good wholesome thing if we well take it, is yet, because it is painful, the thing that we be loath to have.

But this I say yet again and again, that as for far the better thing in this world toward the getting of the very good that God giveth in the world to come, the Scripture undoubtedly so commendeth tribulation, that in respect and comparison thereof it discommendeth this worldly wretched wealth and discomfortable comfort utterly. For to what other thing soundeth the words of Ecclesiastes that I rehearsed you now, that it is better to be in the house of heaviness than to be at a feast? Whereto soundeth this comparison of his, that the wise man's heart draweth thither as folk are in sadness, and the heart of a fool is there as he may find mirth? Whereto draweth this threat of the wise man, that he that delighteth in wealth shall fall into woe? *Risus*, saith he, *dolore miscebitur et extrema gaudii luctus occupat:* Laughter shall be mingled with sorrow, and the end of mirth is taken up with heaviness. And our Saviour saith Himself: *Væ vobis qui ridetis, quia lugebitis et flebitis:* Woe be to you that laugh, for you shall weep and wail. But He saith on the other side: *Beati qui lugent, quoniam illi consolabuntur:* Blessed are they that weep and wail, for they shall be comforted. And He saith to His disciples: *Mundus gaudebit vos autem dolebitis, sed tristitia vestra vertetur in gaudium:* The world shall joy and you shall be sorry, but your sorrow shall be turned into joy. And so is it, you wot well, now; and the mirth of many that then were in joy is now turned all to sorrow. And thus you see by the Scripture plain that in matter of very comfort tribulation is as far above prosperity as the day is above the night.

Another pre-eminence of tribulation over wealth in occasion of merit and reward shall well appear upon certain considerations well marked in them both. Tribulation meriteth in patience and in the obedient conforming of the man's will unto God and in thanks given to God for His visitation, if you reckon me now against these many other good deeds that a wealthy man may do, as by riches give alms, by authority labour in doing many men justice, or if you find farther any such other thing like. First I say that the patient person in tribulation hath in all these virtues of a wealthy man an occasion of merit too, which the wealthy man hath not againward in the forerehearsed virtues of his. For it is easy for the person that is in tribulation to be well willing to do the selfsame if he could, and then shall his goodwill, where the power lacketh, go very near to the merit of the deed. But now is not the wealthy man in a like case with the will of patience and conformity and thanks given to God for tribulation, sith it is not so ready for the wealthy man to be content to be in the tribulation that is the occasion of the patient's desert, as for the troubled person to be content to be in prosperity, to do the good deeds that the wealthy man doth. Besides this, all that the wealthy man doth, though he could not do them without those things that are accounted for wealth and called by that name, as not do great alms without great riches, nor do these many men right by his labour without great authority, yet may he do these things being not in wealth indeed: as where he taketh his wealth for no wealth, nor his riches for no riches, nor in heart setteth by neither nother, but secretly liveth in a contrite heart and a life penitential, as many times did the prophet David being a great king, so that worldly wealth was no wealth to him. And therefore is not of necessity worldly wealth the cause of those good deeds, sith he may do them, and doth them best indeed, to whom the thing that worldly folk call wealth is yet, for his godly set mind, drawn from the delight thereof no pleasure in manner nor no wealth at all. Finally, whensoever the wealthy man doth those good virtuous deeds, if we consider the nature of them right we shall perceive that in the doing of them he doth ever for that rate and portion of those deeds minish the matter of his worldly wealth, as in giving great alms he departeth with so much of his worldly goods which are in that part the matter of his wealth.

In labouring about the doing many good deeds his labour minisheth his quiet and his rest; and for the rate of so much it minisheth his wealth, if pain and wealth be each to other contrary, as I ween you will agree they be.

Now, whosoever then will well consider the thing, he shall, I doubt not, perceive and see therein that in these good deeds that the wealthy man doth, though he doth them by that that his wealth maketh him able, yet in the doing of them he departeth for the portion from the nature of wealth toward the nature of some part of tribulation; and therefore even in those good deeds themself that prosperity doth, doth in goodness the prerogative of tribulation above wealth appear. Now if it hap that some man cannot perceive this point because the wealthy man for all his alms abideth rich still, and for all his good labour abideth still in his authority, let him consider that I speak but after the portion.   And because the portion of all that he giveth of his goods is very little in respect of that he leaveth, therefore is the reason haply with some folk little perceived.   But if it so were that he went forth with giving till he had given out all and left himself nothing, then would a very blind man see it.   For as he were from riches come to poverty, so were he from wealth willingly fallen into tribulation.   And between labour and rest the reason goeth all alike, which whoso can consider shall see that for the portion in every good deed done by the wealthy man the matter is all one.

Then sith we have somewhat weighed the virtues of prosperity, let us consider on the other side the aforenamed things that are the matter of merit and reward in tribulation, that is to wit, patience, conformity, and thanks.   Patience the wealthy man hath not in that that he is wealthy; for if he be pinched in any point wherein he taketh patience, in the part he suffereth some tribulation, and so not by his prosperity but by his tribulation hath the man that merit.   Like is it if we would say that the wealthy man hath another virtue in the stead of patience, that is to wit, the keeping of himself from pride and such other sins as wealth would bring him to. For the resisting of such motions is, as I before told you, without any doubt a minishing of fleshly wealth, and is a very true kind, and one of the most profitable kinds, of tribulation. So that all that good merit groweth to the wealthy man not by his wealth but by the minishing of his wealth with wholesome tribulation. The most colour of comparison is in the other twain, that is to wit, in the conformity of man's will unto God and in thanks given unto God. For like as the good man in tribulation sent him by God conformeth his will to God's will in that behalf and giveth God thank therefore, so doth the wealthy man in his wealth which God giveth him conform his will to God's in that point, sith he is well content to take it of His gift, and giveth God again also right hearty thank therefore. And thus, as I said, in these two things may you catch the most colour to compare the wealthy man's merit with the merit of tribulation. But yet that they be not matches you may soon see by this. For in tribulation can there none conform his will unto God's and give Him thank therefore but such a man as hath in that point a very special good mind. But he that is very naught or hath in his heart but very little good may well be content to take wealth at God's hand, and say : Marry I thank You, Sir, for this with all my heart, and will not fail to love You well while You let me fare no worse. *Confitebitur tibi quum benefeceris ei.*

Now if the wealthy man be very good, yet in conformity of his will and thanks given to God for his wealth his virtue is not like yet to his that doth the same in tribulation. For, as the philosophers said in that thing very well of old, virtue standeth in things of hardness and difficulty. And then, as I told you, much less hardness and less difficulty there is by a great deal to be content and to conform our will to God's will, and to give Him thank too for our ease than for our pain, for our wealth than for our woe. And therefore is the conforming of our will unto God's and the thanks that we give Him for our tribulation more worthy thank again and more reward meriteth in the very fast wealth and felicity of heaven than our conformity with our thanks given for and in our worldly wealth here.   And this thing saw the devil when he said to our Lord of Job, that it was no marvel though Job had a reverent fear unto God, God had done so much for him and kept him in prosperity.   But the devil wist well it was an hard thing for Job to be so loving and so to give thanks to God in tribulation and adversity; and therefore was he glad to get leave of God to put him in tribulation, and thereby trusted to cause him murmur and grudge against God with impatience.   But the devil had there a fall in his own turn; for the patience of Job in the short time of his adversity gat him much more favour and thank of God, and more is he renowned and commended in Scripture for that than for all the goodness of his long prosperous life.   Our Saviour saith Himself also that if we say well by them or yield them thank that do us good, we do no great thing therein, and therefore can we with reason look for no great thank again.   And thus have I shewed you, lo, no little pre-eminence that tribulation hath in merit, and therefore no little pre-eminence of comfort in hope of heavenly reward above the virtues (the merit and cause of good hope and comfort) that cometh of wealth and prosperity.

A summary commendation of tribulation

The Twentieth Chapter

AND therefore, good cousin, to finish our talking for this time lest I should be too long a let unto your other business, if we lay first for a sure ground a very fast faith whereby we believe to be true all that the Scripture saith, understanden truly as the old holy doctors declare it and as the Spirit of God instructeth His Catholic Church, then shall we consider tribulation as a gracious gift of God, a gift that He specially gave His special friends; the thing that in Scripture is highly commended and praised; a thing whereof the contrary long continued is perilous; a thing which, but if God send it, men have need by penance to put upon themself and seek it; a thing that helpeth to purge our sins passed; a thing that preserveth us from sins that else would come; a thing that causeth us to set less by the world; a thing that exciteth us to draw more toward God; a thing that much minisheth our pains in purgatory; a thing that much increaseth our final reward in heaven; the thing by which our Saviour entered His own kingdom; the thing with which all His apostles followed Him thither; the thing which our Saviour exhorteth all men to; the thing without which He saith we be not His disciples; the thing without which no man can get to heaven.

Whoso these things thinketh on and remembereth well shall in his tribulation neither murmur nor grudge, but first by patience take his pain in worth, and then shall he grow in goodness and think himself well worthy; then shall he consider that God sendeth it for his weal, and thereby shall he be moved to give God thank therefore: therewith shall his grace increase, and God shall give him such comfort by considering that God is in his trouble evermore near unto him (*Quia Deus iuxta est iis qui tribulato sunt corde:* God is near, saith the prophet, to them that have their heart in trouble), that his joy thereof shall minish much of his pain, and he shall not seek for vain comfort elsewhere, but specially trust in God and seek for help of Him, submitting his own will wholly to God's pleasure, and pray to God in his heart, and pray his friends pray for him, and specially the priests, as Saint James biddeth, and begin first with confession and make us clean to God, and ready to depart, and be glad to go to God, putting purgatory to His pleasure.

If we thus do, this dare I boldly say, we shall never live here the less of half an hour, but shall with this comfort find our hearts lighted and thereby the grief of our tribulation lessed, and the more likelihood to recover and to live the longer. Now, if God will we shall hence, then doth He much more for us; for he that this way taketh cannot go but well. For of him that is loath to leave this wretched world mine heart is much in fear lest he die not well. Hard it is for him to be welcome that cometh against his will, that saith unto God when He cometh to fetch him: Welcome, my Maker, maugre my teeth. But he that so loveth Him, that he longeth to go to Him, my heart cannot give me but he shall be welcome, all were it so that he should come ere he were well purged. For charity covereth a multitude of sins, and he that trusteth in God cannot be confounded. And Christ saith: He that cometh to Me, I will not cast him out. And therefore let us never make our reckoning of long life, keep it while we may because God hath so commanded; but if God give the occasion that with His goodwill we may go, let us be glad thereof and long to go to Him. And then shall hope of heaven comfort our heaviness, and out of our transitory tribulation shall we go to everlasting glory, to which, my good cousin, I pray God bring us both.

Vincent. Mine own good uncle, I pray God reward you, and at this time will I no longer trouble you. I trow I have this day done you much tribulation with my importune objections of very little substance. And you have even shewed me an ensample of sufferance, in bearing my folly so long and so patiently. And yet shall I be so bold upon you farther as to seek sometime to talk forth of the remnant the most profitable point of tribulation, which you said you reserved to treat of last of all.

Anthony. Let that be hardly, very shortly, cousin, while this is fresh in mind.

Vincent. I trust, good uncle, so to put this in remembrance that it shall never be forgotten with me. Our Lord send you such comfort as He knoweth to be best.

Anthony. That is well said, good cousin, and I pray the

same for you and for all our other friends that have need of comfort, for whom, I think, more than for yourself you needed of some counsel.

Vincent. I shall with this good counsel that I have heard of you do them some comfort, I trust in God, to whose keeping I commit you.

Anthony. And I you also. Farewell, mine own good cousin.

THE SECOND BOOK

Vincent. It is to me, good uncle, no little comfort that as I came in here I heard of your folk that you have had since my last being here (God be thanked) meetly good rest and your stomach somewhat more come to you. For verily, albeit I had heard before that in respect of the great grief that for a month space had holden you, you were a little before my last coming to you somewhat eased and relieved, for else would I not for no good have put you to the pain to talk so much as you then did. Yet after my departing from you, remembering how long we tarried together and that we were all that while in talking, and all the labour yours in talking so long together without interpausing between, and that of matter studious and displeasant, all of disease and sickness and other pain and tribulation, I was, in good faith, very sorry, and not a little wroth with myself for mine own oversight, that I had so little considered your pain; and very feard I was till I heard other word, lest you should have waxed weaker and more sick thereafter. But now I thank our Lord that hath sent the contrary, for else a little casting back were in this great age of yours no little danger and peril.

Anthony. Nay, nay, good cousin, to talk much (except some other pain let me) is to me little grief. A fond old man is often as full of words as a woman. It is, you wot well, as some poets paint us, all the lust of an old fool's life to sit well and warm with a cup and a roasted crab, and drivel and drink and talk. But in earnest, cousin, our talking was to me great comfort and nothing displeasant at all. For though we communed of sorrow and heaviness, yet was the thing that we chiefly thought upon not the tribulation itself but the comfort that may grow thereon. And therefore am I now very glad that you be come to finish up the remnant.

Vincent. Of truth, my good uncle, it was comfortable to me, and hath been since to some other of your friends to whom, as my poor wit and remembrance would serve me, I did, and not needless, report and rehearse your most comfortable counsel. And now come I for the remnant, and am very joyful that I find you so well refreshed and so ready thereto. But this one thing, good uncle, I beseech you heartily, that if I, for delight to hear you speak in the matter, forget myself and you both, and put you to too much pain, remember you your own ease, and when you lust to leave command me to go my way and seek some other time.

Anthony. Forsooth, cousin, many words, if a man were very weak, spoken, as you said right now, without inter-pausing, would peradventure at length somewhat weary him. And therefore wished I the last time after you were gone, when I felt myself (to say the truth) even a little weary, that I had not so told you still a long tale alone, but that we had more often interchanged words and parted the talking between us, with ofter interparling upon your part in such manner as learned men use between the persons whom they devise, disputing in their feigned dialogues. But yet in that point I soon excused you, and laid the lack even where I found it, and that was even upon mine own neck. For I remembered that between you and me it fared as it did once between a nun and her brother.

Very virtuous was this lady, and of a very virtuous place and close religion, and therein had been long, in all which time she had never seen her brother which was in like wise very virtuous too, and had been far off at an university, and had there taken the degree of doctor in divinity. When he was come home he went to see his sister as he that highly rejoiced in her virtue. So came she to the grate that they call (I trow) the locutory; and after their holy watchword spoken on both the sides after the manner used in that place, the one took the other by the tip of the finger, for hand would there none be wrungen through the grate, and forthwith began my lady to

give her brother a sermon of the wretchedness of this world
and the frailty of the flesh and the subtle sleights of the wicked
fiend, and gave him surely good counsel (saving somewhat too
long) how he should be well ware in his living and master well
his body for saving of his soul.   And yet, ere her own tale
came all at an end, she began to find a little fault with him, and
said: In good faith, brother, I do somewhat marvel that you
that have been at learning so long and are doctor and so
learned in the law of God do not now at our meeting (while
we meet so seldom) to me that am your sister and a simple
unlearned soul give of your charity some fruitful exhortation,
and as I doubt not but you can say some good thing yourself.
By my troth, good sister, quoth her brother, I cannot for you,
for your tongue hath never ceased, but said enough for us
both.   And so, cousin, I remember that when I was once
fallen in, I left you little space to say aught between.   But
now will I therefore take another way with you, for I shall of
our talking drive you to the one-half.

Vincent.   Now forsooth, uncle, this was a merry tale.
But now if you make me talk the one-half, then shall you be
contented far otherwise than there was of late a kinswoman of
your own, but which will I not tell you, guess her an you can.
Her husband had much pleasure in the manner and behaviour
of another honest man, and kept him therefore much company, by the reason whereof he was at his meal time the more
oft from home.   So happed it on a time that his wife and he
together dined or supped with that neighbour of theirs, and
then she made a merry quarrel to him for making her husband so good cheer out a door that she could not have him at
home.   Forsooth, mistress, quoth he (as he was a dry, merry
man), in my company nothing keepeth him but one; serve
you him with the same, and he will never be from you.   What
gay thing may that be? quoth our cousin then.   Forsooth,
mistress, quoth he, your husband loveth well to talk, and
when he sitteth with me I let him have all the words.   All the
words! quoth she; marry that am I content he shall have all

the words with goodwill, as he hath ever had.   But I speak
them all myself and give them all to him, and for aught that
I care for them so shall he have them still; but otherwise to
say that he shall have them all, you shall keep him still rather
than he get the half.

Anthony.   Forsooth, cousin, I can soon guess which of our
kin she was.   I would we had none therein, for all her merry
words, that less would let their husbands to talk.

Vincent.   Forsooth, she is not so merry but she is as good.
But where you find fault, uncle, that I speak not enough, I
was, in good faith, ashamed that I spake so much, and moved
you such questions as I found, upon your answer, might better
have been spared, they were so little worth.   But now sith I
see you be so well content that I shall not forbear boldly to
shew my folly, I will be no more so shamefast but ask you
what me lust.

*Whether a man may not in tribulation use some worldly
recreation for his comfort*

THE FIRST CHAPTER

AND first, good uncle, ere we proceed farther, I will be bold to
move you one thing more of that we talked when I was here
before.   For when I revolved in my mind again the things
that were concluded here by you, methought ye would in no
wise that in any tribulation men should seek for comfort,
either in worldly thing or fleshly.   Which mind, uncle, of
yours seemeth somewhat hard; for a merry tale with a friend
refresheth a man much, and without any harm lighteth his
mind and amendeth his courage and his stomach, so that it
seemeth but well done to take such recreation.   And Solomon
saith, I trow, that men should in heaviness give the sorry
man wine to make him forget his sorrow.   And Saint Thomas
saith, that proper pleasant talking, which is called εὐτραπελία,

is a good virtue serving to refresh the mind and make it quick and lusty to labour and study again where continual fatigation would make it dull and deadly.

Anthony. Cousin, I forgot not that point, but I longed not much to touch it, for neither might I well utterly forbear it where the cause might hap to fall that it should not hurt, and on the other side if the case so should fall, methought yet it should little need to give any man counsel to it. Folk are prone enough to such fantasies of their own mind. You may see this by ourself, which, coming now together to talk of as earnest sad matter as men can devise, were fallen yet even at the first into wanton idle tales; and of truth, cousin, as you know very well, myself am of nature even half a giglot and more. I would I could as easily mend my fault as I well know it; but scant can I refrain it, as old a fool as I am. Howbeit, so partial will I not be to my fault as to praise it. But for that you require my mind in the matter, whether men in tribulation may not lawfully seek recreation and comfort themself with some honest mirth, first agree that our chief comfort must be in God, and that with Him we must begin, and with Him continue, and with Him end also. A man to take now and then some honest worldly mirth, I dare not be so sore as utterly to forbid it, sith good men and well learned have in some case allowed it, specially for the diversity of divers men's minds; for else if we were all such as would God we were and such as natural wisdom would we should be, and is not all clean excusable that we be not indeed. I would then put no doubt but that unto any man the most comfortable talking that could be were to hear of heaven; whereas now, God help us, our wretchedness is such that in talking a while thereof men wax almost weary, and, as though to hear of heaven were an heavy burden, they must refresh themself after with a foolish tale. Our affection toward heavenly joy waxeth wonderful cold. If dread of hell were as far gone, very few would fear God; but that yet a little sticketh in our stomachs, mark me, cousin, at the sermon, and commonly towards the end, somewhat the preacher speaketh of hell and heaven. Now, while he preacheth of the pains of hell, still they stand and yet give him the hearing. But as soon as he cometh to the joys of heaven, they be busking them backward and flockmeal fall away. It is in the soul somewhat as it is in the body. Some are there of nature or of evil custom come to that point that a worse thing sometime more steadeth them than a better. Some man if he be sick can away with no wholesome meat, nor no medicine can go down with him but if it be tempered with some such thing for his fantasy as maketh the meat or the medicine less wholesome than it should be. And yet while it will be no better, we must let him have it so.

Cassianus, the very virtuous man, rehearseth in a certain collation of his that a certain holy father in making of a sermon spake of heaven and heavenly things so celestially, that much of his audience with the sweet sound thereof began to forget all the world and fall asleep. Which when the father beheld, he dissembled their sleeping, and suddenly said unto them, I shall tell you a merry tale. At which word they lift up their heads and hearkened unto that, and after the sleep therewith broken heard him tell on of heaven again. In what wise that good father rebuked then their untoward minds so dull unto the thing that all our life we labour for and so quick and lusty toward other trifles, I neither bear in mind nor shall here need to rehearse. But thus much of that matter sufficeth for our purpose, that whereas you demand me whether in tribulation men may not sometime refresh themself with worldly mirth and recreation, I can no more say but he that cannot long endure to hold up his head and hear talking of heaven except he be now and then between (as though heaven were heaviness) refreshed with a merry foolish tale, there is none other remedy but you must let him have it. Better would I wish it, but I cannot help it. Howbeit, let us by mine advice at the least wise make those kinds of recreation as short and as seld as we can. Let them serve us but for sauce and make them not our meat, and let us pray unto God, and all our good friends for us, that we may feel such a savour in the delight of heaven, that in respect of the talking of the joys thereof all worldly recreation be but a grief to think on. And be sure, cousin, that if we might once purchase the grace to come to that point, we never found of worldly recreation so much comfort in a year as we should find in the bethinking us of heaven in less than half an hour.

Vincent. In faith, uncle, I can well agree to this, and I pray God bring us once to take such a savour in it; and surely as you began the other day, by faith must we come to it, and to faith by prayer. But now I pray you, good uncle, vouchsafe to proceed in our principal matter.

Of the short uncertain life in extreme age or sickness

The Second Chapter

Anthony. Cousin, I have bethought me somewhat upon this matter since we were last together. And I find it, if we should go some way to work, a thing that would require many more days to treat thereof than we should haply find meet thereto in so few as myself ween that I have now to live, while every time is not like with me; and among many painful in which I look every day to depart, my mending days come very seld and are very shortly gone. For surely, cousin, I cannot liken my life more meetly now than to the snuff of a candle that burneth within the candlestick's nose. For as the snuff sometime burneth down so low that whoso looketh on it would ween it were quite out, and yet suddenly lifteth up a flame half an inch above the nose, and giveth a pretty short light again, and thus playeth divers times till at last, ere it be looked for, out it goeth altogether, so have I, cousin, divers such days together, as every day of them I look even for to die. And yet

have I then after that some such few days again as you see
me now have yourself, in which a man would ween that I
might yet well continue, but I know my lingering not likely to
last long, but out will my snuff suddenly some day within a
while; and therefore will I with God's help, seem I never so
well amended, nevertheless reckon every day for my last.
For though that to the repressing of the bold courage of blind
youth there is a very true proverb, that as soon cometh a
young sheep's skin to the market as an old, yet this difference
there is at the least between them, that as the young man may
hap sometime to die soon, so the old man can never live long.
And therefore, cousin, in our matter here, leaving out many
things that I would else treat of, I shall for this time speak but
of very few.   Howbeit, if God hereafter send me more such
days, then will we, when you lust farther, talk of more.

*He divideth tribulation into three kinds, of which three the last
he shortly passeth over*

THE THIRD CHAPTER

ALL manner of tribulation, cousin, that any man can have, as
far as for this time cometh to my mind, falleth under some
one at the least of these three kinds: either is it such as himself willingly taketh, or secondly such as himself willingly
suffereth, or finally such as he cannot put from him.   This
third kind I purpose not much more to speak of now, for
thereof shall as for this time suffice those things that we treated
between us this other day.   What kind of tribulation this is I
am sure yourself perceive; for sickness, imprisonment, loss of
goods, loss of friends, or such bodily harm as a man hath
already caught and can in no wise avoid, these things and suchlike are the third kind of tribulation that I speak of, which a
man neither willingly taketh in the beginning, nor can, though
he would, put afterward away.   Now, think I, that as to the

man that lacketh wit and faith no comfort can serve whatsoever counsel be given, so to them that have both I have as for this kind said in manner enough already; and considering that suffer it needs he must while he can by no manner of mean put it from him, the very necessity is half counsel enough to take it in good worth and bear it patiently, and rather of his patience to take both ease and thank than by fretting and fuming to increase his present pain, and by murmur and grudge fall in farther danger after by displeasing of God with his froward behaviour. And yet, albeit that I think that that is said sufficeth, yet here and there I shall in the second kind shew some such comfort as shall well serve unto this last kind too.

THE FOURTH CHAPTER

THE first kind also will I shortly pass over too, for the tribulation that a man willingly taketh himself, which no man putteth upon him against his own will, is, you wot well, as I somewhat touched the last day, such affliction of the flesh or expense of his goods as a man taketh himself or willingly bestoweth in punishment of his own sin and for devotion to God. Now, in this tribulation needeth he no man to comfort him; for while no man troubleth him but himself which feeleth how farforth he may conveniently bear, and of reason and good discretion shall not pass that, wherein if any doubt arise, counsel needeth and not comfort. The courage that for God's sake and his soul's health kindleth his heart and enflameth it thereto shall, by the same grace that put it in his mind, give him such comfort and joy therein, that the pleeasur of his soul shall pass the pain of his body. Yea, and while he hath in heart also some great heaviness for his sin, yet when he considereth the joy that shall come of it his soul shall not fail to feel then that strange case which my body felt once in great a fever.

Vincent.   What strange case was that, uncle?

Anthony.   Forsooth, cousin, even in this same bed, it is now more than fifteen year ago, I lay in a tertian and had passed, I trow, three or four fits.   But after fell there on me one fit out of course, so strange and so marvellous, that I would in good faith have thought it impossible.   For I suddenly felt myself verily both hot and cold throughout all my body, not in some part the one and in some part the other, for that had been, you wot well, no very strange thing to feel the head hot while the hands were cold, but the selfsame parts, I say, so God save my soul, I sensibly felt and right painfully too all in one instant both hot and cold at once.

Vincent.   By my faith, uncle, this was a wonderful thing, and such as I never heard happen any man else in my day, and few men are there of whose mouths I could have believed it.

Anthony.   Courtesy, cousin, peradventure letteth you to say that you believe it not yet of my mouth neither; and surely for fear of that you should not have heard it of me neither, had there not another thing happed me soon after.

Vincent.   I pray you what was that, good uncle?

Anthony.   Forsooth, cousin, this I asked a physician or twain that then looked unto me, how this should be possible; and they twain told me both that it could not be so but that I was fallen into some slumber and dreamed that I felt it so.

Vincent.   This hap hold I little cause you to tell that tale more boldly.

Anthony.   No, cousin, that is true, lo.   But then happed there another, that a young girl in this town, whom a kinsman of hers had begun to teach physic, told me that there was such a kind of fever indeed.

Vincent.   By our Lady, uncle, save for the credence of you the tale would I not yet tell again upon that hap of the maid. For though I know her now for such as I durst well believe her, it might hap her very well at that time to lie because she would you should take her for cunning.

Anthony. Yea, but then happed there yet another hap thereof, cousin, that a work of Galen, *De differentiis febrium,* is ready to be sold in the booksellers' shops. In which work she shewed me then the chapter where Galen saith the same.

Vincent. Marry, uncle, as you say, that hap happed well; and that maid had (as hap was) in that one point more cunning than had both your physicians besides, and hath, I ween, at this day in many points more.

Anthony. In faith so ween I too; and that is well wared on her, for she is very wise and well learned, and very virtuous too. But see now what age is. Lo, I have been so long in my tale that I have almost forgotten for what purpose I told it. Oh, now I remember me. Lo, likewise I say, as myself felt my body then both hot and cold at once, so he that is contrite and heavy for his sin shall have cause to be, and shall indeed be, both sad and glad, and both twain at once, and shall do as I remember holy Saint Jerome biddeth: *Et doleas, et de dolore gaudeas:* Both be thou sorry, saith he, and be thou also of thy sorrow joyful. And thus as I began to say of comfort to be given unto him that is in this tribulation, that is to wit, in fruitful heaviness and penance for his sin, shall we none need to give other than only to remember and consider well the goodness of God's excellent mercy that infinitely passeth the malice of all men's sins, by which He is ready to receive every man, and did spread His arms abroad upon the cross lovingly to embrace all them that will come, and even there accepted the thief at his last end that turned not to God till he might steal no longer, and yet maketh more feast in heaven at one that from sin turneth than of ninety-nine good men that sinned not at all. And therefore of that first kind will I make no longer tale.

*An objection concerning them that turn not to God till they come
at the last cast*

THE FIFTH CHAPTER

Vincent.   Forsooth, uncle, this is unto that kind comfort very
great, and so great also that it may make many a man bold to
abide in his sin, even unto his end, trusting to be then saved
as that thief was.

Anthony.   Very sooth you say, cousin, that some wretches
are there such that in such wise abuse the great goodness of
God, that the better that He is the worse again be they.   But,
cousin, though there be more joy made of his turning that
from the point of perdition cometh to salvation for pity that
God had and His saints all of the peril of perishing that the
man stood in, yet is he not set in like state in heaven as he
should have been if he had lived better before, except it so
fall that he live so well after and do so much good, that he
therein outrun, in the shorter time, those good folk that yet
did not so much in much longer, as it proved in the blessed
apostle Saint Paul.   Which of a persecutor became an apostle,
and last of all came in unto that office, and yet in the labour of
sowing the seed of Christ's faith outran all the remnant, so
farforth that he letted not to say of himself: *Abundantius illis
omnibus laboravi*: I have laboured more than all the remnant
have.   But yet, my cousin, though God, I doubt not, be so
merciful unto them that in any time of their life turn and ask
His mercy, and trust therein (though it be at the last end of a
man's life, and hireth him as well for heaven that cometh to
work in His vineyard toward night, at such time as workmen
leave work, and go home being then in will to work, if the
time would serve, as He hireth him that cometh in the morning), yet may there no man upon the trust of this parable be
bold all his life to lie still in sin.   For let him remember that
into God's vineyard there goeth no man but he that is called

thither. Now, he that in hope to be called toward night will sleep out the morning and drink out the day, is full likely to pass at night unspoken to, and then shall he with shrewd rest go supperless to bed. They tell of one that was wont alway to say that all the while he lived he would do what he lust, for three words when he died should make all safe enough. But then so happed it that long ere he were old his horse once stumbled upon a broken bridge, and as he laboured to recover him, when he saw it would not be, but down into the flood headlong needs he should, in a sudden fright he cried out in the falling: Have all to the devil! And there was he drowned with his three words ere he died, whereon his hope hung all his wretched life. And therefore let no man sin in hope of grace, for grace cometh but at God's will, and that mind may be the let that grace of fruitful repenting shall never after be offered him, but that he shall either graceless go linger on careless, or with a care fruitless fall into despair.

An objection of them that say that tribulation of penance needeth not, but is a superstitious folly

The Sixth Chapter

Vincent. Forsooth, uncle, in this point methinketh you say very well. But then are there some again that say on the other side that heaviness for our sins we shall need none at all, but only change our intent and purpose to do better, and for all that that is passed take no thought at all. And as for fasting and other affliction of the body, they say we should not do it but only to tame the flesh when we feel it wax wanton and begin to rebel. For fasting, they say, serveth to keep the body in temperance, but for to fast for penance, or to do any other good work, alms deed or other, toward satisfaction for our own sin, this thing they call plain injury to the

Passion of Christ, by which only are our sins forgiven freely without any recompense of our own.   And they that would do penance for their own sins, look to be their own Christs, and pay their own ransoms, and save their souls themself.   And with these reasons in Saxony many cast fasting off and all other bodily affliction, save only where need requireth to bring the body to temperance.   For other good, they say, can it none do to ourself, and then to our neighbour can it do none at all, and therefore they condemn it for superstitious folly. Now, heaviness of heart and weeping for our sins, this they reckon shame almost and womanish pevishness.   Howbeit, thanked be God, their women were there now so mannish, that they be not so peevish nor so poor of spirit but that they can sin on as men do, and be neither afraid nor ashamed, nor weep for their sins at all.

And surely, mine uncle, I have marvelled the less ever since that I heard the manner of their preachers there.   For, as you remember, when I was in Saxony these matters were in a manner but in a mammering, nor Luther was not then wedded yet, nor religious men out of their habit, but suffered were those that would be of the sect freely to preach what they would unto the people.   And forsooth I heard a religious man there myself, one that had been reputed and taken for very good, and which, as far as the folk perceived, was of his own living somewhat austere and sharp.   But his preaching was wonderful; methink I hear him yet, his voice was so loud and shrill, his learning less than mean.   But whereas his matter was much part against fasting and all affliction for any penance, which he called men's inventions, he cried ever out upon them to keep well the laws of Christ, let go their peevish penance, and purpose then to mend and seek nothing to sal-vation but the death of Christ, for He is our justice, and He is our Saviour and our whole satisfaction for all our deadly sins; He did full penance for us all upon his painful cross; He washed us there all clean with the water of His sweet side, and brought us out of the devil's danger with His dear precious blood. Leave, therefore, leave, I beseech you, these inventions of men, your foolish Lenten fasts and your peevish penance; minish never Christ's thank, nor look to save yourself; it is Christ's death, I tell you, that must save us all; Christ's death, I tell you yet again, and not our own deeds. Leave your own fasting, therefore, and lean to Christ alone, good Christian people, for Christ's dear bitter Passion. Now, so loud and so shrill he cried Christ in their ears, and so thick he came forth with Christ's bitter Passion, and that so bitterly spoken with the sweat dropping down his cheeks, that I marvelled not though I saw the poor women weep, for he made my own hair stand up upon my head; and with such preaching were the people so brought in, that some fell to break their fasts on the fasting days, not of frailty or of malice first, but almost of devotion, lest they should take from Christ the thank of His bitter Passion. But when they were a while nose-led in that point first, they could abide and endure after many things more, with which had he begun, they would have pulled him down.

Anthony. Cousin, God amend that man whatsoever he be, and God keep all good folk from such manner of preachers. Such one preacher much more abuseth the name of Christ and of His bitter Passion than five hundred hazards that in their idle business swear and forswear themself by His holy bitter Passion at dice. They carry the minds of the people from the perceiving of their craft by the continual naming of the name of Christ; and crying His Passion so shrill into their ears they forget that the Church hath ever taught them that all our Penance without Christ's Passion were not worth a pea; and they make the people ween that we would be saved by our own deeds without Christ's death, where we confess that His only Passion meriteth incomparable more for us than all our own deeds do. But His pleasure is that we shall also take pain our own self with Him, and therefore He biddeth all that will be His disciples take their crosses on their backs as He did, and with their crosses follow him.

And where they say that fasting serveth but for temperance to tame the flesh and keep it from wantonness, I would, in good faith, have weened that Moses had not been so wild, that for the taming of his flesh he should have need to fast whole forty days together. No, nor Elijah neither, nor yet our Saviour Himself which began, and the apostles followed, and all Christendom have kept the Lenten forty days' fast that these folk call now so foolish. King Ahab was not disposed to be wanton in his flesh when he fasted and went clothed in sackcloth and all besprent with ashes. Nor no more was in Nineveh the king and all the city, but they wailed and did painful penance for their sin to procure God to pity them and withdraw His indignation. Anna, that in her widowhood abode so many years with fasting and praying in the temple till the birth of Christ, was not, I ween, in her old age so sore disposed to the wantonness of her flesh that she fasted all therefore. Nor Saint Paul that fasted so much, fasted not all therefore neither. The Scripture is full of places that proveth fasting not to be the invention of man, but the institution of God, and that it hath many more profits than one. And that the fasting of one man may do good unto another our Saviour sheweth Himself where He saith that some kind of devils cannot be by one man cast out of another, *nisi in oratione et ieiunio*, without prayer and fasting. And therefore I marvel that they take this way against fasting and other bodily penance; and yet much more I marvel that they mislike the sorrow and heaviness and displeasure of mind that a man should take in forethinking of his sin. The prophet saith: *Scindite corda vestra et non vestimenta:* Tear your hearts, he saith, and not your clothes. And the prophet David saith: *Cor contritum et humiliatum Deus non despicies:* A contrite heart and an humbled, that is to say, a heart broken, torn, and with tribulation of heaviness for his sins laid alow under foot, shalt thou not, good Lord, despise. He saith also of his own contrition: *Laboravi in gemitu meo, lavabo per singulas noctes lectum meum lacrimis meis, stratum meum rigabo:* I have

laboured in my wailing, I shall every night wash my bed with
my tears, my couch will I water.   But what should I need in
this matter to lay forth one place or twain?   The Scripture is
full of those places by which it plainly appeareth that God
looketh of duty not only that we should amend and be better
in the time to come, but also be sorry and weep and bewail our
sins committed before; and all the old holy doctors be full
and whole of that mind, that men must have for their sins
contrition and sorrow in heart.

What if a man cannot weep, nor in his heart be sorry for his sins?

THE SEVENTH CHAPTER

Vincent.   Forsooth, uncle, yet seemeth me this thing somewhat a sore sentence, not for that I think otherwise, but that
there is good cause and great.   Wherefore a man so should,
but for that of truth some man cannot, be sorry and heavy for
his sin that he hath done, though he never so fain would.
But though he can be content for God's sake to forbear it from
thenceforth, yet for every sin that is passed can he not only
not weep, but some were haply so wanton that when he
happeth to remember them he can scantly forbear to laugh.
Now, if contrition and sorrow of heart be so requisite of
necessity to remission, many a man should stand, as it
seemeth, in a very perilous case.

Anthony.   Many so should indeed, cousin, and indeed
many so do, and the old saints write very sore in this point.
Howbeit, *Misericordia Domini super omnia opera eius:* The
mercy of God is above all His works, and He standeth
bounden to no common rule.   *Et ipse cognovit figmentum
suum et propitiatur infirmitatibus nostris:* And He knoweth
the frailty of this earthen vessel that is of His own making,
and is merciful, and hath pity and compassion upon our
feeble infirmities, and shall not exact of us above the thing

that we may do.   But yet, cousin, he that findeth himself in that case, in that he is minded to do well hereafter, let him give God thanks that he is no worse; but in that he cannot be sorry for his sin passed, let him be sorry hardly that he is no better. And as Saint Jerome biddeth him that for his sin sorroweth in his heart be glad and rejoice in his sorrow, so would I counsel him that cannot be sad for his sin to be sorry yet at the least that he cannot be sorry.   Besides this, though I would in no wise any man should despair, yet would I counsel such a man while that affection lasteth not to be too bold of courage, but live in double fear.   First, for it is a token either of faint faith or of a dull diligence, for surely if we well believe in God and therewith deeply consider His High Majesty with the peril of our sin and the great goodness of God also, either should dread make us tremble and break our stony heart, or love should for sorrow relent it into tears.

Besides this, sith I can scant believe, but sith so little misliking of our old sin is an affection not very pure and clean, and none unclean thing shall enter into heaven, cleansed shall it be and purified, before that we come there.   And therefore would I farther advise one in that case the counsel which Master Gerson giveth every man, that sith the body and the soul together make the whole man, the less affliction that he feeleth in his soul, the more pain in recompense let him put upon his body, and purge the spirit by the affliction of the flesh.   And he that so doth, I dare lay my life, shall have his hard heart after relent into tears, and his soul in an wholesome heaviness and heavenly gladness too, specially if (which must be joined with every good thing) he join faithful prayer therewith.

But, cousin, as I told you the other day before in these matters, with these new men I will not dispute.   But surely for mine own part I cannot well hold with them.   For as far as mine own poor wit can perceive, the Holy Scripture of God is very plain against them, and the whole corps of Christendom in every Christian region and the very places in which they dwell themself have ever unto their own days clearly believed against them, and all the old holy doctors have ever more taught against them, and all the old holy interpreters have construed the Scripture against them. And therefore, if these men have now perceived so late that the Scripture hath be misunderstanden all this while, and that of all those old holy doctors no man could understand it, then am I too old at this age to begin to study it now. And trust these men's cunning, cousin, that dare I not in no wise, sith I cannot see nor perceive no cause wherefore I should think that these men might not now in the understanding of Scripture as well be deceived themself, as they bear us in hand that all those other have been all this while before.

Howbeit, cousin, if it so be that their way be not wrong, but that they have found out so easy a way to heaven as to take no thought but make merry nor take no penance at all, but set them down and drink well for our Saviour's sake, set cock a-hoop and fill in all the cups at once, and then let Christ's Passion pay for all the scot, I am not he that will envy their good hap. But surely counsel dare I give no man to adventure that way with them. But such as fear lest that way be not sure, and take upon them willingly tribulation of penance, what comfort they do take and well may take therein, that have I somewhat told you already. And sith these other folk sit so merry without such tribulation, we need to talk to them, you wot well, of no such manner of comfort. And therefore of this kind of tribulation will I make an end.

*Of that kind of tribulation, which, though they not willingly
take, yet they willingly suffer*

THE EIGHTH CHAPTER

Vincent. Verily, good uncle, so may you well do. For you
have brought it unto very good pass. And now I require
you come to the other kind, of which you purposed alway
to treat last.

Anthony. That shall I, cousin, very gladly do. The other
kind is this which I rehearsed second, and, sorting out the
other twain, have kept it for the last. This kind of tribulation
is, you wot well, of them that willingly suffer tribulation
though that of their own choice they took it not at the first.
This kind, cousin, divide we shall into twain. The first
might we call temptation, the second persecution. But here
must you consider that I mean not every kind of persecution,
but that kind only which though the sufferer would be loath
to fall in, yet will he rather abide it and suffer than by the
flitting from it, fall in the displeasure of God, or leave God's
pleasure unprocured. Howbeit, if we well consider these
two things, temptation and persecution, we may find that
either of them is incident into the other. For both by
temptation the devil persecuteth us, and by persecution the
devil also tempteth us. And as persecution is tribulation to
every man, so is temptation tribulation to a good man. Now,
though the devil, our spiritual enemy, fight against man in
both, yet this difference hath the common temptation from
the persecution, that temptation is, as it were, the fiend's train,
and persecution his plain open fight. And therefore will I
now call all this kind of tribulation here by the name of
temptation, and that shall I divide into two parts. The first
shall I call the devil's trains, the other his open fight.

First of temptation in general, as it is common to both

THE NINTH CHAPTER

To speak of every kind of temptation particularly by itself, this were, ye wot well, in manner an infinite thing. For under that, as I told you, fall persecutions and all. And the devil hath of his trains a thousand subtle ways, and of his open fight as many sundry poisoned darts.

He tempteth us by the world; he tempteth us by our own flesh; he tempteth us by pleasure; he tempteth us by pain; he tempteth us by our foes; he tempteth us by our own friends, and under colour of kindred he maketh many times our next friends our most foes. For, as our Saviour saith: *Inimici hominis domestici eius.*

But in all manner of so divers temptations one marvellous comfort is this, that with the more we be tempted the gladder have we cause to be. For, as Saint James saith: *Omne gaudium existimate fratres mei quum in tentationes varias incideritis:* Esteem it and take it, saith he, my brethren, for a thing of all joy when you fall into divers and sundry manner of temptations. And no marvel, for there is in this world set up, as it were, a game of wrestling wherein the people of God come in on the one side, and on the other side come mighty strong wrestlers and wily, that is to wit, the devils, the cursed proud damned spirits. For it is not our flesh alone that we must wrestle with, but with the devil too. *Non est nobis colluctatio adversus carnem et sanguinem, sed adversus principes et potestates, adversus mundi rectores tenebrarum harum, contra spiritualia nequitiæ in cælestibus:* Our wrestling is not here, saith Saint Paul, against flesh and blood, but against the princes and potestates of these dark regions, against the spiritual wicked ghosts of the air.

But as God unto them that on His part give His adversary the fall hath prepared a crown, so he that will not wrestle shall none have. For, as Saint Paul saith: *Qui certat in agone non coronabitur nisi legitime certaverit:* There shall no man have the crown but he that doth his devoir therefore according to the law of the game.   And then, as holy Saint Bernard saith, how couldest thou fight or wrestle therefore if there were no challenger against thee that would provoke thee thereto? And therefore may it be a great comfort, as Saint James saith, to every man that feeleth himself challenged and provoked by temptation.   For thereby perceiveth he that it cometh to his course to wrestle, which shall be (but if he willingly will play the coward or the fool) the matter of his eternal reward.

A special comfort in all temptation

THE TENTH CHAPTER

BUT now must this needs be to man an inestimable comfort in all temptation if his faith fail him not, that is to wit, that he may be sure that God is alway ready to give him strength against the devil's might, and wisdom against the devil's trains.   For, as the prophet saith: *Fortitudo mea et laus mea Dominus, et factus est mihi in salutem:* My strength and my praise is our Lord, He hath been my safeguarder.   And the Scripture saith: *Pete a Deo sapientiam, et dabit tibi:* Ask wisdom of God, and He shall give it thee, *ut possitis,* as Saint Paul saith, *deprehendere omnes artes,* that you may spy and perceive all the crafts.   A great comfort may this be in all kinds of temptation, that God hath so His hand upon him that is willing to stand and will trust in Him and call upon Him, that He hath made him sure by many faithful promises in Holy Scripture that either he shall not fall, or if he sometime through faintness of faith stagger and hap to fall, yet if he call upon God betimes, his fall shall be no sore bruising to him, but as the Scripture saith: *Iustus si ceciderit non collidetur, quia Dominus supponit manum suam:* The just man, though he fall, shall not be bruised, for our Lord holdeth under His hand.

The prophet expresseth a plain comfortable promise of God against all temptations, where he saith: *Qui habitat in adiutorio altissimi, in protectione Dei cœli commorabitur:* Whoso dwelleth in the help of the highest God, he shall abide in the protection or defence of the God of heaven. Who dwelleth now, good cousin, in the help of the high God? Surely he that through a good faith abideth in the trust and confidence of God's help, and neither for lack of that faith and trust in His help falleth desperate of all help, nor departeth from the hope of His help to seek himself help, as I told you the other day, of the flesh, the world, or the devil.

Now, he then that by fast faith and sure hope dwelleth in God's help and hangeth alway thereupon, never falling from that hope, he shall, saith the prophet, ever dwell and abide in God's defence and protection; that is to say, that while he faileth not to believe well and hope well God will never fail in all temptation to defend him. For unto such a faithful well-hoping man the prophet in the same psalm saith farther: *Scapulis suis obumbrabit tibi, et sub pennis eius sperabis:* With His shoulders shall He shadow thee, and under His feathers shalt thou trust. Lo, here hath every faithful man a sure promise that in the fervent heat of temptation or tribulation (for, as I have said divers times before, they be in such wise coincident that every tribulation the devil useth for temptation to bring us to impatience, and thereby to murmur and grudge and blasphemy, and every kind of temptation to a good man that fighteth against it and will not follow it is a very painful tribulation), in the fervent heat, I say, therefore of every temptation God giveth the faithful man that hopeth in Him the shadow of His holy shoulders, which are broad and large, sufficient to refrigerate and refresh the man in that heat; and in every tribulation He putteth His shoulders for a defence between. And then what weapon of the devil may give us any deadly wound while that impenetrable pavis of the shoulder of God standeth always between?

Then goeth the verse farther, and saith unto such a faithful man: *Et sub pennis eius sperabis:* Thine hope shall be under His feathers; that is to wit, for the good hope thou hast in His help, He will take thee so near Him into His protection that as the hen to keep her young chickens from the kite nestleth them together under her own wings, so from the devil's claws, the ravenous kite of this dark air, will the God of heaven gather the faithful trusting folk near unto His own sides, and set them in surety very well and warm, under the covering of his heavenly wings.

And of this defence and protection, our Saviour spake Himself unto the Jews (as mention is made in the twenty-third chapter of Saint Matthew), to whom He said in this wise: *Hierusalem, Hierusalem, quæ occidis prophetas, et lapidas eos qui ad te missi sunt, quoties volui congregare te, quemadmodum gallina congregat pullos suos sub alas suas, et noluisti?* That is to say: Jerusalem, Jerusalem, that killest the prophets, and stonest unto death them that are sent unto thee, how often would I have gathered thee together, as the hen gathereth her chickens under her wings, and thou wouldest not?

Here are, cousin Vincent, words of no little comfort unto every Christian man, by which we may see with how tender affection God of His great goodness longeth to gather under the protection of His wings and how often like a loving hen He clucketh home unto him even those chickens of His that wilfully walk abroad into the kite's danger, and will not come at His clucking, but ever the more He clucketh for them the farther they go from Him.   And therefore can we not doubt if we will follow Him and with faithful hope come run to Him but that He shall in all matter of temptation take us near unto Him, and set us even under His wing.   And then are we safe if we will tarry there.   For against our will can there no power pull us thence nor hurt our souls there.   *Pone me,* saith the prophet, *iuxta te, et cuiusvis manus pugnet contra me:* Set me near unto thee, and fight against me whose hand that will.   And to shew the great safeguard and surety that we shall have while we sit under His heavenly feathers, the prophet saith yet a great deal farther: *In velamento alarum tuarum exultabo.* That is to wit, that we shall not only when we sit by His sweet side under His holy wing, sit in safeguard, but that we shall also under the covering of His heavenly wings with great exultation rejoice.

Of four kinds of temptations, and therein both the parties of that kind of tribulation that men willingly suffer, touched in the two verses of the psalter.

THE ELEVENTH CHAPTER

Now, in the two next verses following the prophet briefly comprehendeth four kinds of temptations, and therein all the tribulation that we shall now speak of and also some part of that which we have spoken of before. And therefore I shall peradventure (except any farther thing fall in our way) with treating of those two verses finish and end all our matter.

The prophet saith in the ninetieth psalm: *Scuto circumdabit te veritas eius, non timebis a timore nocturno, a sagitta volante in die, a negotio perambulante in tenebris, ab incursu a demonio meridiano:* The truth of God shall compass thee about with a pavis, thou shalt not be afeard of the night's fear, nor of the arrow flying in the day, nor of the business walking about in the darknesses, nor of the incursion or invasion of the devil in the midday.

First, cousin, in these words, The truth of God shall compass thee about with a pavis, the prophet for the comfort of every good man in all temptation and in all tribulation, beside those other things that he said before that the shoulders of God should shadow them and that also they should sit under his wing, here saith he farther that the truth of God shall compass thee with a pavis. That is to wit, that as God hath faithfully promised to protect and defend those that faithfully will dwell in the trust of His help, so will He truly perform it.

And thou that such one art will the truth of His promise defend, not with a little round buckler that scant can cover the head, but with a long large pavis that covereth all along the body, made, as holy Saint Bernard saith, broad above with the Godhead, and narrow beneath with the manhood, so that this pavis is our Saviour Christ himself.   And yet is not this pavis like other pavises of this world, which are not made but in such wise as while it defendeth one part the man may be wounded upon an other.   But this pavis is such that, as the prophet saith, it shall round about enclose and compass thee so that thine enemy shall hurt thy soul on no side.   For *scuto*, saith he, *circumdabit te veritas eius*, with a pavis shall His truth environ and compass thee round about.

And then continently following, to the intent that we should see that it is not without necessity that the pavis of God should compass us about upon every side, he sheweth in what wise we be by the devil with trains and assaults by four kinds of temptations and tribulations environed upon every side, against all which compass of temptations and tribulations that round compassing pavis of God's truth shall in such wise defend us and keep us safe that we shall need to dread none of them all.

The first kind of the four temptations

THE TWELFTH CHAPTER

FIRST he saith: *Non timebis a timore nocturno:* Thou shalt not be afeard of the fear of the night.   By the night is there in scripture sometime understanden tribulation, as appeareth in the thirty-fourth chapter of Job: *Novit enim Deus opera eorum, idcirco inducet noctem:* God hath known the works of them, and therefore shall He bring night upon them, that is to wit, tribulation for their wickedness.   And well you wot that the night is of the nature self discomfortable and full of fear.   And

therefore by the night's fear here I understand the tribulation
by which the devil through the sufferance of God, either by
himself or other that are his instruments, tempteth good folk to
impatience, as he did Job.   But he that, as the prophet saith,
dwelleth and continueth faithfully in the hope of God's help
shall so be clipped in on every side with the shield or pavis
of God, that he shall have no need to be afeard of such tribulation that is here called the night's fear.   And it may be also
conveniently called the night's fear for two causes.   The one,
for that many times the cause of his tribulation is unto him
that suffereth dark and unknown, and therein varieth it and
differeth from that tribulation by which the devil tempteth a
man with open fight and assault, for a known good thing from
which he would withdraw him, or for some known evil thing
into which he would drive him by force of such persecution.

Another cause for which it is called the night's fear may be
for that that the night is so far out of courage and naturally
so casteth folk in fear, that of everything whereof they perceive every manner dread, their fantasy doubleth their fear,
and maketh them often ween that it were much worse than
indeed it is.

The prophet saith in the Psalter: *Posuisti tenebras, et facta
est nox, in ipsa pertransibunt omnes bestiæ sylvæ, catuli leonum
rugientes quærentes a Deo escam sibi:* Thou hast, good Lord,
set the darkness, and made was the night, and in the night
walken all the beasts of the woods, the whelps of the lions
roaring and calling unto God for their meat.

Now though that the lions' whelps walk about roaring in
the night and seek for their prey, yet can they not get such
meat as they would alway, but must hold themself content
with such as God suffereth to fall in their way.   And though
they be not ware thereof, yet of God they ask it, and of Him
they have it.   And this may be comfort to all good men in
their night's fear, in their dark tribulation, that though they
fall into the claws or the teeth of those lions' whelps, yet shall
all that they can do not pass beyond the body which is but as

the garment of the soul. For the soul itself, which is the substance of the man, is so surely fenced in round about with the shield or the pavis of God, that as long as he will abide faithfully *in adiutorio altissimi*, in the hope of God's help, the lions' whelps shall not be able to hurt it. For the great lion himself could never be suffered to go farther in the tribulation of Job than God from time to time gave him leave.

And therefore the deep darkness of the midnight maketh men that stand out of faith and out of good hope in God to be in their tribulation far in the greater fear for lack of the light of faith, whereby they might perceive that the uttermost of their peril is a far less thing than they take it for. But we be so wont to set so much by our body which we see and feel, and in the feeding and fostering whereof we set our delight and our wealth, and so little, alas, and so seld we think upon our soul, because we cannot see that but by spiritual understanding, and most specially by the eye of our faith (in the meditation whereof we bestow, God wot, little time), that the loss of our body we take for a sorer thing and for a greater tribulation a great deal than we do the loss of our soul. And whereas our Saviour biddeth us that we should not fear those lions' whelps that can but kill our bodies, and when that is done have no farther thing in their power wherewith they can do us harm, but biddeth us stand in dread of Him which, when He hath slain the body, is able then beside to cast the soul into everlasting fire, we be so blind in the dark night of tribulation for lack of full and fast belief of God's word, that whereas in the day of prosperity we very little fear God for our soul, our night's fear of adversity maketh us very sore to fear the lion and his whelps, for dread of loss of our bodies. And whereas Saint Paul in sundry places sheweth us that our body is but as the garment of the soul, yet the faintness of our faith to the Scripture of God maketh us with the night's fear of tribulation more to dread not only the loss of our body than of our soul, that is to wit, of the clothing, than of the substance that is clothed therewith, but also of the very outward goods that serve for the clothing of the body. And much more foolish are we in that dark night's fear than were he that would forget the saving of his body for fear of losing his old rain-beaten cloak that is but the covering of his gown or his coat. Now, consider farther yet that the prophet in the fore-remembered verses saith not that in the night walk only the lions' whelps, but also *omnes bestiæ sylvarum*, all the beasts of the wood. Now, wot you well that if a man walk through the wood in the night, many things may make him afeard of which in the day he would not be afeard a whit; for in the night every bush to him that waxeth once afeard seemeth a thief.

I remember that when I was a young man I was once in the war with the king then my master (God assoil his soul), and we were camped within the Turk's ground many a mile beyond Belgrade, which would God were ours now as well as it was then. But so happed it that in our camp about midnight there suddenly rose a rumour and a scry that the Turk's whole army was secretly stealing upon us, wherewith our whole host was warned to arm them in haste and set themself in array to fight. And then were scourers of ours that brought those sudden tidings examined more leisurely by the council what surety or what likelihood they had perceived therein. Of whom one shewed that by the glimmering of the moon he had espied and perceived and seen them himself, coming on softly and soberly in a long range all in good order, not one farther forth than the other in the forefront, but as even as a thread, and in breadth farther than he could see in length. His fellows, being examined, said that he was somewhat pricked forth before them and came so fast back to tell it them, that they thought it rather time to make haste and give warning to the camp than to go nearer unto them. For they were not so far off but that they had yet themself somewhat an unperfect sight of them too. Thus stood we watching all the remnant of the night evermore hearkening when we should hear them come, with Husht, stand still, methink I hear a trampling, so that at last many of us thought we heard them

ourself also.   But when the day was sprungen and that we
saw no man, out was our scourer sent again, and some of our
captains with him, to shew whereabout the place was in which
he perceived them.   And when they came thither they found
that the great fearful army of the Turks, so soberly coming on,
turned (God be thanked) into a fair long hedge standing even
stone still.

And thus fareth it in the night's fear of tribulation in which
the devil, to bear down and overwhelm with dread the faithful hope that we should have in God, casteth in our imagination much more fear than cause.   For while there walk in
that night not only the lion's whelps, but over that all the
beasts of the wood beside, the beast that we hear roar in the
dark night of tribulation and fear it for a lion we sometime
find well afterward in the day that it was no lion at all but a
silly rude roaring ass.   And the thing that on the sea seemeth
sometime a rock is indeed nothing else but a mist.   Howbeit,
as the prophet saith: he that faithfully dwelleth in the hope of
God's help, the pavis of His truth shall so fence him round
about, that be it an ass, colt, or a lion's whelp, or a rock of
stone, or a mist, *non timebit a timore nocturno*, the night's fear
thereof shall he nothing need to dread.

Of pusillanimity

THE THIRTEENTH CHAPTER

THEREFORE find I that in the night's fear one great part is the
fault of pusillanimity, that is to wit, faint and feeble stomach,
by which a man for faint heart is afeard where he needeth not,
by the reason whereof he flieth oftentime for fear of that thing
of which, if he fled not, he should take none harm.   And some
man doth sometime by his flying make his enemy bold on
him, which would, if he fled not, but durst abide thereby, give
over and fly from him.

This fault of pusillanimity maketh a man in his tribulation, for feeble heart, first impatient, and afterward oftentimes driveth him by impatience into a contrary affection, making him frowardly stubborn and angry against God, and thereby to fall into blasphemy, as do the damned souls in hell.

This fault of pusillanimity and timorous mind letteth a man also many times from the doing of many good things which, if he took a good stomach to him in the trust of God's help, he were well able to do. But the devil casteth him in a cowardice, and maketh him take it for humility to think him self unmeet and unable thereto, and therefore to leave the good thing undone whereof God offereth him occasion and had made him convenient thereto.

But such folk have need to lift up their hearts and call upon God, and by the counsel of other good ghostly folk, cast away the cowardice of their own concept which the night's fear by the devil hath framed in their fantasy, and look in the gospel upon him which laid up his talent and left it unoccupied, and therefore utterly lost it with a great reproach of his pusillanimity, by which he had meant he should have excused himself in that he was afeard to put it forth in use and occupy it. And all this fear cometh by the devil's drift, wherein he taketh occasion of the faintness of our good and sure trust in God. And therefore let us faithfully dwell in the good hope of His help, and then shall the pavis of His truth so compass us about that of this night's fear we shall have no fear at all.

Of the daughter of pusillanimity, a scrupulous conscience

THE FOURTEENTH CHAPTER

THIS pusillanimity bringeth forth by the night's fear a very timorous daughter, a silly wretched girl and ever puling, that is called Scrupulosity or a scrupulous conscience. This girl is a meetly good posil in an house, never idle but ever

occupied and busy.   But albeit she hath a very gentle mistress
that loveth her well, and is well content with that she doth,
or if it be not all well (as all cannot alway be well), content to
pardon her as she doth other of her fellows, and so letteth her
know that she will, yet can this peevish girl never cease whining
and puling for fear, lest her mistress be alway angry with her,
and that she shall shrewdly be shent.   Were her mistress,
ween you, like to be content with this condition?   Nay,
surely.

I knew such one myself, whose mistress was a very wise
woman, and (which thing is in women very rare) very mild
also and meek, and liked very well such service as she did her
in the house.   But this continual discomfortable fashion of
hers she so much misliked, that she would sometime say:
Aye, what aileth this girl?   The elvish urchin weenth I were a
devil, I trow.   Surely if she did me ten times better service
than she doth, yet with this fantastical fear of hers I would be
loath to have her in mine house.

Thus fareth, lo, the scrupulous person which frameth
himself many times double the fear that he hath cause, and
many times a great fear where there is no cause at all, and of
that that is indeed no sin maketh a venial, and that that is
venial imagineth to be deadly, and yet for all that falleth in
them, being namely of their nature such as no man long liveth
without.   And then he feareth that he be never full confessed
nor never full contrite, and then that his sins be never full
forgiven him; and then he confesseth and confesseth again,
and cumbreth himself and his confessor both.   And then
every prayer that he saith, though he say it as well as the frail
infirmity of the man will suffer, yet is he not satisfied but if he
say it again, and yet after that again.   And when he hath said
one thing thrice, as little is he satisfied with the last as with
the first, and then is his heart evermore in heaviness, unquiet,
and in fear, full of doubt and dullness, without comfort or
spiritual consolation.

With this night's fear the devil sore troubleth the mind of

many a right good man, and that doth he to bring him to some great inconvenience. For he will, if he can, drive him so much to the fearful minding of God's rigorous justice, that he will keep him from the comfortable remembrance of God's great mighty mercy, and so make him do all his good works wearily, and without consolation or quickness.

Moreover, he maketh him to take for sin something that is none, and for deadly some such as are but venial, to the intent that when he shall fall into them he shall, by reason of his scruple, sin where else he should not, or sin deadly, while his conscience in the deed doing so gave him, whereas else indeed he had offended but venially.

Yea, and farther, the devil longeth to make all his good works and spiritual exercise so painful and so tedious unto him, that with some other subtle suggestion or false wily doctrine of a false spiritual liberty, he should for the false ease and pleasure that he should suddenly find therein be easily conveyed from that evil fault into a much worse, and have his conscience as wide and as large after as ever it was narrow and strait before. For better is yet, of truth, a conscience a little too strait than a little too large.

My mother had, when I was a little boy, a good old woman that took heed to her children; they called her Mother Maud. I trow you have heard of her.

Vincent. Yea, yea, very much.

Anthony. She was wont when she sat by the fire with us to tell us that were children many childish tales. But as Plinius saith that there is no book lightly so bad but that some good thing a man may pick out thereof, so think I that there is almost no tale so foolish but that yet in one matter or other to some purpose it may hap to serve. For I remember me that among other of her fond tales she told us once that the ass and the wolf came upon a time to confession to the fox. The poor ass came to shrift in the Shrovetide a day or two before Ash Wednesday. But the wolf would not come to confession till he saw first Palm Sunday past, and then foded yet forth farther until Good Friday.   The fox asked the ass, before he began *Benedicite*, wherefore he came to confession so soon before Lent begin.   The poor beast answered him again, for fear of deadly sin, if he should lose his part of any of those prayers that the priest in the cleansing days prayeth for them that are then confessed already.   Then in his shrift he had a marvellous grudge in his inward conscience, that he had one day given his master a cause of anger in that that with his rude roaring before his master arose he had awaked him out of his sleep and bereaved him of his rest.   The fox for that fault, like a good discreet confessor, charged him to do so no more, but lie still and sleep like a good son himself till his master were up and ready to go to work, and so should he be sure that he should not wake him no more.

To tell you all the poor ass's confession, it were a long work, for everything that he did was deadly sin with him, the poor soul was so scrupulous.   But his wise, wily confessor accounted them for trifles, as they were, and sware after unto the badger, that he was so weary to sit so long and hear him, that saving for the manner's sake he had liefer have sitten all that while at breakfast with a good fat goose.

But when it came to the penance giving, the fox found that the most weighty sin in all his shrift was gluttony, and therefore he discreetly gave him in penance that he should never for greediness of his meat do any other beast any harm or hindrance, and then eat his meat and study for no more.

Now, as good Mother Maud told us, when the wolf came to Father Reynard (that was, she said, the fox's name), to confession upon Good Friday, his confessor shook his great pair of beads upon him, almost as big as bowls, and asked him wherefore he came so late.   Forsooth, Father Reynard, quoth he, I must needs tell you the truth; I come, you wot well, therefore, I durst come no sooner for fear lest you would for any gluttony have given me in penance to fast some part of this Lent.   Nay, nay, quoth the Father Fox, I am not so unreasonable, for I fast none of it myself.   For I may say to thee, son, between us twain here in confession, it is no commandment of God, this fasting, but an invention of man. The priests make folk fast, and put them to pain about the moonshine in the water, and do but make folk fools. But they shall make me no such fool, I warrant thee, son. For I eat flesh all this Lent myself I. Howbeit, indeed because I will not be occasion of slander, I therefore eat it secretly in my chamber, out of sight of all such foolish brethren as for their weak, scrupulous conscience would wax offended withal. And so would I counsel you to do. Forsooth, Father Fox, quoth the wolf, and so (I thank God) I do as near as I can. For when I go to my meat I take none other company with me, but such sure brethren as are of mine own nature, whose consciences are not weak, I warrant you, but their stomachs as strong as mine. Well, then, no force, quoth Father Fox. But when he heard after by his confession that he was so great a ravener that he devoured and spent sometime so much vitail at one meal as the price thereof would well find some poor man with his wife and his children almost all the week, then he prudently reproved that point in him and preached him a process of his own temperance which never used (as he said) to pass upon himself the value of sixpence at a meal, no nor yet so much neither. For when I bring home a goose, quoth he, not out of the poulter's shop (where folk find them out of the feathers ready plucked and see which is the fattest, and yet for sixpence buy and choose the best), but out of the housewife's house, at the first hand, which may somewhat better cheap afford them, you wot well, than the poulter may; nor yet cannot be suffered to see them plucked and stand and choose them by day, but am fain by night to take at adventure, and when I come home am fain to do the labour to pluck her myself too; yet for all this, though it be but lean and, I ween, not well worth a groat, serveth it me sometime, for all that, both dinner and supper too. And therefore as for that you live of ravin, therein can I find no fault: you have used it so long, that I think you can do none other, and therefore were it folly to forbid it you, and, to say the truth, against good conscience too. For live you must, I wot well, and other craft can you none. And therefore (as reason is) must you live by that. But yet, you wot well, too much is too much, and measure is a merry mean, which I perceive by your shrift you have never used to keep. And therefore surely this shall be your penance, that you shall all this year never pass upon yourself the price of sixpence at a meal, as near as your conscience can guess the price.

Their shrift have I shewed you as Mother Maud shewed it us. But now serveth for our matter the conscience of them both in the true performing of their penance.

The poor ass after his shrift when he waxed an hungered saw a sow lie with her pigs well lapped in new straw, and near he drew and thought to have eaten of the straw. But anon his scrupulous conscience began therein to grudge him; for while his penance was that for greediness of his meat he should do none other body none harm, he thought he might not eat one straw there, lest for lack of that straw some of those pigs might hap to die for cold. So held he still his hunger till one brought him meat. But when he should fall thereto then fell he yet in a far farther scruple. For then it came in his mind that he should yet break his penance if he should eat any of that either, sith he was commanded by his ghostly father that he should not for his own meat hinder any other beast. For he thought that if he eat not that meat some other beast might hap to have it, and so should he by the eating of it peradventure hinder another. And thus stood he still fasting till, when he told the cause, his ghostly father came and informed him better, and then he cast off that scruple and fell mannerly to his meat, and was a right honest ass many a fair day after.

The wolf now coming from shrift, clean soiled from his sins, went about to do as a shrewd wife once told her husband that she would do when she came from shrift. Be merry, man, quoth she now, for this day I thank God was I well shriven. And I purpose now therefore to leave of all mine old shrewdness and begin even afresh.

Vincent. Ah, well, uncle, can you report her so? That word heard I her speak, but she said it in sport to make her goodman laugh.

Anthony. Indeed it seemed she spake it half in sport; for that she said she would cast away all her old shrewdness, therein I trow she sported. But in that she said she would begin it all afresh, her husband found that good earnest.

Vincent. Well I shall shew her what you say, I warrant you.

Anthony. Then will you make me make my word good. But whatsoever she did, at the least wise so fared now this wolf which had cast out in confession all his old ravin, and then hunger pricked him forward that (as the shrewd wife said) he should begin all afresh. But yet the prick of conscience withdrew and held him back, because he would not for breaking of his penance take any prey for his mealtide that should pass the price of sixpence. It happed him, then, as he walked prowling for his gear about he came where a man had in few days before cast off two old lean and lame horses, so sick that no flesh was there left upon them; and the one, when the wolf came by, could scant stand on his legs, and the other already dead and his skin ript off and carried away. And as he looked upon them suddenly, he was first about to feed upon them and whet his teeth on their bones. But as he looked aside he spied a fair cow in a close, walking with her young calf by her side. And as soon as he saw them his conscience began to grudge him against both those two horses. And then he sighed and said unto himself: Alas, wicked wretch that I am, I had almost broken my penance ere I was ware. For yonder dead horse (because I never saw no dead horse sold in the market, and I should even die therefore by the way that my sinful soul shall too), I cannot devise what price I should set upon him. But in my conscience I set him far above sixpence, and therefore I dare not meddle with him. Now then is yonder quick horse of likelihood worth a great deal of money; for horse be dear in this country, specially such soft amblers, for I see by his pace he trotteth not nor can scant shift a foot. And therefore I may not meddle with him, for he very far passeth my sixpence. But kine this country here hath enough, but money have they very little. And therefore, considering the plenty of the kine and the scarcity of the money, as for yonder peevish cow, seemeth unto me in my conscience worth not past a groat, an she be worth so much. Now then, as for her calf, is not so much as she by half. And therefore while the cow is in my conscience worth but fourpence, my conscience cannot serve me for sin of my soul to appraise her calf above twopence; and so pass they not sixpence between them both. And therefore them twain may I well eat at this one meal and break not my penance at all. And so thereupon he did without any scruple of conscience.

If such beasts could speak now (as Mother Maud said they could then) some of them would, I ween, tell a tale almost as wise as this, wherein save for the minishing of old Mother Maud's tale, else would a shorter process have served.

But yet as peevish as the parable is, in this it serveth for our purpose, that the night's fear of a conscience somewhat scrupulous, though it be painful and troublous to him that hath it like as this poor ass had here, is less harm yet than a conscience over large, or such as for his own fantasy the man list to frame himself, now drawing it narrow, now stretching it in breadth, after the manner of a cheverel point, to serve on every side for his own commodity, as did here the wily wolf.

But such folk are out of tribulation, and comfort need they none, and therefore are they out of our matter. But those that are in the night's fear of their own scrupulous conscience, let them be well ware, as I said, that the devil for weariness of the one draw them not into the other, and while he would fly from Scylla drew him into Charybdis. He must do as doth a ship that should come into an haven in the mouth whereof lie secret rocks under the water on both the sides. If he be by mishap entered in among them that are on the one side and cannot tell how to get out, he must get a substantial cunning pilot that so can conduct him from the rocks on that side that yet he bring him not into those that are on the other side, but can guide him in the mid way. Let them, I say therefore, that are in the troublous fear of their own scrupulous conscience, submit the rule of their own conscience to the counsel of some other good man which after the variety and the nature of the scruples may temper his advice. Yea, although a man be very well learned himself, yet let him in this case learn the custom used among physicians. For be one of them never so cunning, yet in his own disease and sickness he never useth to trust all to himself, but sendeth for such of his fellows as he knoweth meet, and putteth himself in their hands for many considerations, whereof they assign the causes. And one of the causes is fear, whereof upon some tokens he may conceive in his own passion a great deal more than needeth and than were good for his health, that for the time he knew no such thing at all.

I knew once in this town one of the most cunning men in that faculty, and the best expert, and therewith the most famous too, and he that the greatest cures did upon other men. And yet when he was himself once very sore sick I heard his fellows that then looked unto him, of all which every one would in their own disease have used his help before any other man, wish yet that for the time of his own sickness, being so sore as it was, he had known no physic at all. He took so great heed unto every suspicious token, and feared so far the worst, that his fear did him sometime much more harm than the sickness gave him cause.

And therefore, as I say, whoso hath such a trouble of his scrupulous conscience, let him for a while forbear the judgment of himself and follow the counsel of some other whom he knoweth for well learned and virtuous, and specially in the place of confession. For there is God specially present with His grace assisting His sacrament. And let him not doubt to acquiet his mind, and follow that he there is bidden, and think for a while less of the fear of God's justice, and be more merry in remembrance of His mercy, and persevere in prayer for grace, and abide and dwell faithfully in the sure hope of His help; and then shall he find, without any doubt, that the pavis of God's truth shall, as the prophet saith, so compass him about, that he shall not dread this night's fear of scrupulosity, but shall have afterward his conscience stablished in good quiet and rest.

Another kind of the night's fear, another daughter of pusillanimity, it is to wit that horrible temptation, by which some folk are tempted to kill and destroy themself.

THE FIFTEENTH CHAPTER

Vincent.   Verily, good uncle, you have in my mind well declared these kinds of the night's fear.

Anthony.   Surely: cousin; but yet are there many more than I can either remember or find.   Howbeit, one yet cometh now to my mind, of which I before nothing thought, and which is yet, in mine opinion, of all the other fears the most horrible, that is to wit, cousin, where the devil tempteth a man to kill and destroy himself.

Vincent.   Undoubtedly this kind of tribulation is marvellous and strange, and the temptation is of such a sort that some men have opinion that such as once fall in that fantasy can never full cast it off.

Anthony.   Yes, yes, cousin, many an hundred, and else God forbid.   But the thing that maketh men so say is because that of those which finally do destroy themself there is much speech and much wondering, as it is well worthy.   But many a good man and woman hath sometime, yea divers years each after other, continually been tempted thereto, and yet have by grace and good counsel well and virtuously withstood it, and been in conclusion clearly delivered of it, and their tribulation nothing known abroad, and therefore nothing talked of. But surely, cousin, an horrible sore trouble it is to any man or woman that the devil tempteth therewith. Many have I heard of, and with some have I talked myself, that have been sore cumbered with that temptation, and marked have I not a little the manner of them.

Vincent. I require you, good uncle, shew me somewhat of such things as you perceive therein. For first, where you call this kind of temptation the daughter of pusillanimity, and thereby so near of sib unto the night's fear, methinketh on the other side, that it is rather a thing that cometh of a great courage and boldness when they dare their own hands put themself to death, from which we see almost every man shrink and fly, and that many such as we know by good proof and plain experience for men of great heart and excellent hardy courage.

Anthony. I said, cousin Vincent, that of pusillanimity cometh this temptation, and very truth it is that indeed so it doth. But yet I meant it not that of only faint heart and fear it cometh and groweth alway. For the devil tempteth sundry folks by sundry ways. But the cause wherefore I spake of none other kind of that temptation than of only that which is the daughter that the devil begetteth upon pusillanimity, was for that, that those other kinds of the temptation fall not under the nature of tribulation and fear, and therefore fall they far out of our matter here, and are such temptations, as only need counsel and not comfort or consolation, for that the persons therewith tempted be with that kind of temptation not troubled in their mind, but verily well content, both in the tempting and following. For some hath there been, cousin, such that they have been tempted thereto by mean of a foolish pride, and some by the mean of anger without any dread at all, and very glad to go thereto. To this I say not nay. But where you ween that none fall thereto by fear, but that they have all a strong mighty stomach, that shall you well see the contrary, and that peradventure in those of whom you would ween the stomach most strong and their heart and courage most hardy.

Vincent. Yet is it marvel, uncle, unto me that it should be as you say it is, that this temptation is unto them that do it for pride or for anger no tribulation, nor that they should need in so great a distress and peril both of body and soul to be lost no manner of good ghostly comfort.

Anthony. Let us therefore, cousin, consider a sample or two, for thereby shall we the better perceive it.

There was here in Buda, in King Ladislaus's days, a good, poor, honest man's wife. This woman was so fiendish, that the devil, perceiving her nature, put her in the mind that she should anger her husband so sore that she might give him occasion to kill her, and then should he be hanged for her.

Vincent. This was a strange temptation indeed. What the devil should she be the better then?

Anthony. Nothing, but that it eased her shrewd stomach before to think that her husband should be hanged after. And peradventure, if you look about the world and consider it well, you shall find more such stomachs than a few. Have you never heard no furious body plainly say that to see some such man have a mischief he would with goodwill be content to lie as long in hell as God liveth in heaven?

Vincent. Forsooth, and some such have I heard of.

Anthony. This mind of his was not much less mad than hers, but rather haply the more mad of the twain. For the woman peradventure did not cast so far peril therein. But to tell you now to what good pass her charitable purpose came: As her husband (the man was a carpenter) stood hewing with his chip-axe upon a piece of timber, she began after her old guise so to revile him that the man waxed wroth at last and bade her get her in, or he would lay the helm of his axe about her back, and said also that it were little sin even with that axe-head to chop off that unhappy head of hers that carried such an ungracious tongue therein. At that word the devil took his time, and whetted her tongue against her teeth. And when it was well sharped she sware to him in very fierce anger: By the mass, whoreson husband, I would thou wouldest; here lieth mine head, lo (and therewith down she laid her head upon the same timber log), if thou smite it not off, I beshrew thine whoreson's heart. With that, likewise as the devil stood at her elbow, so stood (as I heard say) his good angel at his, and gave him ghostly courage, and bade him be bold and do it. And so the good man up with his chip-axe, and at a chop chopped off her head indeed. There were standing other folk by, which had a good sport to hear her chide, but little they looked for this chance till it was done ere they could let it. They said they heard her tongue babble in her head, and call Whoreson whoreson, twice after that the head was from the body. At the least wise, afterward unto the king thus they reported all, except only one, and that was a woman, and she said that she heard it not.

Vincent. Forsooth, this was a wonderful work. What came, uncle, of the man?

Anthony. The king gave him his pardon.

Vincent. Verily he might in conscience do no less.

Anthony. But then was it farther almost at another point, that there should have been a statute made that in such case there should never after pardon be granted, but the truth being able to be proved, none husband should need any pardon, but should have leave by the law to follow the sample of that carpenter and do the same.

Vincent. How happed it, uncle, that that good law was left unmade?

Anthony. How happed it? As it happeth, cousin, that many more be left unmade as well as it, and within a little as good as it too, both here and in other countries, and sometime some worse made in their stead. But, as they say, the let of that law was the queen's grace (God forgive her soul). It was the greatest thing, I ween, good lady, that she had to answer for when she died. For surely, save for that one

thing, she was a full blessed woman.   But letting now that
law pass, this temptation in procuring her own death was unto
this carpenter's wife no tribulation at all, as far as ever men
could perceive.   For it liked her well to think thereon, and
she even longed therefore.   And therefore if she had before
told you or me her mind, and that she would so fain bring it so
to pass, we could have had none occasion to comfort her as
one that were in tribulation.   But, marry, counsel her (as I
told you before) we might to refrain and amend that malicious
devilish mind.

Vincent.   Verily that is truth.   But such as are well willing
to do any purpose that is so shameful will never tell their mind
to nobody for very shame.

Anthony.   Some will not indeed.   And yet are there some
again that, be their intent never so shameful, find some yet
whom their heart serveth them to make of their counsel
therein.   Some of my folk here can tell you that no longer
ago than even yesterday one that came out of Vienna shewed
us among other talking that a rich widow (but I forgot to ask
him where it happed) having all her life an high proud mind
and a fell, as those two virtues are wont alway to keep company together, was at debate with another neighbour of hers
in the town.   And on a time she made of her counsel a poor
neighbour of hers whom she thought for money she might
induce to follow her mind.   With him she secretly brake, and
offered him ten ducats for his labour, to do so much for her
as in a morning early to come to her house and with an axe
unknown privily strike off her head; and when he had so done
then convey the bloody axe into the house of him with whom
she was at debate, in some such manner wise as it might be
thought that he had murdered her for malice; and then she
thought she should be taken for a martyr.   And yet had she
farther devised that another sum of money should after be
sent to Rome, and there should be means made to the Pope
that she might in all haste be canonized.   This poor man
promised but intended not to perform it; howbeit, when he

deferred it she provided the axe herself; and he appointed with her the morning when he should come and do it, and thereupon into her house he came. But then set he such other folk as he would should know her frantic fantasy in such place appointed as they might well hear her and him talk together. And after that he had talked with her thereof what he would, so much as he thought was enough, he made her lie down and took up the axe in his own hand, and with the other hand he felt the edge and found a fault that it was not sharp, and that therefore he would in no wise do it till he had grounden it sharp. He would not else, he said, for pity, it would put her to so much pain. And so full sore against her will for that time she kept her head still. But because she would no more suffer any more deceive her so and fode her forth with delays, ere it was very long after she hung herself with her own hands.

Vincent. Forsooth, here was a tragical story whereof I never heard the like.

Anthony. Forsooth, the party that told it me sware that he knew it for a truth. And himself is, I promise you, such as I reckon for right honest and of substantial truth.

Now here she letted not, as shameful a mind as she had, to make one of her counsel yet, and yet as I remember another too, whom she trusted with the money that should procure her canonization. And here I wot well that her temptation came not of fear but of high malice and pride. But then was she so glad in the pleasant device thereof that, as I shewed you, she took it for no tribulation, and therefore comforting of her could have no place; but if men should anything give her toward her help, it must have been, as I told you, good counsel. And therefore, as I said, this kind of temptation to a man's own destruction, which requireth counsel and is out of tribulation, was out of our matter, that is to treat of comfort in tribulation.

Of him that were moved to kill himself by illusion of the devil,
which he reckoned for a revelation

THE SIXTEENTH CHAPTER

BUT lest you might reject both these samples, weening they
were but feigned tales, I shall put you in remembrance of one
which I reckon yourself have read in the *Collations* of Cassianus, and if you have not there you may soon find it.   For
myself have half forgotten the thing, it is so long since I read
it.   But thus much I remember, that he telleth there of one
that was many days a very special holy man in his living, and
among the other virtuous monks and anchors that lived there in
wilderness was marvellously much esteemed, saving that
some were not all out of fear of him, lest his revelations,
whereof he told many by himself, would prove illusions of the
devil.   And so proved it after indeed.   For the man was by
the devil's subtle suggestions brought into such an high
spiritual pride, that in conclusion the devil brought him to
that horrible point that he made him go kill himself.   And as
far as my mind giveth me now without new sight of the book,
he brought him to it by this persuasion, that he made him
believe that it was God's will he should so do and that thereby
should he go straight to heaven.   And then if it were by that
persuasion, with which he took very great comfort in his own
mind himself, then was it, as I said, out of our case, and
needed not comfort but counsel against giving credence to the
devil's persuasion.

But marry, if he made him first perceive how he had been
deluded, and then tempted him to his own death by shame
and by despair, then was it within our matter, lo; for then was
his temptation fallen down from pride to pusillanimity, and
was waxen that kind of the night's fear that I spake of,
wherein a good part of the counsel that were to be given him
should have need to stand in good comforting, for then was he
brought into right sore tribulation.

But, as I was about to tell you, strength of heart and courage is there none therein, not only for that very strength (as it hath the name of virtue in a reasonable creature) can never be without prudence, but also for that (as I said) even in them that seem men of most hardiness, it shall well appear to them that well weigh the matter that the mind whereby they be led to destroy themself groweth of pusillanimity and very foolish fear.

Take for the sample Cato Uticensis, which in Africa killed himself after the great victory that Julius Cæsar had. Saint Austin well declareth in his work *De Civitate Dei* that there was no strength nor magnanimity therein, but plain pusillanimity and impotency of stomach, whereby he was forced to the destruction of himself because his heart was too feeble for to bear the beholding of another man's glory or the suffering of other worldly calamities that he feared should fall on himself. So that, as Saint Austin well proveth, that horrible deed is none act of strength, but an act of a mind either drawn from the consideration of itself with some devilish fantasy, wherein the man hath need to be called home with good counsel, or else oppressed by faint heart and fear, wherein a good part of the counsel must stand in lifting up his courage with good consolation and comfort. And therefore if we found any such religious person, as was that father which Cassian writeth of, that were of such austerity and apparent ghostly living, that he were with such as well knew him reputed for a man of singular virtue, and that it were perceived that he had many strange visions appearing unto him, if it should now be perceived after that that the man went about secretly to destroy himself, whoso should hap to come to the knowledge thereof and intended to do his devoir in the let, first must he find the means to search and find out whether the man be in his manner and his countenance lightsome, glad, and joyful, or dumpish, heavy, and sad, and whether he go thereabout as one that were full of the glad hope of heaven or as one that had his breast farced full of tediousness and weariness of the world. If he were founden of the first fashion, it were a token that the devil hath by his fantastical apparitions puffed him up in such a peevish pride, that he hath finally persuaded him by some illusion shewed him for the proof that God's pleasure is that he shall for His sake with his own hands kill himself.

Vincent. Now, if a man so found it, uncle, what counsel should a man give him then?

Anthony. That were somewhat out of our purpose, cousin, sith (as I told you before) the man were not then in sorrow and tribulation, whereof our matter speaketh, but in a perilous merry mortal tentation. So that if we should, beside our own matter that we have in hand, enter into that too, we might make a longer work between both than we could well finish this day. Howbeit, to be short, it is soon seen that therein the sum and effect of the counsel must in manner rest in giving him warning of the devil's sleights. And that must be done under such sweet pleasant manner, as the man should not abhor to hear it. For while it could lightly be none other but that the man were rocked and sungen asleep by the devil's craft and his mind occupied as it were in a delectable dream, he should never have good audience of him that would rudely and boisterously shog him and wake him and so shake him out thereof. Therefore must you fair and easily touch him, and with some pleasant speech awake him so that he wax not wayward as children do that are waked ere they list to rise.

But when a man hath first begun with his praise (for if he be proud ye shall much better please him with a commendation than with a dirge), then, after favour won therewithal, a man may little and little insinuate the doubt of such revelations, not at the first as it were for any doubt of his, but of some other that men in some other places talk of. And peradventure it shall not miscontent himself to shew great perils that may fall therein in another man's case than his own, and shall begin to preach upon it. Or if you were a man

that had not so very great scrupulous conscience of an harmless lie, devised to do good withal (which kind Saint Austin,
though he take alway for sin, yet he taketh but for venial;
and Saint Jerome, as by divers places in his books appeareth,
taketh not fully for so much), then may you feign some secret
friend of yours to be in such case, and that yourself somewhat
fear his peril and have made of charity this voyage for his sake,
to ask this good father's counsel.   And in the communication
upon these words of Saint John: *Nolite omni spiritui credere,
sed probate spiritus si ex Deo sint:* Give not credence to every
spirit, but prove the spirits whether they be of God, and
these words of Saint Paul: *Angelus Sathanæ transfigurat se in
angelum lucis:* The angel of Satan transfigureth himself into
the angel of light, you shall take occasion the better if they
hap to come in on his side, but yet not lack occasion neither if
those texts, for lack of his offer, come in upon your own.
Occasion, I say, shall you not lack to inquire by what sure and
undeceivable tokens a man may discern the true revelations
from the false illusions, whereof a man shall find many both
here and there in divers other authors, and whole together
divers goodly treatises of that good godly doctor, Master John
Gerson, entitled *De probatione spirituum,* as whether the
party be natural wise or anything seem fantastical, whether
the party be poor-spirited or proud, which will somewhat
appear by his delight in his own praise, or if of wiliness or of
another pride for to be praised of humility he refuse to hear
thereof, yet any little fault found in himself, or diffidence
declared and mistrust of his own revelations and doubtful
tokens told wherefore himself should fear lest they be the
devil's illusion, such things, as Master Gerson saith, will make
him spit out somewhat of his spirit, if the devil lie in his breast.

Or if the devil be yet so subtle that he keep himself close in
his warm den and blow out never an hot word, yet is it to
be considered what end his revelations draw to, whether to
any spiritual profit to himself or other folk, or only to vain
marvels and wonders.

Also whether they withdraw him from such other good virtuous business as by the common rules of Christendom or any rules of his profession he was wont to use, or were bounden to be occupied in.

Or whether he fall into any singularity of opinions against the Scripture of God or against the common faith of Christ's Catholic Church.

Many other tokens are there in the work of Master Gerson spoken of to consider by, whether the person, neither having revelations of God nor illusions from the devil, do either for winning of money or worldly favour, feign his revelations himself and delude the people withal.

But now, for our purpose, if among any of the marks by which the true revelations may be known from false illusions that man himself bring forth for one mark the doing or teaching of anything against the Scripture of God or the common faith of the Church, then have you an entry made you by which when you list you may enter into the special matter wherein he can never well flit from you. Or else may you yet, if you list, feign that your secret friend, for whose sake you come to him for counsel, is brought in that mind by a certain apparition shewed unto him, as himself saith by an angel, as you fear by the devil, that he can be by you none other wise persuaded as yet, but that the pleasure of God is that he shall go kill himself, and that if he so do then shall he be thereby so specially participant of Christ's Passion that he shall forthwith be carried up with angels into heaven. For which he is so joyful, that he firmly purposeth upon it, no less glad to do it than another man would be glad to avoid it. And therefore may you desire his good counsel to instruct you with some substantial good advice, wherewith you may turn him from this error that he be not under hope of God's true revelation, in body and soul destroyed by the devil's false illusion.

If he will in this thing study and labour to instruct you, the things that himself shall find of his own invention, though they be less effectual, shall peradventure more work with himself toward his own amendment, sith he shall of likelihood better like them, than shall double so substantial told him by another man.

If he be loath to think upon that side, and therefore shrink from the matter, then is there none other way but adventure after the plain fashion to fall into the matter, and shew what you hear, and to give him counsel and exhortation to the contrary, but if you list to say that thus and thus hath the matter been reasoned already between your friend and you. And therein may you rehearse such things as should prove that the vision which moveth him is no true revelation, but a very false illusion.

Vincent. Verily, uncle, I well allow this, that a man should as well in this thing as every other wherein he longeth to do another man good, seek such a pleasant way as the party should be likely to like or at the least wise well to take in worth his communication, and not so to enter in thereunto as he whom he would help should abhor him, and be loath to hear him, and therefore take no profit by him. But now, uncle, if it come by the one way or the other to the point that hear me he will or shall, what be the reasons effectual with which I should by my counsel convert him?

Anthony. All those by which you may make him perceive that himself is deceived and that his visions be no godly revelations but very devilish illusion. And those reasons must you gather of the man, of the matter, and of the law of God, or of some one of these. Of the man, if you can perad-venture shew him that in such a point or such he is waxen worse since such revelations have haunted him than he was before, as in those that are deluded whoso be well acquainted with them shall well mark and perceive. For they wax more proud, more wayward, more envious, suspicious, misjudging, and depraving other men with the delight of their own praise, and such other spiritual vices of the soul.

Of the matter may you gather, if it have happed his revela-tions before to prove false, or that they be things rather strange than profitable. For that is a good mark between God's miracles and the devil's wonders. For Christ and His saints have their miracles alway tending to fruit and profit. The devil and his witches and necromancers, all their wonderful works, draw to no fruitful end, but to a fruitless ostentation and shew, as it were a juggler that would for a shew before the people play masteries at a feast. Of the law of God you must draw your reasons in shewing by the Scripture that the thing which he weeneth God by His angel biddeth, God hath his own mouth forbidden. And that is, you wot well, in the case that we speak of so easy to find, that I need not to rehearse it to you, sith there is plain among the ten commandments forboden the unlawful killing of any man, and therefore of himself, as Saint Austin saith, all the Church teacheth, except himself be no man.

Vincent. This is very true, good uncle, nor I will not dispute upon any glossing of that prohibition. But sith we find not the contrary but that God may dispense with that commandment Himself, and both license and command also, if Himself list, any man to go kill either another man or himself either this man that is now by such a marvellous vision induced to believe that God so biddeth him, and therefore thinketh himself in that case of that prohibition discharged, and charged with the contrary commandment, with what reason may we make him perceive that his vision is but an illusion and not a true revelation?

Anthony. Nay, cousin Vincent, ye shall in this case not need to require those reasons of me. But taking the Scripture of God for a ground for this matter, you know very well yourself you shall go somewhat a shorter way to work if you ask this question of him, that sith God hath forboden once the thing Himself, though He may dispense therewith if He will, yet sith the devil may feign himself God and with a marvellous vision delude one and make as though God did it, and sith the devil is also more likely to speak against God's commandment than God against His own, you shall have good cause, I say, to demand of the man himself whereby he knoweth that his vision is God's true revelation and not the devil's false delusion.

Vincent. Indeed, uncle, I think that would be an hard question to him. May a man, uncle, have in such a thing even a very sure knowledge of his own mind?

Anthony. Yea, cousin, God may cast into the mind of a man, I suppose, such an inward light of understanding that he cannot fail but be sure thereof. And yet he that is deluded by the devil may think himself as sure and yet be deceived indeed. And such a difference is there in a manner between them as is between the sight of a thing while we be waking and look thereon, and the sight with which we see a thing in our sleep while we dream thereof.

Vincent. This is a pretty similitude, uncle, in this thing; and then is it easy for the monk that we speak of to declare how he knoweth his vision for a true revelation and not a false delusion, if there be so great difference between them.

Anthony. Not so easy, cousin, yet as you ween it were. For how can you now prove unto me that you be awake?

Vincent. Marry, lo, do I not now wag my hand, shake my head, and stamp with my foot here in the floor?

Anthony. Have you never dreamed ere this, that you have done the same?

Vincent. Yes, that have I, and more too than that. For I have ere this in my sleep dreamed that I doubted whether I were asleep or awake, and have in good faith thought that I did thereupon even the same things that I do now indeed, and thereby determined that I was not asleep. And yet have I dreamed in good faith, farther, that I have been afterward at dinner, and there making merry with good company have told the same dream at the table and laughed well thereat, that while I was asleep I had by such means of moving the parts of my body and considering thereof so verily thought myself waking.

Anthony. And will you not now soon, trow you, when you

wake and rise, laugh as well at yourself when you see that you lie now in your warm bed asleep again, and dream all this time while you ween so verily that you be waking and talking of these matters with me?

Vincent. Good Lord, uncle, you go now merrily to work with me indeed when you look and speak so sadly and would make me ween I were asleep.

Anthony. It may be that you be so, for anything that you can say or do whereby you may with any reason that you make drive me to confess that yourself be sure of the contrary, sith you can do nor say nothing now whereby you be sure to be waking, but that you have ere this, or hereafter may, think yourself as surely to do the selfsame things indeed while you be all the while asleep, and nothing do but lie dreaming.

Vincent. Well, well, uncle, though I have ere this thought myself awake while I was indeed asleep, yet for all this I know well enough that I am awake now, and so do you too, though I cannot find the words by which I may with reason force you to confess it, but that alway you may drive me off, by the sample of my dream.

Anthony. This is, cousin, as meseemeth, very true; and likewise seemeth me the manner and difference between some kind of true revelations and some kind of false illusions as it standeth between the things that are done waking and the things that in our dreams seem to be done while we be sleeping, that is to wit, that he which hath that kind of revelation from God is as sure of the truth as we be of our own deed while we be waking. And he that is illuded by the devil, is in such wise deceived, and worse too, than be they by their dream; and yet reckoneth for the time himself as sure as the other, saving that the one falsely weeneth, the other truly knoweth. But I say not, cousin, that this kind of sure knowledge cometh in every kind of revelation, for there are many kinds, whereof were too long to talk now. But I say that God doth, or may do to man in something, certainly send some such.

Vincent. Yet then may this religious man of whom we speak, when I shew him the Scripture against his revelation and therefore call it an illusion, bid me with reason go care for myself. For he knoweth well and surely himself that his revelation is very good and true and not any false illusion, sith for all the general commandment of God in the Scripture God may dispense where He will, and when He will, and may command him do the contrary as He commanded Abraham to kill his own son, and as Samson had by inspiration of God commandment to kill himself with pulling down the house upon his own head at the feast of the Philistines.

Now if I would then do as you bade me right now, tell him that such apparitions may be illusions, and sith God's word is in the Scripture against him plain for the prohibition, he must perceive the truth of his revelation, whereby that I may know it is not a false illusion; then shall he bid me again tell him whereby that I can prove myself to be awake and talk with him and not to be asleep and dream so, sith in my dream I may as surely ween so as I know that I do so. And thus shall he drive me to the same bay to which I would bring him.

Anthony. This is well said, cousin; but yet could he not scape you so. For the dispensation of God's common precept, which dispensation he must say that he hath by his private revelation, is a thing of such sort as sheweth itself naught and false. For it never hath had any sample like since the world began unto now, that ever man hath read or heard of among faithful people commended. First in Abraham touching the death of his son, God intended it not, but only tempted the towardness of the father's obedience.

In Samson all men make not the matter very sure, whether he be saved or not; but yet therein some matter and cause appeareth. For the Philistines, being enemies to God and using Samson for their mocking-stock in scorn of God, it is well likely that God gave him the mind to bestow his own life upon the revenging of the displeasure that those blasphemous Philistines did unto God. And that appeareth meetly clear by this, that though his strength failed him when he wanted his hair, yet had he not, as it seemeth, that strength evermore at hand while he had his hair but at such times as it pleased God to give it him.   Which thing appeareth by these words that the scripture in some place of that matter saith: *Irruit virtus Domini in Sampsonem:* The power or might of God rushed into Samson.   And so, therefore, while this thing that he did in the pulling down of the house was done by the special gift of strength then at that point given him by God, it well declareth that the strength of God, and therewith the spirit of God, entered into him therefore.

Saint Austin also rehearseth that certain holy virtuous virgins in time of persecution, being by God's enemies infidels pursued upon to be deflowered by force, ran into a water and drowned themself rather than they would be bereaved of their virginity.   And albeit that he thinketh it is not lawful for any other maid to follow their sample, but rather suffer other to do her any manner violence by force and commit sin of his own upon her against her will, than willingly and thereby sinfully herself become an homicide of herself, yet he thinketh that in them it happed by the special instinct of the Spirit of God that for causes seen unto Himself would rather that they should avoid it with their own temporal death than abide the defiling and violation of their chastity.

But now this good man neither hath any of God's enemies to be by his own death revenged on, nor any woman that violently pursue him by force to bereave him of his virginity, nor never find we that God proved any man's obedient mind by the commandment of his own slaughter of himself. Therefore is his case both plain against God's open precept, and the dispensation strange and without sample, no cause appearing nor well imaginable, but if he would think, that God could neither any longer live without him nor take him to Him in such wise as He doeth other men, but command him to come by a forboden way, by which without other cause we never heard that ever He bade any man else before.

Now, where you think, if you should after this bid him tell
you by what way he knoweth that his intent riseth upon a
true revelation and not upon a false illusion, he would bid
you then again tell him by what mean you know that you be
talking with him well waking and not dream it sleeping, you
may tell him again that men thus to talk together as you do
and in such manner wise, and to prove and perceive that
they so do, by the moving of themself, with putting the
question thereof unto themself for their pleasure, and the
marking and considering thereof, is in waking a daily common
thing that every man doeth or may do when he will, and
when they do it they do it but of pleasure. But in sleep it
happeth very seld that men dream that they so do, nor in the
dream never put the question but for doubt. And therefore it is more reason that sith this revelation is such also as
happeth so seld, and ofter happeth that men dream of such
than have such indeed, therefore is it more reason, you may
tell him, that he shew you whereby he knoweth in such a rare
thing, and a thing more like a dream, that himself is not asleep
than you in such a common thing among folk that are waking,
and so seldom happing in a dream, should need to shew him
whereby you know that you be not asleep.

Besides this, himself to whom you should shew it seeth
and perceiveth the thing that he would bid you prove. But
the thing that he would make you believe, the truth of his
revelation which you bid him prove, you see not, he wotteth
well himself. And therefore ere you believe it against the
Scripture it were well consonant unto reason that he should
shew you whereby he knoweth it for a true waking revelation
and not a false dreaming delusion.

Vincent. Then shall he peradventure say to me again, that
whether I believe him or not maketh him no matter; the thing
toucheth himself and not me, and himself is in himself as sure
that it is a true revelation as that he can tell that he dreameth
not but talketh with me waking.

Anthony. Without doubt, cousin, if he abide at that point

and can be by no reason brought to do so much as doubt, nor can by no mean be shogged out of his dead sleep, but will needs take his dream for a very truth, and as some by night rise and walk about their chamber in their sleep will so rise and hang himself, I can then none other way see but either bind him fast in his bed or else assay whether that might hap to help him with which the common tale goeth that a carver's wife in such a frantic fantasy holp her husband. To whom, when he would upon a Good Friday needs have killed himself for Christ's sake as Christ was killed for him, she would not in vain plead against his mind, but well and wisely put him in remembrance, that if he would die for Christ as Christ died for him, it were then convenient for him to die even after the same fashion, and that might not be by his own hands, but the hand of some other. For Christ, pardy, killed not Himself. And because her husband should need to make no more of counsel (for that would he not in no wise), she offered him that for God's sake she would secretly crucify him herself upon a great cross that he had made to nail a new-carved crucifix upon. Whereof when he was very glad, yet she bethought her that Christ was bounden to a pillar and beaten first, and after crowned with thorn. Whereupon, when she had by his own assent bound him fast to a post, she left not beating with holy exhortation to suffer so much and so long, that ere ever she left work and unbound him, praying him nevertheless that she might put on his head, and drive it well down, a crown of thorn that she had wreathen for him and brought him, he said he thought this was enough for that year. He would pray God forbear him of the remnant till Good Friday come again. But when it came again the next year, then was his lust past; he longed to follow Christ no farther.

Vincent. Indeed, uncle, if this help him not, then will nothing help him, I trow.

Anthony. And yet, cousin, the devil may peradventure make him toward such a purpose first gladly suffer other pain, yea, and minish his feeling too therein, that he may thereby the less fear his death. And yet are peradventure sometime such things and many more to be assayed. For as the devil may hap to make him suffer, so may he hap to miss, namely if his friends fall to prayer for him against his temptation. For that can himself never do while he taketh it for none. But for conclusion, if the man be surely proved so inflexibly set upon the purpose to destroy himself, as commanded thereto by God, that no good counsel that men can give him nor any other thing that men may do to him can refrain him, but that he would surely shortly kill himself, then, except only good prayer by his friends made for him, I can find no farther shift, but either have him ever in sight, or bind him fast in his bed. And so must he needs of reason be content to be ordered. For though himself take his fantasy for a true revelation, yet sith he cannot make us perceive it for such, likewise as he thinketh himself by his secret commandment bounden to follow it, so must he needs agree that sith it is against the plain open prohibition of God, we be by the plain open precept bounden to keep him from it.

Vincent. In this point, uncle, I can go no farther. But now if he were upon the other side perceived to mind his destruction, and to go thereabout with heaviness of heart and thought and dullness, what way were there to be used to him then?

Anthony. Then were his temptation, as I told you before, properly pertaining to our matter; for then were he in a sore tribulation and a very perilous. For then were it a token that the devil had either by bringing him into some great sin brought him in despair, or peradventure by his revelations founden false and reproved, or by some secret sin of his deprehended and divulged, cast him both in despair of heaven through fear, and in a weariness of this life for shame, sith he seeth his estimation lost among other folk of whose praise he was wont to be proud. And therefore, cousin, in such case as this is the man is to be fair handled and sweetly, and with douce and tender loving words to be put in good courage, and comforted in all that men godly may.

Here must they put him in mind that if he despair not but pull up his courage and trust in God's great mercy, he shall have in conclusion great cause to be glad of this fall. For before he stood in greater peril than he was ware of while he took himself for better than he was. And God, for favour that He beareth him, hath suffered him to fall deep into the devil's danger, to make him thereby know what he was while he took himself for so sure. And therefore as He suffered him then to fall for a remedy against overbold pride, so will God now (if the man meek himself, not with fruitless despair, but with fruitful penance) so set him up again upon his feet, and so strength him with His grace, that for this one fall that the devil hath given him he shall give the devil an hundred.

And here must he be put in remembrance of Mary Magdalene, of the prophet David, and specially of Saint Peter, whose high bold courage took a foul fall. And yet because he despaired not of God's mercy, but wept and called upon it, how highly God took him into His favour again in his Holy Scripture is well testified, and well through Christendom known.

And now shall it be charitably done if some good virtuous folk, such as himself somewhat esteemeth and hath afore longed to stand in estimation with, do resort sometime unto him, not only to give him counsel, but also to ask advice and counsel of him in some cases of their own conscience, to let him thereby perceive that they no less esteem him now, but rather more than they did before, sith they think him now by this fall better expert of the devil's craft, and thereby not only better instructed himself, but also better able to give good advice and counsel unto other. This thing will in my mind well amend and lift up his courage from the peril of that desperate shame.

Vincent. Methinketh, uncle, that this were a perilous thing. For it may peradventure make him set the less by his fall, and thereby cast him into his first pride or into his other sin again that falling whereinto drave him into this despair.

Anthony. I do not mean, cousin, that every fool should at adventure fall in hand with him, for so, lo, might it hap for to do harm indeed.   But, cousin, if a cunning physician have a man in hand, he can well discern when and how long some certain medicine is necessary which at another time ministered or at that time overlong continued might put the patient in peril.   If he have his patient in an ague to the cure whereof he needeth his medicines in their working cold, yet if he hap ere that fever be full cured to fall into some such other disease as except it were holpen with hot medicines were likely to kill the body before the fever could be cured, he would for the while have his most care to the cure of that thing wherein were most present peril; and when that were once out of jeopardy do then the more exact diligence after about the further cure of the fever.

And likewise if the ship were in peril to fall into Scylla, the fear of falling into Charybdis on the other side shall never let any wise master thereof to draw him from Scylla toward Charybdis first, in all that ever he may.   But when he hath him once so far away from Scylla that he seeth him safe out of that danger, then will he begin to take good heed to keep him well from the other.

And in like wise, while this man is falling down to despair and to the final destruction of himself, a good wise spiritual leech will first look unto that, and by good comfort lift up his courage, and when he seeth that peril well past care for the cure of his other faults after.   Howbeit, even in the giving of his comfort he may find ways enough in such wise to temper his words that the man may take occasion of good courage, and yet far from occasion giving of new recidivation into his former sin, sith the great part of his counsel shall be to courage him to amendment, and that is, pardy, far from falling into sin again.

Vincent.   I think, uncle, that folk fall into this ungracious mind, through the devil's temptation by many more means than one.

Anthony.   That is, cousin, very true.   For the devil taketh his occasions as he seeth them fall meet for him.   Some he stirreth to it for weariness of themselves after some great loss, some for fear of horrible bodily harm, and some, as I said, for fear of worldly shame.

One wist I myself that had been long reputed for a right honest man, which was fallen in such a fantasy that he was well near worn away therewith. But what he was tempted to do, that would he not tell no man. But he told unto me that he was sore cumbered, and that it alway ran in his mind that folk's fantasies were fallen from him, and that they esteemed not his wit as they were wont to do, but ever his mind gave him that the people began to take him for a fool. And folk of truth nothing so did at all, but reputed him both for wise and honest.

Two other knew I that were marvellous feard that they should kill themself, and could tell me no cause wherefore they so feared it, but only that their own mind so gave them. Neither loss had they any had, nor no such thing toward them, nor none occasion of any worldly shame, the one in body very well liking and lusty, but wondrous weary were they both twain of that mind. And alway they thought that do it they would not for nothing; and, nevertheless, even they feared they should, and wherefore they so feared neither of them both could tell. And the one, lest he should do it, desired his friends to bind him.

Vincent. This is, uncle, a marvellous strange manner.

Anthony. Forsooth, cousin, I suppose many of them are in this case. The devil, as I said before, seeketh his occasions. For as Saint Peter saith: *Adversarius vester diabolus quasi leo rugiens circuit quærens quem devoret:* Your adversary the devil as a roaring lion goeth about seeking whom he may devour. He marketh well, therefore, the state and the condition that every man standeth in, not only concerning these outward things, lands, possessions, goods, authority, fame, favour, or hatred of the world, but also men's complexions within them, health or sickness, good humours or bad, by which they be light-hearted or lumpish, strong-hearted or faint and feeble of spirit, bold and hardy or timorous and fearful of courage. And after as these things minister him matter of temptation, so useth he himself in the manner of his temptation.

Now, likewise as in such folk as are full of young warm lusty blood and other humours exciting the flesh to filthy voluptuous living, the devil useth to make those things his instruments in tempting them and provoking them thereunto; and where he findeth some folk full of hot blood and choler he maketh those humours his instruments to set their heart on fire in wrath and fierce furious anger, so where he findeth some folk which through some dull melancholious humours are naturally disposed to fear, he casteth sometime such a fearful imagination in their mind, that without help of God they can never cast it out of their heart.

Some at the sudden falling of some horrible thought into their mind have not only had a great abomination thereat (which abomination they well and virtuously had thereat), but the devil, using their melancholious humour and thereby their natural inclination to fear for his instrument, hath caused them to conceive therewith such a deep dread beside, that they ween themself with that abominable thought to be fallen into such an outrageous sin, that they be ready to fall into despair of grace, weening that God hath given them over for ever. Whereas that thought (were it never so horrible and never so abominable) is yet unto them that never like it but ever still abhor it and strive still there against matter of conflict and merit, and not any sin at all.

Some have with holding a knife in their hand suddenly thought upon the killing of themself, and forthwith in devising what an horrible thing it were if they should mishap so to do, have fallen in a fear that they should so do indeed, and have with long and often thinking thereon imprinted that fear so sore in their imagination, that some of them have not after cast it off without great difficulty. And some could never in their life be rid thereof, but have after in conclusion miserably done it indeed. But likewise as where the devil useth the blood of a man's own body toward his purpose in provoking him to lechery the man must, and doth, with grace and wisdom resist it, so must that man do whose melancholious humours the devil abuseth toward the casting of such a desperate dread into his heart.

Vincent.   I pray you, uncle, what advice were to be given him in such case?

Anthony.   Surely methinketh his help standeth in two things, counsel and prayer. First as concerning counsel: likewise as it may be that he hath two things that hold him in his temptation, that is to wit, some evil humours of his own body and the cursed devil that abuseth them to his pernicious purpose, so must he need against them twain the counsel of two manner of folk, that is to wit, physicians for the body and physicians for the soul. The bodily physician shall consider what abundance the man hath of those evil humours that the devil maketh his instruments in moving the man toward that fearful affection, and as well by diet convenient and medicines meet therefore to resist them, as by purgations to disburden the body of them.

Nor let no man think strange that I would advise a man to take counsel of a physician for the body in such a spiritual passion. For sith the soul and the body be so knit and joined together that they both make between them one person, the distemperance of either other engendereth sometime the distemperance of both twain.

And therefore, like as I would advise every man in every sickness of the body be shriven and seek of a good spiritual physician the sure health of his soul, which shall not only serve against peril that may peradventure farther grow by that sickness than in the beginning men would ween were likely (but the comfort thereof and God's favour increasing therewith shall also do the body good, for which cause the blessed apostle Saint James exhorteth men that they shall in their bodily sickness induce the priests, and saith that it shall do them good both in body and soul), so would I sometime advise some men in some sickness of the soul, beside their spiritual leech, take also some counsel of the physician for the body. Some that are wretchedly disposed, and yet long to be more vicious than they be, go to physicians and poticaries, and inquire what things may serve to make them more lusty to their foul fleshly delight. And were it then any folly upon the other side, if he that feeleth himself against his will much moved unto such uncleanness should inquire of the physician what things, without minishing of his health, were meet for the minishment of such foul fleshly motion?

Of spiritual counsel, the first is to be shriven, that by reason of his other sins the devil have not the more power upon him.

Vincent. I have heard some say, uncle, that when such folk have been at shrift their temptation hath been the more brim upon them than it was before.

Anthony. That think I very well, but that is a special token that shrift is wholesome for them while the devil is with that most wroth. You find in some places of the gospel that the devil the person whom he possessed did most trouble when he saw that Christ would cast him out. We must else let the devil do what he will if we fear his anger, for with every good deed will he wax angry.

Then is it in his shrift to be shewed him that he not only feareth more than he needeth, but also feareth where he needeth not, and, over that, is sorry of that thing whereof (but if he will willingly turn his good into his harm) he hath more cause to be glad.

First if he have cause to fear, yet feareth he more than he needeth. For there is no devil so diligent to destroy him as God is to preserve him, nor no devil so near him to do him harm, as God is to do him good, nor all the devils in hell so strong to invade and assault him as God is to defend him, if he distrust Him not, but faithfully put his trust in Him.

He feareth also where he needeth not. For where he dreadeth that he were out of God's favour because such horrible thoughts fall in his mind, he must understand that while they fall in his mind against his will they be not imputed

unto him.   He is, finally, sad of that he may be glad.   For
sith he taketh such thoughts displeasantly and striveth and
fighteth against them, he hath thereby a good token that he is
in God's favour and that God assisteth him and helpeth him,
and may make himself sure that so will God never cease to do,
but if himself fail and fall from Him first.   And over that, this
conflict that he hath against his temptation shall (if he will not
fall where he need not) be an occasion of his merit and of a
right great reward in heaven.   And the pain that he taketh
therein shall for so much, as Master Gerson well sheweth,
stand him instead of his purgatory.

The manner of the fight against his temptation must stand
in three things, that is to wit, in resisting, and in contemning,
and in the invocation of help.

Resist must a man for his own part with reason, considering
what a folly it were to fall where he need not, while he is not
driven to it in avoiding of any other pain or in hope of winning
any manner of pleasure, but contrariwise should by that pain
lose everlasting bliss and fall into everlasting pain.   And if it
were in avoiding of other great pain, yet could he avoid none
so great thereby as he should thereby fall into.

He must also consider that a great part of this temptation
is in effect but the fear of his own fantasy, the dread that he
hath lest he shall once be driven to it, which thing he may be
sure that (but if himself will of his own folly) all the devils in
hell can never drive him to, but his own foolish imagination
may.   For likewise as some man going over an high bridge
waxeth so feard through his own fantasy, that he falleth down
indeed (which were else able enough to pass over without any
danger), and as some man shall upon such a bridge, if folk call
upon him, You fall, you fall, fall with the fantasy that he
taketh thereof (which bridge, if folk looked merrily upon him
and said, There is no danger therein, he would pass over well
enough, and would not let to run thereon if it were but a
foot from the ground), thus fareth it in this temptation.   The
devil findeth the man of his own fond fantasy afeard; and then

crieth he in the ear of his heart, Thou fallest, thou fallest, and maketh the fond man afeard that he should at every foot fall indeed.   And the devil so wearieth him with that continual fear (if he give the ear of his heart unto him), that at the last he withdraweth his mind from due remembrance of God and then driveth him to that deadly mischief indeed.   Therefore, like as against the vice of the flesh the victory standeth not all whole in the fight, but sometime also in the flight (saving that it is indeed a part of a wise warrior's fight to flee from his enemies' trains), so must a man in this temptation too not only resist it alway with reasoning thereagainst, but sometime set it clear at right nought and cast it off when it cometh, and not once regard it so much as to vouchsafe to think thereon.

Some folk have been clearly rid of such pestilent fantasies with very full contempt thereof, making a cross upon their hearts and bidding the devil avaunt, and sometime laugh him to scorn too, and then turn their mind unto some other matter.   And when the devil hath seen that they have set so little by him after certain assays made in such times as he thought most meet, he hath given that temptation quite over, both for that the proud spirit cannot endure to be mocked, and also lest with much tempting the man to the sin whereto he could not in conclusion bring him, he should much increase his merit.

The final fight is by invocation of help unto God, both praying for himself and desiring other also to pray for him, both poor folk for his alms and other good folk of their charity, specially good priests in that holy sacred service of the mass, and not only them, but also his own good angel and other holy saints, such as his devotion specially stand unto; or if he be learned, use then the litany with the holy suffrages that follow which is a prayer in the Church of marvellous old antiquity, not made first (as some ween it were) by that holy man Saint Gregory, which opinion rose of that that in the time of a great pestilence in Rome he caused the whole city go in

solemn procession therewith, but it was in use in the Church
many year before Saint Gregory's days, as well appeareth by
the books of other holy doctors and saints that were dead
hundreds of years before Saint Gregory was born.   And holy
Saint Bernard giveth counsel that every man should make suit
unto angels and saints to pray for him to God in the things
that he would have sped at His holy hand.   If any man will
stick at that and say it need not because God can hear us
Himself, and will also say that it is perilous so to do because
they say we be not so counselled by no Scripture, I will not
dispute the matter here.   He that will not do it I let him not
to leave it undone.   But yet for mine own part I will as well
trust to the counsel of Saint Bernard and reckon him for as good
and as well learned in Scripture as any man that I hear say the
contrary.   And better dare I jeopard my soul with the soul of
Saint Bernard than with his that findeth that fault in his doctrine.

Unto God Himself every good man counselleth to have
recourse above all, and in this temptation to have special
remembrance of Christ's Passion, and pray Him for the
honour of His death, the ground of man's salvation, keep this
person thus tempted from that damnable death.

Special verses may there be drawn out of the Psalter,
against the devil's wicked temptations.   As for example:
*Exurgat Deus et dissipentur inimici eius, et fugiant qui oderunt
eum a facie eius.*   And many other, which are in such horrible
temptation to God pleasant and to the devil very terrible,
but none more terrible nor more odious to the devil than the
words with which our Saviour drave him away Himself: *Vade
Sathana*, nor no prayer more acceptable unto God, nor
more effectual for the matter, than those words which our
Saviour hath taught us Himself: *Ne nos inducas in tentationem,
sed libera nos a malo.*   And I doubt not by God's grace but he
that in such a temptation will use good counsel and prayer,
and keep himself in good virtuous business and good virtuous
company, and abide in the faithful hope of God's help, shall
have the truth of God (as the prophet saith in the verse afore

rehearsed) so compass him about with a pavis, that he shall not need to dread this night's fear of this wicked temptation. And thus will I finish this piece of the night's fear; and glad am I that we be passed it and comen once unto the day, to those other words of the prophet: *A sagitta volante in die.* For methinketh I have made it a long night.

Vincent. Forsooth, uncle, so have you; but we have not slept in it, but been very well occupied. But now I fear that, except you make here a pause till you have dined, you shall keep yourself from your dinner overlong.

Anthony. Nay, nay, cousin, for both brake I my fast even as you came in, and also you shall find this night and this day like a winter day and a winter night. For as the winter hath short days and long nights, so shall you find that I made you not this fearful night so long but I shall make you this light courageous day as short. And so shall the matter require well of itself indeed. For in these words of the prophet: *Scuto circumdabit te veritas eius, a sagitta volante in die:* The truth of God shall compass thee round about with a pavis, from the arrow fleeing in the day, I understand the arrow of pride with which the devil tempteth a man not in the night, that is to wit, in tribulation and adversity, for that time is too discomfortable and too fearful for pride, but in the day, that is to wit, in prosperity. For that time is full of lightsome lust and courage. But surely this worldly prosperity, wherein a man so rejoiceth and whereof the devil maketh him so proud, is but even a very short winter day. For we begin many full poor and cold, and up we fly like an arrow that were shot up into the air. And yet when we be suddenly shot up into the highest, ere we be well warm there, down we come unto the cold ground again, and then even there stick we still. And yet for the short while that we be upward and aloft, Lord, how lusty and how proud we be, buzzing above busily, like as a bumble bee flieth about in summer, never ware that she shall die in winter. And so fare many of us, God help us. For in the short winter day of worldly wealth and prosperity this flying arrow of the devil, this high spirit of pride, shot out of the devil's bow and piercing through our heart, beareth us up in our affection aloft into the clouds, where we ween we sit on the rainbow and overlook the world under us, accounting in the regard of our own glory such other poor souls as were peradventure wont to be our fellows for silly poor pismires and ants.

But this arrow of pride, fly it never so high in the clouds, and be the man that it carrieth up so high never so joyful thereof, yet let him remember that, be this arrow never so light, it hath yet an heavy iron head, and therefore, fly it never so high, down must it needs come and on the ground must it light, and falleth sometime not in a very cleanly place, but the pride turneth into rebuke and shame, and there is then all the glory gone.

Of this arrow speaketh the wise man in the fifth chapter of Sapience, where he saith in the person of them that in pride and vanity passed the time of this present life and after that so spent passed hence into hell: *Quid profuit nobis superbia, aut divitiarum iactantia quid contulit nobis?   Transierunt omnia illa tanquam umbra, etc., aut tanquam sagitta emissa in locum destinatum, divisus aer continuo in se reclusus est, ut ignoretur transitus illius.   Sic et nos nati continuo desivimus esse, et virtutis quidem nullum signum valuimus ostendere, in malignitate autem nostra consumpti sumus.   Talia dixerunt in inferno hi qui peccaverunt:* What hath pride profited us, or what good hath the glory of our riches done unto us?   Passed are all those things like a shadow, etc., or like an arrow shot out into the place appointed, the air that was divided is by and by returned into the place, and in such wise closed together again that the way is not perceived in which the arrow went.   And in like wise we, as soon as we were born, be by and by vanished away, and have left no token of any good virtue behind us but are consumed and wasted and come to naught in our malignity. They, lo, that have lived here in sin, such words have they spoken when they lay in hell.

Here shall you, good cousin, consider that whereas the

Scripture here speaketh of the arrow shot into his place
appointed or intended, in the shooting of this arrow of pride
there be divers purposings and appointings. For the proud
man himself hath no certain purpose or appointment at any
mark, butt, or prick upon earth whereat he determineth to
shoot and there to stick and tarry, but ever he shooteth as
children do, that love to shoot up a cop high to see how high
their arrow can fly up. But now doth the devil intend and
appoint a certain prick surely set in a place into which he
purposeth (fly this arrow never so high and the proud heart
thereon) to have them light both at last. And that place is in
the very pit of hell. There is set the devil's well-acquainted
prick and his very just mark, down upon which prick with his
pricking shaft of pride he hath by himself a plain proof and
experience that (but if it be stopped by some grace of God in
the way) the soul that flieth up therewith can never fail to fall.
For when himself was in heaven and began to fly up a cop
high with the lusty light flight of pride, saying: *Ascendam super
astra, et ponam solium meum ad latera Aquilonis, et ero similis
altissimo* (I will fly up above the stars, and set my throne on
the sides of the north and will be like unto the highest), long
ere he could fly up half so high as he said in his heart he would
he was turned from a bright glorious angel into a dark
deformed devil, and from flying any farther upward down was
he thrown into the deep dungeon of hell. Now may it peradventure, cousin, seem, that sith this kind of temptation of
pride is no tribulation or pain, all this that we speak of this
arrow of pride flying forth in the day of prosperity were beside
our matter.

Vincent. Verily, mine uncle, and so seemed it unto me;
and somewhat was I minded so to say to you too, saving that
were it properly pertaining to the present matter or somewhat
disgressing therefrom, good matter methought it was and
such as I had no lust to let.

Anthony. But now must you, cousin, consider that though
prosperity be contrary to tribulation, yet unto many a good

man the devil's temptation unto pride in prosperity is a greater tribulation, and more need hath of good comfort and good counsel both than he that never felt it would ween.   And that is the thing, cousin, that maketh me speak thereof as of a thing proper to this matter.   For, cousin, as it is a thing right hard to touch pitch and never file the fingers, to put flax unto fire and yet keep them from burning, to keep a serpent in thy bosom and yet be safe from stinging, to put young men with young women without danger of foul fleshly desire, so is it hard for any person, either man or woman, in great worldly wealth and much prosperity so to withstand the suggestions of the devil and occasions given by the world, that they keep themself from the deadly desire of ambitious glory.   Where-upon there followeth (if a man fall thereto) an whole flood of all unhappy mischief, arrogant manner, high, sullen, solemn port, overlooking the poor in word and countenance, dis-pleasant and disdainous behaviour, ravin, extortion, oppres-sion, hatred, and cruelty.

Now, many a good man, cousin, comen into great authority, casting in his mind the peril of such occasions of pride as the devil taketh of prosperity to make his instruments of, where-with to move men to such high point of presumption as engendereth so many great inconveniences, and feeling the devil therewith offering to themself suggestions thereunto, they be sore troubled therewith; and some fall so feard thereof, that even in the day of prosperity they fall into the night's fear of pusillanimity, and, doubting overmuch lest they should misuse themself, leave the things undone wherein they might use themself well, and mistrusting the aid and help of God in holding them upright in their temptations, give place to the devil in the contrary temptation, whereby for faint heart they leave off good business wherein they were well occupied. And under pretext (as it seemeth to themself) of humble heart and meekness, and serving God in contemplation and silence, they seek their own ease and earthly rest unware, wherewith (if it so be) God is not well content.   Howbeit, if it so be that a man feel himself such indeed as by the experience that he hath of himself he perceiveth that in wealth and authority he doth his own soul harm and cannot do therein the good that to his part appertaineth, but seeth the things that he should set his hands to sustain decay through his default and fall to ruin under him, and that to the amendment thereof he leaveth his own duty undone, then would I in any wise advise him to leave off that thing, be it spiritual benefice that he have, parsonage, or bishopric, or temporal room and authority, and rather give it over quite and draw himself aside and serve God, than take the worldly worship and commodity for himself with incommodity of them whom his duty were to profit. But on the other side, if he see not the contrary, but that he may do his duty conveniently well and feareth nothing but that the temptations of ambition and pride may peradventure turn his good purpose and make him decline unto sin, I say not nay but that well done it is to stand in moderate fear alway. Whereof the Scripture saith: *Beatus homo qui semper est pavidus:* Blessed is the man that is alway fearful. And Saint Paul saith: *Qui stat, videat ne cadat:* He that standeth, let him look that he fall not. Yet is overmuch fear perilous, and draweth toward the mistrust of God's gracious help, which immoderate fear and faint heart Holy Scripture forbiddeth saying: *Noli esse pusillanimis,* Be not feeble-hearted or timorous. Let such a man, therefore, temper his fear with good hope, and think that sith God hath set him in that place (if he think that God have set him therein) God will assist him with His grace to the well using thereof. Howbeit, if he came thereto by simony or some such other evil mean, then were the thing one good reason wherefore he should the rather leave it off, but else let him continue in his good business, and against the devil's provocation unto evil bless himself and call unto God and pray, and look what thing the devil tempteth him to lean the more toward the contrary.

Let him be piteous and comfortable to those that are in distress and affliction. I mean not to let every malefactor pass forth unpunished and freely run out and rob at rovers, but in his heart be sorry to see that of necessity for fear of decaying the commonweal men are driven to put malefactors to pain.   And yet where he findeth good tokens and likelihood of amendment, therein all that he may help that mercy may be had.   There shall never lack desperately disposed wretches enow beside upon whom for ensample justice may proceed. Let him think in his own heart every poor beggar his fellow.

Vincent.   That will be very hard, uncle, for an honourable man to do when he beholdeth himself richly apparelled and the beggar rigged in his rags.

Anthony.   If here were, cousin, two men that were beggars both, and afterward a great rich man would take yet one unto him and tell him that for a little time he would have him in his house, and thereupon arrayed him in silk, and give him a great bag by his side filled even full of gold, but giving him this knot therewith that within a little while, out he should in his old rags again and bear never a penny with him; if this beggar met his fellow now while his gay gown were on, might he not, for all his gay gear, take him for his fellow still?   And were he not a very fool if for a wealth of a few weeks he would ween himself far his better?

Vincent.   Yes, uncle, if the difference of their state were none other.

Anthony.   Surely, cousin, methinketh that in this world between the richest and the most poor the difference is scant so much.   For let the highest look on the most base and consider how poor they came both into this world, and then consider further therewith how rich soever he be now he shall yet within a while, peradventure less than one week, walk out again as poor as that beggar shall; and then, by my troth, methinketh this rich man much more than mad if for the wealth of a little while, haply less than one week, he reckon himself in earnest any better than the beggar's fellow.   And less than thus can no man think that hath any natural wit and well useth it.

But now a Christian man, cousin, that hath the light of faith, he cannot fail to think in this thing much farther. For he will think not only upon his bare coming hither and his bare going hence again, but also upon the dreadful judgment of God, and upon the fearful pains of hell and the inestimable joys of heaven. And in the considering of these things he will call to remembrance that peradventure when this beggar and he be both departed hence the beggar may be suddenly set up in such royalty, that well were himself that ever was he born if he might be made his fellow. And he that well bethinketh him, cousin, upon these things, I verily think that the arrow of pride flying forth in the day of worldly wealth shall never so wound his heart that ever it shall bear him up one foot. But now, to the intent he may think on such things the better, let him use often to resort to confession and there open his heart, and by the mouth of some virtuous ghostly father have such things oft renewed in his remembrance.

Let him also choose himself some secret solitary place in his own house, as far from noise and company as he conveniently can, and thither let him sometime secretly resort alone, imagining himself as one going out of the world even straight into the giving up his reckoning unto God of his sinful living. Then let him there before an altar or some pitiful image of Christ's bitter Passion (the beholding whereof may put him in remembrance of the thing, and move him to devout compassion) kneel down or fall prostrate as at the feet of Almighty God, verily believing Him to be there invisibly present, as without any doubt He is. There let him open his heart to God and confess his faults such as he can call to mind, and pray God of forgiveness. Let him call to remembrance the benefits that God hath given him, either in general among other men or privately to himself, and give Him humble hearty thanks therefore. There let him declare unto God the temptations of the devil, the suggestions of the flesh, the occasions of the world and of his worldly friends, much worse many times in drawing a man from God than are his most mortal enemies.   Which thing our Saviour witnesseth Himself where he saith: *Inimici hominis domestici eius:* The enemies of a man are they that are his own familiars.   There let him lament and bewail unto God his own frailty, negligence, and sloth in resisting and withstanding of temptation, his readiness and pronity to fall thereunto.   There let him lamentably beseech God of His gracious aid and help to strength his infirmity withal, both in keeping him from falling and, when he by his own fault misfortuneth to fall, then with the helping hand of His merciful grace to lift him up and set him on his feet in the state of His grace again. And let this man not doubt but that God heareth him and granteth him gladly his boon.   And so, dwelling in the faithful trust of God's help, he shall well use his prosperity and persevere in his good profitable business, and shall have therein the truth of God so compass him about with a pavis of His heavenly defence, that of the devil's arrow flying in the day of worldly wealth he shall not need to dread.

Vincent.   Forsooth, uncle, I like this good counsel well, and I would ween that such as are in prosperity and take such order therein may do both to themself and other folk about much good.

Anthony.   I beseech our Lord, cousin, put this and better in the mind of every man that needeth it.   And now will I touch one word or twain of the third temptation whereof the prophet speaketh in these words: *A negotio perambulante in tenebris,* from the business walking in the darknesses.   And then will we call for our dinner, leaving the last temptation, that is to wit, *ab incursu et demonio meridiano,* from the incursion and the devil of the midday, till after noon; and then shall we therewith (God willing) make an end of all this matter.

Vincent.   Our Lord reward you, good uncle, for your good labour with me.   But, for our Lord's sake, take good heed, uncle, that you forbear not your dinner overlong.

Anthony.   Fear not that, cousin, I warrant you: for this piece will I make you but short.

Of the devil named Negotium perambulans in tenebris, *that is to wit, business walking in the darknesses*

THE SEVENTEENTH CHAPTER

THE prophet saith in the said psalm: *Qui habitat in adiutorio altissimi, in protectione Dei cœli commorabitur. Scuto circumdabit te veritas eius, non timebis, etc., a negotio perambulante in tenebris:* He that dwelleth in the faithful hope of God's help, he shall abide in the protection or safeguard of God of heaven. And thou that art such one shall the truth of Him so compass about with a pavis that thou shalt not be afeard of the business walking about in the darknesses.

Negotium is here, cousin, the name of a devil that is ever full of business in tempting folk to much evil business. His time of tempting is in the darknesses. For you wot well that beside the very full night which is the deep dark there are two times of darknesses, the one ere the morning wax light, the other when the evening waxeth dark.

Two times of like manner darkness are there also in the soul of man, the one ere the light of grace be well in the heart sprungen up, the other when the light of grace out of the soul beginneth to walk fast away.

In these two darknesses this devil that is called business busily walketh about, and such fond folk as will follow him he carrieth about with him and setteth them a-work with many manner bumbling business.

He setteth, I say, some to seek the pleasures of the flesh in eating, drinking, and other filthy delight. And some he setteth about incessant seeking for these worldly goods. And of such busy folk whom this devil called business walking about in the darknesses setteth a-work with such business our Saviour saith in the gospel: *Qui ambulat in tenebris nescit quo vadit:* He that walketh in darknesses wotteth not whither he goeth. And surely in such case are they. They neither wot which way they go nor whither. For verily they walk round

about, as it were, in a round maze. When they ween themself at an end of their business they be but at the beginning
again. For is not the going about the serving of the flesh a
business that hath none end, but evermore from the end
cometh to the beginning again? Go they never so full fed to
bed, yet evermore on the morrow as new be they to be fed
again as they were the day before. Thus fareth it by the
belly; thus fareth it by those parts that are beneath the
belly. And as for covetise, fareth like the fire: the more
wood that cometh thereto, the more fervent and the more
greedy it is.

But now hath this maze a centre or a middle place, into
which sometime they be conveyed suddenly when they ween
they were not yet far from the brink. The centre or middle
place of this maze is hell, and into that place be these
busy folk, that with this devil of business walk about in
this busy maze in the darknesses, suddenly sometime conveyed, nothing ware whither they be going, and even while
they ween that they were not far walked from the beginning, and that they had yet a great way to walk about
before they should come to the end. But of these fleshly folk
walking in this busy pleasant maze the Scripture declareth the
end: *Ducunt in bonis dies suos et in puncto ad inferna descendunt* :
They lead their life in pleasure, and at a pop down they
descend into hell.

Of the covetous men saith Saint Paul: *Qui volunt divites
fieri incidunt in tentationem et in laqueum diaboli, et desideria
multa inutilia et nociva, quæ mergunt homines in interitum et
perditionem:* They that long to be rich do fall into temptation and into the grin of the devil, and into many desires
unprofitable and harmful which drown men into death and
into destruction.

Lo, here is the middle place of this busy maze, the grin of
the devil, the place of perdition and destruction, that they fall
and be caught and drowned in ere they be ware.

The covetous rich man also that our Saviour speaketh of in

the gospel, that had so great plenty of corn that his barns would not receive it, but intended to make his barns larger and said unto himself that he would make merry many days, had weened, you wot well, that he had had a great way yet to walk. But God said unto him: *Stulte, hac nocte tollent a te animam tuam, quæ autem parasti, cuius erunt?* Fool, this night shall they take thy soul from thee, and then all this good that thou hast gathered, whose shall it be? Here you see that he fell suddenly into the deep centre of this busy maze, so that he was fallen full therein long ere ever he had weened he should have come near thereto.

Now, this wot I very well, that those that are walking about in this busy maze take not their business for any tribulation. And yet are there many of them forwearied as sore, and as sore panged and pained therein, their pleasures being so short, so little, and so few, and their displeasures and their griefs so great, so continual, and so many, that it maketh me think upon a good worshipful man which, when he divers times beheld his wife, what pain she took in strait binding up her hair to make her a fair large forehead, and with strait bracing in her body to make her middle small, both twain to her great pain for the pride of a little foolish praise, he said unto her: Forsooth, madam, if God give you not hell, He shall do you great wrong; for it must needs be your own of very right. For you buy it very dear and take very great pain therefore.

They that now lie in hell for their wretched living here do now perceive their folly in the more pain that they took here for the less pleasure. There confess they now their folly and cry out: *Lassati sumus in via iniquitatis:* We have been wearied in the way of wickedness. And yet while they were walking therein they would not rest themself, but run on still in their weariness, and put themself still unto more pain and more for the little peevish pleasure short and soon gone, that they took all that labour and pain for, beside the everlasting pain that followed it for their farther advantage after. So help me God and none other wise, but as I verily think that many a man buyeth hell here with so much pain that he might have bought heaven with less than the one-half. But yet, as I say, while these fleshly and worldly busy folk are walking about in this round busy maze of this devil that is called business that walketh about in these two times of darkness, their wits are so by the secret enchantment of the devil bewitched, that they mark not the great long miserable weariness and pain that the devil maketh them take and endure about nought, and therefore they take it for no tribulation, so that they need no comfort.

And therefore is it not for their sakes that I speak all this, saying that it may serve them for counsel toward the perceiving of their own foolish misery through the good help of God's grace beginning to shine upon them again. But there are very good folk and virtuous that are in the daylight of grace, and yet because the devil tempteth them busily to such fleshly delight and sith they see plenty of worldly substance fall unto them and feel the devil in like wise busily tempt them to set their heart thereupon, they be sore troubled therewith, and begin to fear thereby that they be not with God in the light, but with this devil that the prophet calleth *Negotium*, that is to say, business walking about in the two times of darknesses.

Howbeit, as I said before, of those good folk and gracious that are in the worldly wealth of great power and authority, and thereby fear the devil's arrow of pride, so say I now here again of these that stand in dread of fleshly foul sin and covetise, sith they be but tempted therewith and follow it not (albeit that they do well to stand ever in moderate fear lest with waxing overbold and setting the thing over light, they might peradventure mishap to fall in thereto), yet sore to vex and trouble themself with the fear of loss of God's favour therefore is without necessity and not alway without peril. For, as I said before, it withdraweth the mind of a man far from spiritual consolation of the good hope that he should have in

God's help. And as for those temptations, while he that is tempted followeth them not, the fight against them serveth a man for matter of merit and reward in heaven if he not only flee the deed, the consent, and the delectation, but also, in that he conveniently may, flee from all occasions thereof. And this point is in those fleshly temptations a thing eath to perceive and meetly plain enough. But in these worldly business pertaining unto covetise, therein is the thing somewhat more dark and in the perceiving more difficulty. And very great troublous fear doth there oftentimes arise thereof in the hearts of very good folk when the world falleth fast unto them, because of the sore words and terrible threats that God in Holy Scripture speaketh against those that are rich. As where Saint Paul saith: *Qui volunt divites fieri, incidunt in tentationem et in laqueum diaboli:* They that will be rich fall into temptation, and into the grin of the devil. And where our Saviour saith Himself: *Facilius est camelum per foramen acus transire quam divitem intrare in regnum Dei:* It is more easy for a camel, or (as some say, for *camelus* so signifieth in the Greek tongue) for a great cable rope, to go through a needle's eye than for a rich man to enter into the kingdom of God.

No marvel now though good folk that fear God take occasion of great dread at so dreadful words, when they see the worldly goods fall to them. And some stand in doubt whether it be lieful for them to keep any good or no. But evermore in all those places of Scripture the having of the worldly goods is not the thing that is rebuked and threatened, but the affection that the haver unliefully beareth thereto. For where Saint Paul saith: *Qui volunt divites fieri, etc.,* They that will be made rich, he speaketh not of the having, but of the will and the desire and affection to have, and the longing for it. For that cannot be lightly without sin. For the thing that folk sore long for they will make many shifts to get, and jeopard themself therefore. And to declare that the having of riches is not forboden, but the inordinate affection of the mind sore set thereupon, the prophet saith: *Divitiæ si affluant, nolite cor apponere:* If riches flow unto you, set not your heart thereupon.   And albeit that our Lord by the said ensample of the camel or cable rope to come through the needle's eye said that it is not only hard but also impossible for a rich man to enter into the kingdom of heaven, yet He declared that though the rich man cannot get into heaven of himself, yet God, He said, can get him in well enough.   For unto men, He said, it was impossible, but not unto God.   For unto God, He said, all things are possible.   And yet, over that, He told of which manner rich men He meant that could not get into the kingdom of heaven, saying: *Filioli, quam difficile est confidentes in pecuniis in regnum Dei introire:* My babes, how hard is it for them that put their trust and confidence in their money to enter into the kingdom of God.

Vincent.   This is, I suppose, uncle, very true, and else God forbid.   For else were the world in a full hard case, if every rich man were in such danger and peril.

Anthony.   That were it, cousin, indeed; and so I ween is it yet.   For I fear me that to the multitude there be very few but that they long sore to be rich, and of those that so long to be very few reserved also but that they set their heart very sore thereon.

Vincent.   This is, uncle, I fear me, very true, but yet not the thing that I was about to speak of.   But the thing that I would have said was this, that I cannot well perceive (the world being such as it is, and so many poor people therein) how any man may be rich and keep him rich without danger of damnation therefore.   For all the while that he seeth poor people so many that lack while himself hath to give them, and whose necessity (while he hath therewith) he is bounden in such case of duty to relieve, so far forth that holy Saint Ambrose sayeth that whoso that die for default where we might help them, we kill them, I cannot see but that every rich man hath great cause to stand in great fear of damnation. Nor I cannot perceive, as I say, how he can be delivered of that fear as long as he keepeth his riches. And therefore, though he might keep his riches if there lacked poor men and yet stand in God's favour therewith, as Abraham did and many another holy rich man since, yet in such abundance of poor men as there be now in every country any man that keepeth any riches, it must needs be that he hath an inordinate affection thereunto while he giveth it not out unto the poor needy persons that the duty of charity bindeth and straineth him to. And thus, uncle, in this world at this day meseemeth your comfort unto good men that are rich and troubled with fear of damnation for the keeping can very scantly serve.

Anthony. Hard is it, cousin, in many manner things to bid or forbid, affirm or deny, reprove or allow, a matter nakedly proponed and put forth, or precisely to say this thing is good or this thing is naught, without consideration of the circumstances.

Holy Saint Austin telleth of a physician that gave a man a medicine in a certain disease, that holp him. The selfsame man at another time in the selfsame disease took the selfsame medicine himself, and had thereof more harm than good; which thing when he shewed unto the physician, and asked him whereof the harm should hap, That medicine, quoth he, did thee no good but harm because thou tookest it when I gave it thee not. This answer Saint Austin very well alloweth. For that though the medicine were one, yet might there be peradventure in the sickness some such difference as the patient perceived not; yea, or in the man himself, or in the place, or the time of the year, many things might make the let, for which the physician would not then have given him the selfsame medicine that he gave him before.

To peruse every circumstance that might, cousin, in this matter be touched, and were to be considered and weighed, would indeed make this part of this devil of business a very busy piece of work and a long. But I shall a little open the point that you speak of, and shall shew you what I think therein with as few words as I conveniently can, and then will we go to dinner.

First, cousin, he that is a rich man and keepeth all his good, he hath, I think, very good cause to be very feard indeed. And yet I fear me that such folk fear it least. For they be very far from the state of good men, sith if they keep still all, then are they very far from charity, and do (you wot well) alms either little or none at all.

But now is our question, cousin, not in what case that rich man standeth that keepeth all, but whether we should suffer men to stand in a perilous dread and fear for the keeping of any great part. For if that by the keeping still of so much as maketh a rich man still they stand in the state of damnation, then are the curates bounden plainly to tell them so according to the commandment of God given unto them all in the person of Ezekiel: *Si dicente me ad impium morte morieris, non annunciaveris ei, etc.:* If when I say to the wicked man, Thou shalt die, thou do not shew it unto him nor speak unto him that he may be turned from his wicked way and may live, he shall soothly die in his wickedness and his blood shall I require of thine hand. But, cousin, though God invited men unto the following of Himself in wilful poverty by the leaving of all together at once for His sake as the thing whereby (with being out of the solicitude of worldly business, and far from the desire of earthly commodities) they may the more speedily get and attain the state of spiritual perfection and the hungry desire and longing for celestial things, yet doth He not command every man so to do upon the peril of damnation. For where He saith: *Qui non renunciaverit omnibus quæ possidet, non potest meus esse discipulus:* He that forsaketh not all that ever he hath cannot be My disciple, He declareth well by other words of His own in the selfsame place a little before what he meaneth. For there saith He more: *Si quis venit ad me, et non odit patrem suum et matrem et uxorem et filios et fratres et sorores, adhuc autem et animam suam, non potest meus esse discipulus:* He that cometh to Me, and hateth not his father and his mother and his wife and his children and his brethren and his sisters, yea, and his own life too, cannot be

My disciple. Here meaneth our Saviour Christ that none can be His disciple but if he love Him so far above all his kin and above his own life too, that for the love of Him rather than to forsake him he shall forsake them all. And so meaneth He by those other words, that whosoever do not so renounce and forsake all that ever he hath in his own heart and affection, that he will rather lose it all and let it go every whit than deadly displease God with the reserving of any one part thereof, he cannot be Christ's disciple, sith Christ teacheth us to love God above all thing. And he loveth not God above all thing that contrary to God's pleasure keepeth anything that he hath. For that thing he sheweth himself to set more by than by God while he is better content to lose God than it. But, as I said, to give away all, or that no man should be rich or have substance, that find I no commandment of. There are, as our Saviour saith, in the house of His Father many mansions. And happy shall he be that shall have the grace to dwell even in the lowest.

It seemeth verily by the gospel that those which for God's sake patiently suffer penury shall not only dwell above those in heaven that live here in plenty in earth, but also that heaven in some manner of wise more properly belongeth unto them, and is more specially prepared for them than it is for the rich, by that that God in the gospel counselleth the rich folk to buy in a manner heaven of them, where He saith unto the rich men: *Facite vobis amicos de mammona iniquitatis, ut cum defeceritis recipiant vos in eterna tabernacula:* Make you friends of the wicked riches, that when you fail here they may receive you into everlasting tabernacles.

But now, although this be thus in respect of the riches and the poverty compared together, yet they being good men both, there may be some other virtue beside wherein the rich man may so peradventure excel, that he may in heaven be far above that poor man that was here in earth in other virtues far under him, as the proof appeareth clear in Lazarus and Abraham.

Nor I say not this to the intent to comfort rich men in heaping up of riches. For a little comfort is bent enough thereto for them. They be not so proud-hearted and obstinate but that they would, I ween, to that counsel be with right little exhortation very conformable. But I say this for those good men to whom God giveth substance and the mind to dispose it well, and yet not the mind to give it all away at once, but for good causes to keep some substance still, should not despair of God's favour for the not doing of the thing which God hath given them no commandment of nor drawn by any special calling thereunto.

Zacchæus, lo, that climbed up into the tree for desire that he had to behold our Saviour at such time as Christ called aloud unto him and said: Zacchæus, make haste and come down, for this day must I dwell in thy house, was so glad thereof and so touched inwardly with special grace to the profit of his soul, that whereas all the people murmured much that Christ would call him and be so familiar with him as of His own offer to come unto his house (considering that they knew him for the chief of the publicans that were customers or toll gatherers of the emperor's duties, all which whole company were among the people sore infamed of ravin, extortion, and bribery; and then Zacchæus not only the chief of the fellowship, but also grown greatly rich, whereby the people accounted him in their own opinion for a man very sinful and naught), he forthwith by the instinct of the Spirit of God, in reproach of all such temerarious, bold, and blind judgment given upon a man whose inward mind and sudden change they cannot see, shortly proved them all deceived, and that our Lord had at those few words outwardly spoken to him so wrought in his heart within, that whatsoever he was before, he was then, unware unto them all, suddenly waxen good. For he made haste and came down, and gladly received Christ and said: Lo, Lord, the one half of my good here I give unto poor people; and yet over that, if I have in anything deceived any man, here am I ready to recompense him fourfold as much.

Vincent. This was, uncle, a gracious hearing. But yet I marvel me somewhat wherefore Zacchæus used his words in that manner of order. For methinketh he should first have spoken of making restitution unto those whom he had beguiled and then speak of giving his alms after. For restitution is, you wot well, duty and a thing of such necessity that in respect of restitution alms deed is but voluntary. Therefore it might seem that, to put men in mind of their duty in making restitution first and doing their alms after, Zacchæus should have said more conveniently, if he had said first that he would make every man restitution whom he had wronged, and then give half in alms of that that remained after. For only that might he call clearly his own.

Anthony. This is true, cousin, where a man hath not enough to suffice for both; but he that hath is not bounden to leave his almsgiving to the poor man that is at his hand and peradventure calleth upon him, till he go seek up all his creditors and all those that he hath wronged, so far peradventure asunder, that leaving the one good deed undone the while, he may, before they come together, change that good mind again, and do neither the one nor the other. It is good alway to be doing some good out of hand while we think thereon; grace shall the better stand with us and increase also to go the farther in the other after.

And this I answer, if the man had there done the one out of hand, the giving, I mean, half in alms, and not so much as speak of restitution till after (whereas now, though he speak the one in order before the other, and yet all at one time), the thing remained still in his liberty to put them both in execution after such order as he should then think expedient. But now, cousin, did the Spirit of God temper the tongue of Zacchæus in the utterance of these words in such wise as it may well appear the saying of the wise man to be verified in them, where he sayeth: *Domini est gubernare linguam:* To God it belongeth to govern the tongue. For here when he said he would give half of his whole good unto poor people, and yet beside that not only recompense any man whom he had wronged, but more than recompense him by three times as much again, he double reproved the false suspicion of the people that accounted him for so evil that they reckoned in their mind all his good gotten in effect with wrong, because he was grown to substance in that office that was commonly misused extortiously. But his words declared that he was deep enough in his reckoning, that if half his good were given away, yet were he well able to yield every man his duty with the other half, and yet leave himself no beggar neither. For he said not he would give away all.

Would God, cousin, that every rich Christian man that is reputed right worshipful, yea, and (which yet in my mind more is) reckoned for right honest too, would and were able to do the thing that little Zacchæus, that same great publican (were he Jew, or were he paynim) said, that is to wit, with less than half his goods recompense every man whom he had wronged four times as much; yea, yea, cousin, as much for as much hardly. And then they that shall receive it shall be content (I dare promise for them) to let the other thrice as much go, and forgive it, because it was one of the hard points of the old law, whereas Christian men must be full of forgiving and not use to require and exact their amends to the uttermost.

But now for our purpose here, notwithstanding that he promised not neither to give away all nor to become a beggar neither, no, nor yet to leave of his office neither, which albeit that he had not used before peradventure in every point so pure as Saint John the Baptist had taught them the lesson, *Nihil amplius quam constitutum est vobis faciatis* (Do no more than is appointed unto you), yet forasmuch as he might both lawfully use his substance that he minded to reserve, and lawfully might use his office too, in receiving the prince's duty (according to Christ's express commandment: *Reddite quæ sunt Cæsaris Cæsari*: Give the emperor those things that are his, refusing all extortion and bribery beside), our Lord well allowing his good purpose, and exacting no further forth of him concerning his worldly behaviour, answered and said: *Hodie salus facta est huic domui, eo quod et ipse filius sit Abrahæ:* This day is health comen to this house, for that he too is the son of Abraham.

But now forget I not, cousin, that in effect thus far you condescended unto me, that a man may be rich, and yet not out of the state of grace nor out of God's favour. Howbeit, you think that though it may be so in some time or in some place, yet at this time and in this place, or any such other like wherein be so many poor people upon whom they be, you think, bounden to bestow their good, they can keep no riches with conscience.

Verily, cousin, if that reason would hold, I ween the world was never such anywhere in which any man might have kept any substance without the danger of damnation. As for since Christ's days to the world's end, we have the witness of His own word that there hath never lacked poor men nor never shall. For He said Himself: *Pauperes semper habebitis vobiscum quibus quum vultis benefacere potestis:* Poor men shall you alway have with you, whom when you will you may do good unto. So that, as I tell you, if your rule should hold, then were there, I ween, no place in no time since Christ's days hitherto, nor as I think in as long before that neither, nor never shall there hereafter, in which there could any man abide rich without the danger of eternal damnation even for his riches alone, though he demeaned it never so well. But, cousin, men of substance must there be, for else shall you have more beggars pardy than there be, and no man left able to relieve another. For this I think in my mind a very sure conclusion, that if all the money that is in this country were to-morrow next brought together out of every man's hand and laid all upon one heap, and then divided out unto every man alike, it would be on the morrow after worse than it was the day before. For I suppose when it were all equally thus divided among all, the best should be left little better then than almost a beggar is now. And yet he that was a beggar before, all that he shall be the richer for that he should thereby receive shall not make him much above a beggar still; but many one of the rich men, if their riches stood but in movable substance, shall be safe enough from riches haply for all their life after.

Men cannot, you wot well, live here in this world but if that some one man provide a mean of living for some other many. Every man cannot have a ship of his own, nor every man be a merchant without a stock (and these things, you wot well, needs must be had), nor every man cannot have a plough by himself. And who might live by the tailor's craft if no man were able to put a gown to make? Who by the masonry or who could live a carpenter if no man were able to build neither church nor house? Who should be the makers of any manner cloth if there lacked men of substance to set sundry sorts a-work? Some man that hath not two ducats in his house were better forbear them both and leave himself not a farthing but utterly lose all his own than that some rich man by whom he is weekly set a-work should of his money lose the one half. For then were himself like to lack work. For surely the rich man's substance is the wellspring of the poor man's living. And therefore here would it fare by the poor man as it fared by the woman in one of Æsop's fables, which had an hen that laid her every day a golden egg, till on a day she thought she would have a great many eggs at once, and therefore she killed her hen and found but one or twain in her belly, so that for a few she lost many.

But now, cousin, to come to your doubt how it may be that a man may with conscience keep riches with him when he seeth so many poor men upon whom he may bestow it: verily that might he not with conscience do if he must bestow it upon as many as he may. And so must, of truth, every rich man do, if all the poor folk that he seeth be so specially by God's commandment committed unto his charge alone, that because our Saviour saith: *Omni petenti te da:* Give every man that asketh thee, therefore he be bounden to give out still to every beggar that will ask him, as long as any penny lasteth in his purse. But verily, cousin, that saying hath (as Saint Austin saith other places in Scripture hath) need of interpretation. For, as holy Saint Austin saith, though Christ say give every man that asketh thee, He saith not yet give them all that they will ask thee. But surely all were one if he meant to bind me by commandment to give every man without exception somewhat, for so should I leave myself nothing.

Our Saviour in that place of the sixth chapter of Saint Luke, speaketh both of the contempt that we should in heart have of these worldly things and also of the manner that men should use toward their enemies. For there He biddeth us love our enemies, give good words for evil, and not only suffer injuries patiently both by taking away of our good and harm done unto our body, but also be ready to suffer the double, and over that to do them good again that do us the harm. And among these things He biddeth us give every man that asketh, meaning that in the thing that we may conveniently do a man good we should not refuse it, what manner of man soever he be, though he were our mortal enemy, namely where we see that but if we help him ourself the person of the man should stand in peril of perishing. And therefore saith Saint Paul: *Si esurierit inimicus tuus da illi cibum:* If thine enemy be in hunger give him meat. But now, though I be bounden to give every manner man in some manner of his necessity, were he my friend or my foe, Christian man or heathen, yet am I not unto all men bounden alike nor unto any man in every case alike, but (as I began to tell you) the differences of the circumstances make great change in the matter. Saint Paul saith: *Qui non providet suis est infideli deterior:* He that provideth not for those that are his is worse than an infidel. Those are ours that are belonging to our charge either by nature or by law or any commandment of God. By nature as our children, by law as our servants in our household. So that, albeit these two sorts be not ours all alike, yet would I think that the least ours of the twain (that is to wit, our servants) if they need and lack, we be bounden to look to them and provide for their need, and see so far forth as we may that they lack not the things that should serve for their necessity while they dwell in our service.   Meseemeth also that if they fall sick in our service so that they cannot do the service that we retain them for, yet may we not in any wise turn them then out of doors and cast them up comfortless while they be not able to labour and help themself.   For this were a thing against all humanity.   And surely if he were but a wayfaring man that I received into my house as a guest, if he fall sick therein and his money gone, I reckon myself bounden to keep him still, and rather to beg about for his relief than cast him out in that case to the peril of his life, what loss soever I should hap to sustain in the keeping of him.   For when God hath by such chance sent him to me and there once matched me with him I reckon myself surely charged with him till I may without peril of his life be well and conveniently discharged of him.

By God's commandment are in our charge our parents, for by nature we be in theirs, sith (as Saint Paul saith) it is not the children's part to provide for the parents, but the parents' to provide for the children.   Provide, I mean, conveniently good learning or good occupations to get their living by with truth and the favour of God, but not to make provision for them of such manner living as to Godward they should live the worse for, but rather if they see by their manner that too much would make them naught, the father should then give them a great deal the less.   But although that nature put not the parents in charge of the children, yet not only God commandeth, but the order of nature also compelleth, that the children should both in reverent behaviour honour their father and mother and also in all their necessity maintain them.   And yet as much as God and nature both bindeth us to the sustenance of our own father, his need may be so little, though it be somewhat, and a fremd man's so great, that both nature and God also would I should in such unequal need relieve that urgent necessity of a stranger; yea, my foe,

and God's enemy too, the very Turk or Saracen, before a
little need and unlikely to do great harm in my father and my
mother too.   For so ought they both twain themself to be well
content I should.

But now, cousin, out of the case of such extreme needs well
perceived and known unto myself I am not bounden to give
every beggar that will ask, nor to believe every faitour that I
meet in the street that will say himself that he is very sick,
nor to reckon all the poor folk committed by God only so to
my charge alone, that none other man should give them
nothing of his till I have first given out all mine; nor am not
bounden neither to have so evil opinion of all other folk save
myself, as to think that but if I help the poor folk shall all fail
at once, for God hath left in all this quarter no more good folk
now but me.   I may think better by my neighbours and
worse by myself than so, and yet come to heaven by God's
grace well enough.

Vincent.   Marry, uncle, but some man will peradventure
be right well content in such cases to think his neighbours
very charitable, to the intent that he may think himself at
liberty to give nothing at all.

Anthony.   That is, cousin, very true.   So will there some
be content either to think or make as though they thought;
but those are they that are content to give naught because
they be naught.   But our question is, cousin, not of them, but
of good folk that by the keeping of worldly good stand in great
fear to offend God.   For the acquieting of their conscience
speak we now, to the intent that they may perceive what
manner of having of worldly good and keeping thereof may
stand with the state of grace.   Now think I, cousin, that if a
man keep riches about him for a glory and royalty of the world
in the consideration whereof he taketh a great delight and
liketh himself therefore, taking the poorer for the lack thereof
as one far worse than himself, such a mind is very vain foolish
pride, and such a man is very naught indeed.   But on the
other side, if there be a man (such as would God there were

many) that hath unto riches no love, but having it fall abun-
dantly unto him taketh to his own part no great pleasure thereof
but as though he had it not; keepeth himself in like abstinence
and penance privily as he would do in case he had it not; and,
in such things as he doth openly, bestow somewhat more
liberally upon himself in his house after some manner of the
world, lest he should give other folk occasion to marvel and
muse and talk of his manner and misreport him for an hypo-
crite; therein between God and him doth truly protest and
testify, as did the good Queen Esther, that he doth it not for
any desire thereof in the satisfying of his own pleasure, but
would with as goodwill or better forbear the possession of
riches, saving for the commodity that other men have by his
disposing thereof, as percase in keeping a good household in
good Christian order and fashion, and in setting other folk a-
work with such things as they gain their living the better by
his means.   This man's having of riches I might, methinketh,
in merit match in a manner with another man's forsaking of
all, if there were none other circumstance more pleasant unto
God added farther unto the forsaking beside, as percase for
the more fervent contemplation by reason of the solicitude of
all worldly business left off, which was the thing that made
Mary Magdalene's part the better. For else would Christ
have canned her much more thank to go about and be busy in
the helping her sister Martha to dress His dinner, than to take
her stool and sit down at her ease and do nought.

  Now if he that have this good and riches by him have not
haply fully so perfect a mind, but somewhat loveth to keep
himself from lack, and not so fully as a pure Christian fashion
requireth determined to abandon his pleasure, well, what will
you more?   The man is so much the less perfect than I would
he were, and haply than himself would wish if it were as easy
to be it as to wish it; but yet not by and by in state of damnation for all that, no more than every man is forthwith in
state of damnation that, forsaking all and entering into
religion, is not yet alway so clear depured from all worldly

affections as himself would very fain he were and much bewaileth that he is not. Of whom some man that hath in the world willingly forsaken the likelihood of right worshipful rooms hath afterward had much ado to keep himself from the desire of the office of cellarer, or sexton, to bear yet at the least wise some rule and authority, though it were but among the bellies. But God is more merciful to man's imperfection, if the man know it and knowledge it and mislike it and little and little labour to mend it, than to reject and cast off to the devil him that, after as his frailty can bear and suffer, hath a general intent and purpose to please Him and to prefer or set by nothing in all this world before Him.

And therefore, cousin, to make an end of this piece withal: *A negotio perambulante in tenebris*, of this devil, I mean, that the prophet calleth business walking in the darknesses. If a man have a mind to serve God and please Him, and rather lose all the good he hath than wittingly do deadly sin, and would without murmur or grudge give it every whit away in case that God should so command him, and intend to take it patiently if God would take it from him, and glad would be to use it unto God's pleasure and do his diligence to know and to be taught what manner using thereof God would be pleased with, and therein from time to time be glad to follow the counsel of good virtuous men, though he neither give away all at once, nor give every man that asketh him neither.

Let every man fear and think in this world that all the good that he doth or can do is a great deal too little. But yet for all that fear, let him dwell therewith in the faithful hope of God's help, and then shall the truth of God so compass him about, as the prophet saith, with a pavis, that he shall not so need to dread the trains and the temptations of this devil that the prophet calleth business walking about in the darknesses, but that he shall for all the having of riches and worldly substance so avoid his trains and his temptations, that he shall in conclusion by the great grace and almighty mercy of God get into heaven well enough. And now was I, cousin, about, lo, after this piece thus ended, to bid them bring in our dinner; but now shall I not need, lo, for here they come with it already.

Vincent.   Forsooth, good uncle, God disposeth and timeth your matter and your dinner both I trust.   For the end of your good tale (for which our Lord reward you) and the beginning here of your good dinner too (from which it were more than pity that you should any longer have tarried) meet even at the close together.

Anthony.   Well, cousin, now will we say grace, and then for a while will we leave talking and assay how our dinner shall like us and how fair we can fall to feeding.   Which done, you know my customable guise (for manner I may not call it, because the guise is unmannerly) to bid you not farewell, but steal away from you to sleep.   But you wot well I am not wont at afternoon to sleep long, but even a little to forget the world.   And when I wake I will again come to you, and then is (God willing) all this long day ours, wherein we shall have time enough to take much more than shall suffice for the finishing of this one part of our matter which only now remaineth.

Vincent.   I pray you, good uncle, keep your customable manner, for manner may you call it well enough.   For as it were against good manner to look that a man should kneel down for courtesy when his knee is sore, so is it very good manner that a man of your age, aggrieved with such sundry sicknesses beside that suffer you not alway to sleep when you should, let his sleep not slip away, but take it when he may. And I will, uncle, in the meanwhile steal from you too, and speed a little errand and return to you again.

Anthony.   Tarry while you will, and when you have dined go at your pleasure, but I pray you tarry not long.

Vincent.   You shall not need, uncle, to put me in mind of that, I would so fain have up the remnant of our matter.

THE THIRD BOOK

Vincent. Somewhat have I tarried the longer, uncle, partly
for that I was loath to come over soon, lest my soon coming
might have happed to have made you wake too soon, but
specially by the reason that I was letted with one that shewed
me a letter dated at Constantinople, by which letter it
appeareth that the great Turk prepareth a marvellous mighty
army. And yet whither he will therewith, that can there yet
no man tell; but I fear in good faith, uncle, that his voyage shall
be hither. Howbeit, he that wrote the letter saith that it is
secretly said in Constantinople that great part of his army
shall be shipped and sent either into Naples or into Sicily.

Anthony. It may fortune, cousin, that the letter of the
Venetian dated at Constantinople was devised at Venice.
From thence come there some among, and sometime from
Rome too, and sometime also from some other places, letters
all farced full of such tidings that the Turk is ready to do some
great exploit, which tidings they blow about for the furtherance of some such affairs as they then have themself in hand.

The Turk hath also so many men of arms in his retinue at
his continual charge, that lest they should lie still and do
nothing, but peradventure fall in devising of some novelties
among themself, he is fain yearly to make some assemblies and
some changing of them from one place unto another and part
some sort asunder that they wax not over well acquainted by
dwelling overlong together.

By these ways also he maketh those that he mindeth
suddenly to invade indeed the less to look therefore, and
thereby the less preparation to make before while they see
him so many times make a great visage of war when he

mindeth it not.   But then at one time or other they suddenly
feel it when they fear it not.   Howbeit, full likely, cousin, it
is of very truth that into this realm of Hungary he will not
fail to come.   For neither is there any country through
Christendom that lieth for him so meet, nor never was there
any time till now in which he might so well and surely win
it.   For now call we him in ourself, God save us, as Æsop
telleth that the sheep took in the wolf unto them to keep them
from the dogs.

Vincent.   Then are there very like, good uncle, all those
tribulations to fall upon us here that I spake of in the beginning of our first communication here the other day.

Anthony.   Very truth it is, cousin, that so there will of
likelihood in a while, but not forthwith all at the first.   For
while he cometh under the colour of aid for the one against
the other, he will somewhat see the proof before he fully shew
himself.   But in conclusion, if he be able to get it for him, you
shall see him so handle it that he shall not fail to get it from
him, and that forthwith out of hand, ere ever he suffer him
settle himself over-sure therein.

Vincent.   Yet say they, uncle, that he useth not to force
any man to forsake his faith.

Anthony.   Not any man, cousin?   They say more than
they can make good that tell you so.   He maketh a solemn
oath among the ceremonies of that feast, in which he first
taketh upon him his authority, that he shall in all that he
possible may minish the faith of Christ and dilate the faith
of Mahomet.   But yet hath he not used to force every whole
country at once to forsake their faith; for of some countries
hath he been content only to take a tribute yearly and let
them then live as they list.   Out of some he taketh the whole
people away, dispersing them for slaves among many sundry
countries of his very far from their own, without any sufferance of regret.   Some country, so great and populous that
they cannot well be carried and conveyed thence, he de-
stroyeth the gentlemen and giveth the lands, part to such as he

bringeth, and part to such as willingly will reney their faith,
and keepeth the other in such misery that they were in manner
as good be dead at once.   In rest he suffereth else no Christian
man almost, but those that resort as merchants or those that
offer themself to serve him in his war.

But as for those Christian countries that he useth not for
only tributaries, as he doth Chios, Cyprus, Crete, but
reckoneth for clear conquest and utterly taketh for his own, as
Morea, Greece, and Macedonia and such other like, and as I
verily think he will Hungary if he get it, in all those useth
he Christian people after sundry fashions.   He letteth them
dwell there indeed because they were too many to carry all
away, and too many to kill them all too, but if he should either
leave the land dispeopled and desolate or else some other
countries of his own from whence he should (which would not
well be done) convey the people thither to people that land
withal.   There, lo, those that will not be turned from their
faith, of which God keepeth (lauded be His holy name) very
many, he suffereth to dwell still in peace; but yet is their peace
for all that not very peaceable.   For lands he suffereth them
to have none of their own; office or honest room they bear
none; with occasions of his wars he pilleth them with taxes
and tallages unto the bare bones.   Their children he chooseth
where he list in their youth and taketh them from their
parents, conveying them whither he list where their friends
never see them after, and abuseth them as he list: some young
maidens maketh harlots, some young men he bringeth up in
war, and some young children he causeth to be gelded, not
their stones cut out as the custom was of old, but cutteth off
their whole members by the body.   How few scape and live
he little forceth, for he will have enough.   And all that he so
taketh young to any use of his own are betaken unto such
Turks or false renegades to keep, that they be turned from the
faith of Christ every one, or else so handled that as for this
world they come to an evil cheving.   For beside many
other contumelies and despites that the Turks and the false

renegade Christians many times do to good Christian people
that still persevere and abide by the faith, they find the mean
sometime to make some false shrews say that they heard such
a Christian man speak opprobrious words against Mahomet.
And upon that point falsely testified will they take occasion
to compel him forsake the faith of Christ and turn to the
profession of their shameful superstitious sect, or else will
they put him unto death with cruel intolerable torments.

Vincent. Our Lord, uncle, for His mighty mercy keep
those wretches hence. For, by my troth, if they hap to come
hither methink I see many more tokens than one that we shall
have of our own folk here ready to fall in unto them. For
like as before a great storm the sea beginneth sometime to
work and roar in itself ere ever the winds wax boisterous, so
methink I hear at mine ear some of our own here among us,
which within these few years could no more have borne the
name of a Turk than the name of the devil, begin now to find
little fault therein, yea, and some to praise them too, little and
little as they may, more glad to find faults at every state of
Christendom, priests, princes, rites, ceremonies, sacraments,
laws, and customs spiritual, temporal, and all.

Anthony. In good faith, cousin, so begin we to fare here
indeed, and that but even now of late. For since the title of
the crown hath comen in question the good rule of this realm
hath very sore decayed as little while as it is. And undoubtedly Hungary shall never do well as long as it standeth
in this case, that men's minds hearken after novelty and have
their hearts hanging upon a change; and much the worse I
like it when their words walk so large toward the favour of the
Turk's sect which they were ever wont to have in so great
abomination as every true-minded Christian man, and Christian
woman too, must have.

I am of such age as you see, and verily from as far as I can
remember it hath been marked and often proved true that
when children have in Buda fallen in a fantasy by themself
to draw together, and in their playing make as it were corpses

carried to church and sing after their childish fashion the tune of the *Dirige*, there hath great death there shortly followed after. And twice or thrice I may remember in my days when children in divers parts of this realm have gathered themself in sundry companies and made as it were parties and battles, and after their battles in sport, wherein some children have yet taken great hurt, there hath fallen very battle and deadly war indeed.

These tokens were somewhat like your ensample of the sea, sith they be of things that after follow tokens foregoing, through some secret motion or instinct whereof the cause is unknown. But by Saint Mary, cousin, these tokens like I much worse, these tokens I say, not of children's plays nor of children's songs, but old shrews' large open words so boldly spoken in the favour of Mahomet's sect in this realm of Hungary, that hath been ever hitherto a very sure key of Christendom. And, out of doubt, if Hungary be lost and that the Turk have it once fast in his possession, he shall ere it be long after have an open ready way into almost the remnant of all Christendom. Though he win it not all in a week, the great part will be won after, I fear me, within very few years.

Vincent. But yet evermore I trust in Christ, good uncle, that He shall not suffer that abominable sect of His mortal enemies in such wise to prevail against His Christian countries.

Anthony. That is very well said, cousin. Let us have our sure hope in Him, and then shall we be very sure that we shall not be deceived. For either shall we have the thing that we hope for or a better thing in the stead. For as for the thing it self that we pray for and hope to have, God will not alway send us. And therefore (as I said in our first communication) in all thing save only for heaven our prayer nor our hope may never be too precise, although the thing be lieful to require. Verily, if we people of the Christian nations were such as would God we were, I would little fear all the preparations that the great Turk could make. No, nor yet being as bad as we be, I nothing doubt at all but that in conclusion, how base

soever Christendom be brought, it shall spring up again till
the time be come very near to the day of doom, whereof some
tokens as methinketh are not comen yet.   But somewhat
before that time shall Christendom be straited sore and
brought into so narrow a compass, that according to Christ's
words: *Filius hominis veniens putas inveniet fidem in terra?*
When the Son of Man shall come again, that is to wit, to the
day of general judgment, weenest thou that He shall find faith
in the earth? as who say, but a little.   For as appeareth in the
Apocalypse and other places of Scripture, the faith shall be at
that time so far faded, that He shall for the love of His elects,
lest they should fall and perish too, abridge those days and
accelerate His coming.   But as I say, methinketh I miss yet
in my mind, some of those tokens that shall, by the Scripture,
come a good while before that; and among other, the coming
in of the Jews and the dilating of Christendom again before the
world come to that strait.   So that I say for mine own
mind I little doubt but this ungracious sect of Mahomet
shall have a foul fall and Christendom spring and spread,
flower and increase again.   Howbeit, the pleasure and the
comfort shall they see that shall be born after that we be
buried, I fear me, both twain.   For God giveth us great
likelihood that for our sinful wretched living He goeth about
to make these infidels, that are His open professed enemies,
the sorrowful scourge of correction over evil Christian people
that should be faithful, and are of truth His falsely professed
friends.   And surely, cousin, albeit that methinketh I see
divers tokens of this misery coming to us, yet can there not in
my mind be a worse prognostication thereof than this
ungracious token that you note here yourself.   For undoubtedly, cousin, this new manner here of men's favourable
fashion in their language toward these ungracious Turks
declareth plainly that not only their minds give them that
hither in shall he come, but also that they can be content
both to live under him and over that from the true faith of
Christ to fall into Mahomet's false abominable sect.

Vincent. Verily, mine uncle, as I go more about than you, so must I needs more hear (which is an heavy hearing in mine ear) the manner of men in this matter, which increaseth about us here (I trust in other places of this realm by God's grace it is otherwise). But in this quarter here about us many of these fellows that are meet for the war first were wont as it were in sport and, in a while after, half between game and earnest and, by our Lady, now not far from fair flat earnest indeed, talk as though they looked for a day when with a turn unto the Turk's faith they should be made masters here of true Christian men's bodies and owners of all their goods.

Anthony. Though I go little abroad, cousin, yet hear I sometime, when I say little, almost as much as that. But while there is no man to complain to for the redress, what remedy but patience, and fain to sit still and hold my peace? For of these two that strive whether of them both shall reign upon us, and each of them calleth himself king, and both twain put the people to pain, the one is, you wot well, too far from our quarter here to help us in this behalf, and the other, while he looketh for the Turk's aid, either will not or (I ween) well dare not find any fault with them that favour the Turk and his sect. For of Turks natural this country lacketh none now, which are here conversant under divers pretexts, and of every thing advertise the great Turk full surely. And therefore, cousin, albeit that I would advise every man pray still and call unto God to hold His gracious hand over us, and keep away this wretchedness if His pleasure be, yet would I farther advise every good Christian body to remember and consider that it is very likely to come, and therefore make his reckoning and cast his pennyworths before, and every man and every woman both appoint with God's help in their own mind beforehand what thing they intend to do if the very worst fall.

Whether a man should cast in his mind and appoint in his heart before, that if he were taken with Turks he would rather die than forsake the faith.

THE FIRST CHAPTER

Vincent. Well fare your heart, good uncle, for this good counsel of yours. For surely methinketh that this is marvellous good. But yet heard I once a right cunning and a very good man say that it were great folly and very perilous too that a man should think upon any such thing or imagine any such case in his mind, for fear of double peril that may follow thereupon; for either shall he be likely to answer himself to that case put by himself, that he will rather suffer any painful death than forsake his faith, and by that bold appointment should he fall in the fault of Saint Peter that of oversight made a proud promise and soon had a foul fall, or else were he likely to think that rather than abide the pain he would forsake God indeed; and by that mind should he sin deadly through his own folly, whereas he needeth not, as he that shall peradventure never come in the peril, to be put thereunto, and that therefore it were most wisdom never to think upon any such manner case.

Anthony. I believe well, cousin, that you have heard some man that would so say. For I can shew almost as much as that left of a very good man and a great solemn doctor in writing. But yet, cousin, although I should hap to find one or two more, as good men and as well learned too that would both twain say and write the same, yet would I not fear for my part to counsel my friend to the contrary. For, cousin, if his mind answer him as Saint Peter answered Christ, that he will rather die than forsake Him, though he say therein more unto himself than he should be peradventure able to make good if it came to the point, yet perceive I not that he doth in that thought any deadly displeasure unto God. Nor Saint Peter, though he said more than he could perform, yet in his so saying offended not God greatly neither. But his offence was when he did not after so well as he said before. But now may this man be likely never to fall in the peril of breaking that appointment, sith some ten thousand that so shall examine themself, never one shall fall in the peril. And yet to have that good purpose all their life seemeth me no more harm the while than a poor beggar that hath never a penny to think that if he had great substance he would give great alms for God's sake.

But now is all the peril if the man answer himself that he would in such case rather forsake the faith of Christ with his mouth and keep it still in his heart than for the confessing of it to endure a painful death. For by this mind he falleth in deadly sin which, while he never cometh in the case indeed, if he never had put himself the case he never had fallen in. But in good faith methinketh that he which upon that case put unto himself by himself will make himself that answer hath the habit of faith so faint and so cold that, to the better knowledge of himself and of his necessity to pray for more strength of grace, he had need to have the question put him either by himself or some other man.

Besides this, to counsel a man never to think on that case is in my mind as much reason as the medicine that I have heard taught one for the toothache, to go thrice about a churchyard and never think on a fox tail. For if the counsel be not given them it cannot serve them. And if it be given them it must put the point of the matter in their mind, which by and by to reject and think therein neither one thing nor other is a thing that may be sooner bidden than obeyed.

I ween also that very few men can escape it, but that though they would never think thereon by themself, yet in one place or other where they shall hap to come in company they shall have the question by adventure so proponed and put forth; that like as while he heareth one talking to him he may well wink if he will but he cannot make himself sleep, so shall he, whether he will or no, think one thing or other therein.

Finally, when Christ spake so often and so plain of the matter, that every man should upon pain of damnation openly confess His faith, if men took him and by dread of death would drive him to the contrary, it seemeth me in a manner implied therein that we be bounden conditionally to have evermore that mind actually sometime, and evermore habitually, that if the case so should fall, then with God's help so we would.   And thus much thinketh me necessary for every man and woman to be alway of this mind and often to think thereupon.   And where they find in the thinking thereon their hearts agrise and shrink in the remembrance of the pain that their imagination representeth to the mind, then must they call to mind and remember the great pain and torment that Christ suffered for them, and heartily pray for grace that if the case should so fall God should give them strength to stand. And thus with exercise of such meditation, though men should never stand full out of fear of falling, yet must they persevere in good hope and in full purpose of standing.   And this seemeth me, cousin, so farforth the mind that every Christian man and woman must needs have, that methinketh every curate should often counsel all his parishions, and every man and woman their servants and their children, even beginning in their tender youth, to know this point and to think thereon, and little and little from their very childhood to accustom them dulcely and pleasantly in the meditation thereof, whereby the goodness of God shall not fail so to aspire the grace of His Holy Spirit into their hearts in reward of that virtuous diligence, that through such actual meditation He shall confirm them in such a sure habit of spiritual faithful strength that all the devils in hell with all the wrestling that they can make shall never be able to wrest it out of their heart.

Vincent.   By my troth, uncle, methinketh that you say very well.

Anthony.   I say surely, cousin, as I think.   And yet all this have I said concerning them that dwell in such places as they be never like in their lives to come in the danger to be put to the proof. Howbeit, many a man may ween himself far therefrom that yet may fortune by some one chance or other to fall in the case that either for the truth of faith or for the truth of justice (which go almost all alike) he may fall in the case. But now be you and I, cousin, and all our friends here far in another point. For we be so likely to fall in the experience thereof soon, that it had been more time for us, all other things set aside, to have devised upon this matter and firmly to have settled ourself upon a fast point long ago than to begin to commune and counsel upon it now.

Vincent. In good faith, uncle, you say therein very truth, and would God it had come sooner in my mind. But better is it yet late than never. And I trust God shall yet give us respite and time, whereof, uncle, that we lose no part I pray you proceed now with your good counsel therein.

Anthony. Very gladly, cousin, shall I now go forth in the fourth temptation which only remaineth to be treated of, and properly pertaineth whole unto this present purpose.

Of the fourth temptation, which is persecution for the faith, touched in these words of the prophet: Ab incursu et demonio meridiano.

THE SECOND CHAPTER

THE fourth temptation, cousin, that the prophet speaketh of in the fore-remembered psalm, *Qui habitat in adiutorio altissimi, etc.*, is plain open persecution. Which is touched in these words: *Ab incursu et demonio meridiano.* And of all his temptations this is the most perilous, the most bitter sharp, and the most rigorous. For whereas in other temptations he useth either pleasant allectives unto sin, or other secret sleights and trains, and cometh in the night, and stealeth on in the dark unware (or in some other part of the day flieth and passeth by like an arrow, so shaping himself, sometime in one fashion, sometime in another, and so dissimuling himself and his high mortal malice, that a man is thereby so blinded and beguiled that he may not sometime perceive well what he is), in this temptation, this plain open persecution for the faith, he cometh even in the very midday, that is to wit, even upon them that have an high light of faith shining in their heart, and openly suffereth himself so plainly be perceived by his fierce malicious persecution against the faithful Christians for hatred of Christ's true Catholic faith, that no man having faith can doubt what he is. For in this temptation he sheweth himself such as the prophet nameth him, *demonium meridianum*, the midday devil; he may be so lightsomely seen with the eye of a faithful soul by his fierce furious assault and incursion. For therefore saith the prophet, that the truth of God shall compass that man round about that dwelleth in the faithful hope of His help with a pavis, *ab incursu et demonio meridiano*, from the incursion and the devil of the midday, because this kind of persecution is not a wily temptation, but a furious force and a terrible incursion. In other of his temptations he stealeth on like a fox, but in this Turk's persecution for the faith he runneth on roaring with assault like a ramping lion.

This temptation is of all temptations also the most perilous. For whereas in temptations of prosperity he useth only delectable allectives to move a man to sin, and in other kinds of tribulation and adversity he useth only grief and pain to pull a man into murmur, impatience, and blasphemy, in this kind of persecution for the faith of Christ he useth both twain, that is to wit, both his allectives of quiet and rest, by deliverance from death and pain with other pleasures also of this present life, and beside that, the terror and infliction of intolerable pain and torment.

In other tribulation, as loss, or sickness, or death of our friends, though the pain be peradventure as great and sometime greater too, yet is not the peril nowhere nigh half so much. For in other tribulations (as I said before) that necessity that the man must of fine force abide and endure the pain, wax he never so wroth and impatient therewith, is a great reason to move him to keep his patience therein and be content therewith and thank God thereof, and of necessity to make a virtue that he may be rewarded for. But in this temptation, this persecution for the faith, I mean not by fight in the field, by which the faithful man standeth at his defence and putteth the faithless in half the fear and half the harm too, but where he is taken and in hold, and may for the forswearing or the denying of his faith be delivered and suffered to live in rest, and some in great worldly wealth also; in this case, I say, this thing that he needeth not to suffer this trouble and pain but he will is a marvellous great occasion for him to fall into the sin that the devil would drive him to, that is to wit, the forsaking of the faith.

And therefore, as I say, of all the devil's temptations is this temptation, this persecution for the faith, the most perilous.

Vincent. The more perilous, uncle, that this temptation is (as indeed of all temptations the most perilous it is), the more need have they that stand in peril thereof to be before with substantial advice and good counsel well armed against it, that we may with the comfort and consolation thereof the better bear that tribulation when it cometh, and the better withstand the temptation.

Anthony. You say, cousin Vincent, therein very truth, and I am content to fall therefore in hand therewith. But forasmuch, cousin, as methinketh that of this tribulation somewhat you be more feard than I, and of truth somewhat more excusable it is in you than it were in me, mine age considered and the sorrow that I have suffered already, with some other considerations upon my part beside, rehearse you therefore the griefs and the pains that you think in this tribulation possible to fall unto you, and I shall against each of them give you counsel and rehearse you such occasion of comfort and consolation as my poor wit and learning can call unto my mind.

Vincent. In good faith, uncle, I am not all thing afeard

in this case only for myself, but well you wot I have cause to care also for many more, and that folk of sundry sorts, men and women both, and that not all of one age.

Anthony. All that you have cause to fear for, cousin, for all them have I cause to fear with you too, sith all your kinsfolk and allies within a little be likewise unto me. Howbeit, to say the truth, every man hath cause in this case to fear, both for himself and also for every other. For sith as the Scripture saith: *Unicuique dedit Deus curam de proximo suo*: God hath given every man cure and charge of his neighbour, there is no man that hath any spark of Christian love and charity in his breast, but that in a matter of such peril as this is, wherein the soul of man standeth in so great danger to be lost, he must needs care and take thought, not for his friends only but also for his very foes. We shall therefore, cousin, not rehearse your harms or mine that may befall in this persecution, but all the great harms in general as near as we can call to mind that may hap unto any man.

THE THIRD CHAPTER

SITH a man is made of the body and the soul, all the harm that any man may take, it must needs be in one of these two, either immediately or by the mean of some such thing as serveth for the pleasure, weal, or commodity of the one of these two. As for the soul first, we shall need no rehearsal of any harm that by this kind of tribulation may attain thereto, but if that by some inordinate love and affection that the soul bear to the body she consent to slide from the faith, and thereby do her harm herself. Now remain there the body, and these outward things of fortune which serve for the maintenance of the body, and minister matter of pleasure to the soul also through the delight that she hath in the body for the while that she is matched therewith.

Consider, then, first the loss of those outward things as

somewhat the less in weight than is the body itself.   In them what may a man lose, and thereby what pain may he suffer?

Vincent. He may lose, uncle, of which I should somewhat lose myself, money, plate, and other movable substance, then offices, authority, and finally all the lands of his inheritance for ever that himself and his heirs perpetually might else enjoy.   And of all these things, uncle, you wot well that myself have some, little in respect of that that some other have here, but somewhat more yet than he that hath most here would be well content to lose.

Upon the loss of these things follow neediness and poverty, the pain of lacking, the shame of begging (of which twain I wot not well which is the most wretched necessity), beside the grief and heaviness of heart in beholding good men and faithful and his dear friends bewrapped in like misery, and ungracious wretches and infidels and his mortal enemies enjoy the commodities that himself and his friends have lost. Now for the body, very few words shall serve us.   For therein I see none other harm but loss of liberty, labour, imprisonment, painful and shameful death.

Anthony. There needeth not much more, cousin, as the world is now.   For I fear me that less than a fourth part of this will make many a man sore stagger in his faith and some man fall quite therefrom, that yet at this day, before he come to the proof, weeneth himself that he would stand very fast. And I beseech our Lord that all they that so think and would yet when they were brought unto the point fall therefrom for fear or for pain, may get of God the grace to ween still as they do, and not to be brought to the assay where pain or fear should shew them, as it shewed Saint Peter, how far they be deceived now.

But now, cousin, against these terrible things what way shall we take in giving men counsel of comfort?   If the faith were in our days as fervent as it hath been ere this in time before passed, little counsel and little comfort would suffice. We should not much need with words and reasoning to extenuate and minish the vigour and asperity of the pains; but the greater and the more bitter that the passion were, the more ready was of old time the fervour of faith to suffer it. And surely, cousin, I doubt it little in my mind, but that if a man had in his heart so deep a desire and love, longing to be with God in heaven, to have the fruition of His glorious face, as had those holy men that were martyrs in old time, he would no more now stick at the pain that he must pass between than at that time those old holy martyrs did. But alas, our faint and feeble faith with our love to God less than lukewarm by the fiery affection that we bear to our own filthy flesh maketh us so dull in the desire of heaven, that the sudden dread of every bodily pain woundeth us to the heart and striketh our devotion dead. And therefore hath there every man, cousin (as I said before), much the more need to think upon this thing many a time and oft aforehand, ere any such peril fall, and by much devising thereupon before they see cause to fear it. While the thing shall not appear so terrible unto them, reason shall better enter, and through grace working with their diligence engender and set sure not a sudden slight affection of sufferance for God's sake, but by a long continuance a strong deep-rooted habit, not like a reed ready to wave with every wind, nor like a rootless tree scant set up on end in a loose heap of light sand, that will with a blast or two be blown down.

THE FOURTH CHAPTER

FOR if we now consider, cousin, these causes of terror and dread that you have recited, which in his persecution for the faith this midday devil may by these Turks rear against us to make his incursion with, we shall well perceive, weighing them well with reason, that albeit somewhat they be indeed, yet, every part of the matter pondered, they shall well appear in conclusion things nothing so much to be dread and fled from as to folk at the first sight they do suddenly seem.

Of the loss of the goods of fortune

THE FIFTH CHAPTER

FOR first, to begin at the outward goods (that neither are the proper goods of the soul nor of the body but are called the goods of fortune) that serve for the sustenance and commodity of man for the short season of this present life, as worldly substance, offices, honour, and authority, what great good is there in these things of themself for which they were worthy so much as to bear the name by which the world of a worldly favour customably calleth them? For if the having of strength make a man strong, and the having of heat make a man hot, and the having of virtue make a man virtuous, how can those things be verily and truly good which he that hath them may by the having of them, as well be the worse as the better, and, as experience proveth, more oft is the worse than the better? What should a good man greatly rejoice in that, that he daily seeth most abound in the hands of many that be nought? Do not now this great Turk and his bashaws, in all these advancements of fortune surmount very far above any Christian estate, and any lords living under him? And was there not yet hence upon twenty years the great sultan of Syria, which many a year together bare as great a port as the great Turk, and after in one summer unto the great Turk that whole empire was lost? And so may all his empire now, and shall hereafter by God's grace, be lost into Christian men's hands likewise, when Christian people shall be mended and grow in God's favour again. But when that whole kingdoms and mighty great empires are of so little surety to stand, but be so soon translated from one man unto another, what great thing can you or I, yea or any lord the greatest in this land, reckon himself to have by the possession of an heap of silver or gold, white and yellow metal, not so profitable of their own nature, save for a little glittering, as the rude rusty metal of iron.

Of the unsurety of lands and possessions

THE SIXTH CHAPTER

LANDS and possessions many men yet much more esteem than money, because the lands seem not so casual as money is or plate, for that though their other substance may be stole and taken away, yet evermore they think that their land will lie still where it lay.   But what are we the better that our land cannot be stirred but will lie still where it lay while ourself may be removed and not suffered to come near it ?   What great difference is there to us whether our substance be movable or unmovable, sith we be so movable ourself, that we may be removed from them both, and lose them both twain ?   Saving that sometime in the money is the surety somewhat more; for when we be fain ourself to flee we may make shift to carry some of our money with us, whereof our land we cannot carry one inch.

If our land be a thing of more surety than our money, how happeth it then that in this persecution we be more feard to lose it ?   For if it be a thing of more surety, then can it not so soon be lost.   In the translation of these two great empires, Greece first sith myself was born, and after Syria since you were born too, the land was lost before the money was found.   Oh, cousin Vincent, if the whole world were animated with a reasonable soul (as Plato had weened it were), and that it had wit and understanding to mark and perceive all thing, Lord God, how the ground on which a prince buildeth his palace would loud laugh his lord to scorn when he saw him proud of his possession and heard him boast himself that he and his blood are for ever the very lords and owners of the land !   For then would the ground think the while in himself: Ah, thou silly poor soul, that weenest thou were half a god, and art amid thy glory but a man in a gay gown, I that am the ground here over whom thou art so proud have had an hundred such owners of me as thou callest thyself, more than ever thou hast heard the names of. And some of them that proudly went over mine head lie now low in my belly, and my side lieth over them. And many one shall, as thou dost now, call himself mine owner after thee that neither shall be sib to thy blood, nor any word hear of thy name. Who ought your castle, cousin, three thousand year ago?

Vincent. Three thousand, uncle? Nay, nay, in any king, Christian or heathen, you may strike off a third part of that well enough, and, as far as I ween, half of the remnant too. In far fewer years than three thousand it may well fortune that a poor plowman's blood may come up to a kingdom, and a king's right royal kin on the other side fall down to the plow and cart, and neither that king know that ever he came from the cart, nor that carter know that ever he came from the crown.

Anthony. We find, cousin Vincent, in full antique stories many strange changes as marvellous as that come about in the compass of very few years in effect. And be such things then in reason so greatly to be set by, that we should esteem the loss at so great when we see that in keeping our surety is so little?

Vincent. Marry, uncle, but the less surety that we have to keep it, sith it is a great commodity to have it, the farther by so much and the more loath we be to forgo it.

Anthony. That reason shall I, cousin, turn against yourself. For if it be so (as you say) that sith the things be commodious the less surety that you see you have of the keeping, the more cause you have to be afeard of the losing. Then on the other side the more that a thing is of his nature such that the commodity thereof bringeth a man little surety and much fear, that thing of reason the less have we cause to love. And then the less cause that we have to love a thing, the less cause have we to care therefore or fear the loss thereof or be loath to go therefrom.

These outward goods or gifts of fortune are by two manner wise to be considered

THE SEVENTH CHAPTER

WE shall yet, cousin, consider in these outward goods of fortune, as riches, good name, honest estimation, honourable fame, and authority, in all these things we shall, I say, consider that either we love them and set by them as things commodious unto us for the state and condition of this present life, or else as things that we purpose by the good use thereof to make them matter of our merit with God's help in the life after to come. Let us then first consider them as things set by and beloved for the pleasure and commodity of them for this present life.

The little commodity of riches, being set by but for this present life

THE EIGHTH CHAPTER

Now, riches loved and set by for such, if we consider it well, the commodity that we take thereof is not so great as our own fond affection and fantasy maketh us imagine it. It maketh us (I say not nay) go much more gay and glorious in sight, garnished in silk; but cloth is within a little as warm. It maketh us have great plenty of many kind of delicate and delicious vitail and thereby to make more excess, but less exquisite and less superfluous fare with fewer surfeits, and fewer fevers growing thereon too, were within a little as wholesome. Then the labour in the getting, the fear in the keeping, and the pain in the parting from do more than counterpoise a great part of all the pleasure and commodity that they bring; besides this, that riches is the thing that taketh many times from his master all his pleasure and his life too. For many a man is for his riches slain. And some that keep their riches as a thing pleasant and commodious for their life take none other pleasure in a manner thereof in all their life than as though they bare the key of another man's coffer, and rather are content to live in neediness miserably all their days than they could find in their heart to minish their hoard, they have such fantasy to look thereon. Yea, and some men, for fear lest thieves should steal it from them, be their own thieves and steal it from themself while they dare not so much as let it lie where themself may look thereon, but put it in a pot and hide it in the ground, and there let it lie safe till they die and sometime seven year after. From which place if the pot had been stolen away five year before his death, all the same five year that he lived after weening alway thathis pot lay safe still, what had he been the poorer while he never occupied it after?

Vincent. By my troth, uncle, not one penny for aught that I perceive.

The little commodity of fame, being desired but for worldly pleasure

THE NINTH CHAPTER

Anthony. Let us now consider good name, honest estimation, and honourable fame, for these three things are of their own nature one and take their difference, in effect, but of the manner of the common speech in diversity of degrees. For a good name may a man have, be he never so poor. Honest estimation in the common taking of the people belongeth not unto any man but him that is taken for one of some countenance and haviour, and among his neighbours had in some reputation. In the word of honourable fame folk conceive the renown of great estates much and far spoken of by reason of their laudable acts. Now all this gear, used as a thing pleasant and commodious for this present life, pleasant it may seem to him that fasteneth his fantasy therein, but of the nature of the thing itself, I perceive no great commodity that it hath, I say of the nature of the thing itself because it may be by chance some occasion of commodity.   As if it hap that for the good name the poor man hath, or for the honest estimation that a man of some haviour and substance standeth in among his neighbours, or for the honourable fame wherewith the great estate is renowned, if it hap, I say, that any man bearing them the better will therefore do them therefore any good. And yet as for that, like as it may sometime so hap and sometime so happeth indeed, so may it hap sometime on the other side, and on the other side so it sometime happeth indeed, that such folk are of some other envied and hated, and as readily by them that envy them and hate them take harm as they take by them that love them good.

But now to speak of the thing itself in his own proper nature, what is it but a blast of another man's mouth, as soon passed as spoken?   Whereupon he that setteth his delight feedeth himself but with wind, whereof be he never so full, he hath little substance therein, and many times shall he much deceive himself.   For he shall ween that many praise him that never speak word of him, and they that do say yet much less than he weeneth, and far more seldom too.   For they spend not all the day, he may be sure, in talking of him alone. And whoso commend him most will yet, I ween, in every four and twenty hours wink and forget him once.   Besides this, that while one talketh well of him in one place another sitteth and saith as shrewdly of him in another.   And finally, some that most praise him in his presence behind his back mock him as fast and loud laugh him to scorn, and sometime slyly to his own face too.   And yet are there some fools so fed with this fond fantasy of fame, that they rejoice and glory to think how they be continually praised all about, as though all the world did nothing else day nor night but ever sit and sing, *Sanctus, sanctus, sanctus*, upon them.

Of flattery

THE TENTH CHAPTER

AND into this pleasant fantasy of much foolish vainglory be there some men brought sometime by such as themself do in a manner hire to flatter them, and would not be content if a man should do otherwise, but would be right angry not only if a man told them truth when they do naught indeed, but also if they praise it but slenderly.

Vincent. Forsooth, uncle, this is very truth. I have been ere this, and not very long ago, where I saw so proper experience of this point that I must stop your tale for so long while I tell you mine.

Anthony. I pray you, cousin, tell on.

Vincent. When I was first in Almaine, uncle, it happed me to be somewhat favoured with a great man of the church, and a great state, one of the greatest in all that country there. And indeed, whosoever might spend as much as he might in one thing and other were a right great estate in any country of Christendom. But glorious was he very far above all measure, and that was great pity, for it did harm and made him abuse many great gifts that God had given him. Never was he satiate of hearing his own praise.

So happed it one day that he had in a great audience made an oration in a certain manner wherein he liked himself so well that at his dinner he sat, him thought, on thorns till he might hear how they that sat with him at his board would commend it. And when he had sit musing awhile, devising (as I thought after) upon some pretty proper way to bring it in withal, at the last, for lack of a better (lest he should have letted the matter too long), he brought it even bluntly forth and asked us all that sat at his board's end (for at his own mess in the midst there sat but himself alone) how well we liked his oration that he had made that day. But in faith, uncle, when that problem was once proponed, till it was full answered no man, I ween, eat one morsel of meat more; every man was fallen in so deep a study for the finding of some exquisite praise. For he that should have brought out but a vulgar and a common commendation would have thought himself shamed for ever. Then said we our sentences by row as we sat, from the lowest unto the highest in good order, as it had been a great matter of the commonweal in a right solemn council. When it came to my part (I will not say it, uncle, for no boast), methought, by our Lady, for my part I quit myself meetly well.

And I liked myself the better because methought my words, being but a stranger, went yet with some grace in the Almaine tongue wherein letting my Latin alone me listed to shew my cunning. And I hoped to be liked the better because I saw that he that sat next me and should say his sentence after me was an unlearned priest, for he could speak no Latin at all. But when he came forth for his part with my lord's commendation, the wily fox had been so well accustomed in court with the craft of flattery that he went beyond me to too far. And then might I see by him what excellence a right mean wit may come to in one craft, that in all his whole life studieth and busieth his wit about no more but that one. But I made after a solemn vow unto myself that if ever he and I were matched together at that board again, when we should fall to our flattery, I would flatter in Latin, that he should not contend with me no more. For though I could be content to be outrun of an horse, yet would I no more abide it to be outrun of an ass. But, uncle, here began now the game. He that sat highest and was to speak was a great beneficed man, and not a doctor only but also somewhat learned indeed in the laws of the Church. A world it was to see how he marked every man's word that spake before him. And it seemed that every word the more proper it was the worse he liked it for the cumbrance that he had to study out a better to pass it. The man even sweat with the labour, so that he was fain in the while now and then to wipe his face. Howbeit, in conclusion, when it came to his course we that had spoken before him had so taken up all among us before, that we had not left him one wise word to speak after.

Anthony. Alas, good man! Among so many of you some good fellow should have lent him one.

Vincent. It needed not as hap was, uncle, for he found out such a shift that in his flattering he passed us all the many.

Anthony. Why, what said he, cousin?

Vincent. By our Lady, uncle, not one word. But like as I trow Plinius telleth, that when Apelles the painter in the table that he painted of the sacrifice and the death of Iphigenia had in the making of the sorrowful countenances of the other noblemen of Greece that beheld it, spent out so much his craft and his cunning, that when he came to make the countenance of King Agamemnon her father (which he reserved for the last, lest if he had made his visage before he must in some of the other after either have made the visage less dolorous than he could, and thereby have forborne some part of his praise, or, doing the uttermost of his craft, might have happed to make some other look more heavily for the pity of her pain than her own father, which had been yet a far greater fault in his painting), when he came, I say, to the making of his face therefore last of all, he could devise no manner of new heavy cheer and countenance for her father, but that he had made there already in some of the other a much more heavy before. And therefore, to the intent that no man should see what manner countenance it was that her father had, the painter was fain to paint him holding his face in his handkercher.

The like pageant in a manner played us there this good ancient honourable flatterer. For when he saw that he could find no words of praise that would pass all that had been spoken before already, the wily fox would speak never a word but as he that were ravished unto heavenward with the wonder of the wisdom and eloquence that my lord's grace had uttered in that oration, he set a long sigh with an Oh from the bottom of his breast, and held up both his hands, and lift up his head, and cast up his eyes into the welkin and wept.

Anthony. Forsooth, cousin, he played his part very properly. But was that great prelate's oration, cousin, anything praiseworthy? For you can tell, I see well. For you would not, I ween, play as Juvenal merrily describeth the blind senator, one of the flatterers of Tiberius the emperor, that among the remnant so magnified the great fish that the emperor had sent for them to shew them which this blind senator (Montanus I trow they called him) marvelled of as much as any that marvelled most, and many things he spake thereof with some of his words directed thereunto, looking himself toward his left side while the fish lay on his right side. You would not, I trow, cousin, have take upon you to praise it so but if you had heard it.

Vincent. I heard it, uncle, indeed, and to say the truth, it was not to dispraise. Howbeit, surely, somewhat less praise might have served it, by more a great deal than the half. But this am I sure, had it been the worst that ever was made, the praise had not been the less of one hair. For they that used to praise him to his face never considered how much the thing deserved, but how great a laud and praise themself could give his good grace.

Anthony. Surely, cousin, as Terence saith, such folk make men of fools even stark mad, and much cause have their lords to be right angry with them.

Vincent. God hath indeed and is, I ween. But as for their lords, uncle, if they would after wax angry with them therefore, they should in my mind do them very great wrong, when it is one of the things that they specially keep them for. For those that are of such vainglorious mind (be they lords or be they meaner men) can be much better contented to have their devices commended than amended. And require they their servant and their friend never so specially to tell them the very truth, yet shall he better please them if he speak them fair than if he telleth them truth.

For they be in the case that Martial speaketh of in an epigram unto a friend of his that required his judgment how he liked his verses but he prayed him in any wise to tell him even the very truth.   To whom Martial made answer in this wise:

> The very truth of me thou dost require.
> The very truth is this, my friend dear :
> The very truth thou wouldest not gladly hear.

And in good faith, uncle, the selfsame prelate that I told you my tale of (I dare be bold to swear it, I know it so surely) had on a time made of his own drawing a certain treaty that should serve for a league between that country and a great prince.   In which treaty himself thought that he had devised his articles so wisely and indited them so well, that all the world would allow them.   Whereupon longing sore to be praised, he called unto him a friend of his, a man well learned and of good worship and very well expert in those matters, as he that had been divers times ambassador for that country and had made many such treaties himself. When he took him the treaty and that he had read it he asked him how he liked it and said: But I pray you heartily, tell me the very truth.   And that he spake so heartily that the other had weened he would fain have heard the truth; and in trust thereof he told him a fault therein, at the hearing whereof he sware in great anger: By the mass, thou art a very fool.   The other afterward told me that he would never tell him truth again.

Anthony.   Without question, cousin, I cannot greatly blame him.   And thus themself make every man mock them, flatter them, and deceive them, those, I say, that are of such vainglorious mind.   For if they be content to hear the truth let them then make much of those that tell them the truth and withdraw their ear from them that falsely flatter them, and they shall be more truly served than with twenty requests praying men to tell them true.   King Ladislaus (our Lord assoil his soul) used much this manner among his servants. When one of them praised any deed of his or any condition in him, if he perceived that they said but the truth he would let it pass by uncontrolled.   But when he saw that they set a gloss upon it for his praise of their own making beside, then would he shortly say unto them: I pray thee, good fellow, when thou sayest grace at my board never bring in *Gloria Patri* without a *sicut erat*.   Any act that ever I did, if thou report it again to mine honour with a *Gloria Patri* never report it but with a *sicut erat*, that is to wit, even as it was and none otherwise.   And lift me not up with no lies, for I love it not.   If men would use this way with them that this noble king used it would minish much of their false flattery.   I can well allow that men should commend (keeping them within the bonds of truth) such things as they see praiseworthy in other men, to give them the greater courage to the increase thereof.   For men keep still in that point one condition of children, that praise must prick them forth.   But better it were to do well and look for none.   Howbeit, they that cannot find in their heart to commend another man's good deed shew themself either envious or else of nature very cold and dull.   But out of question, he that putteth his pleasure in the praise of the people hath but a fond fantasy.   For if his finger do but ache of an hot blain, a great many men's mouths blowing out his praise will scantly do him among them all half so much ease as to have one little boy blow upon his finger.

The little commodity that men have of rooms, offices, and authority, if they desire them but for their worldly commodity

THE ELEVENTH CHAPTER

LET us now consider in like wise what great worldly wealth ariseth unto men by great offices, rooms, and authority, to those worldly disposed people, I say, that desire them for no better purpose.   For of them that desire them for better we shall speak after anon.   The great thing that they chief like all therein is that they may bear a rule, command and control other men, and live uncommanded and uncontrolled themself. And yet this commodity took I so little heed of, that I never was ware it was so great till a good friend of ours merrily told me once that his wife once in a great anger taught it him. For when her husband had no list to grow greatly upward in the world, nor neither would labour for office of authority, and over that forsook a right worshipful room when it was offered him, she fell in hand with him, he told me, and all-to rated him and asked him: What will you do that you list not to put forth yourself as other folk do? Will you sit still by the fire and make goslings in the ashes with a stick as children do? Would God I were a man, and look what I would do. Why wife, quoth her husband, what would you do? What? By God, go forward with the best. For as my mother was wont to say (God have mercy on her soul), it is evermore better to rule than to be ruled. And therefore, by God, I would not, I warrant you, be so foolish to be ruled where I might rule. By my troth, wife, quoth her husband, in this I dare say you say truth. For I never found you willing to be ruled yet.

Vincent. Well, uncle, I wot where you be now well enough; she is indeed a stout master woman. And in good faith, for aught that I can see, even that same womanish mind of hers is the greatest commodity that men reckon upon in rooms and offices of authority.

Anthony. By my troth, and methinketh very few there are of them that attain any great commodity therein. For first there is in every kingdom but one that can have an office of such authority that no man may command him or control him. None officer can there stand in that case but the king himself which only uncontrolled or uncommanded may control and command all. Now of all the remnant each is under him. And yet beside him almost every one is under more commanders and controllers too than one. And some man that is in a great office commandeth fewer things and less labour to many men that are under him than someone that is over him commandeth him alone.

Vincent. Yet it doth them good, uncle, that men must make courtesy to them, and salute them with reverence, and stand barehead before them, or unto some of them kneel peradventure too.

Anthony. Well, cousin, in some part they do but play at gleek, receive reverence, and to their cost pay honour again therefore. For except, as I said, only a king, the greatest in authority under him receiveth not so much reverence of no man as according to reason himself doth honour to him. Nor twenty men's courtesies do him not so much pleasure as his own once kneeling doth him pain if his knee hap to be sore.

And I wist once a great officer of the king's say (and in good faith I ween he said but as he thought) that twenty men standing barehead before him keep not his head half so warm as to keep on his own cap. Nor he never took so much ease with their being barehead before him as he caught once grief with a cough that came upon him by standing barehead long before the king. But let it be that these commodities be somewhat such as they be, yet then consider whether that any incommodities be so joined therewith that a man were almost as good lack both as have both. Goeth all thing evermore as every one of them would have it? That were as hard as to please all the people at once with one weather while in one house the husband would have fair weather for his corn and his wife would have rain for her leeks. So while they that are in authority be not all evermore of one mind, but sometime variance among them, either for the respect of profit or for contention of rule or for maintenance of matters, sundry parts for their sundry friends, it cannot be that both the parties can have their own mind; nor often are they content which see their conclusion quail, but ten times they take the missing of their mind more displeasantly than other poor men do. And this goeth not only to men of mean authority but unto the very greatest. The princes themself cannot have, you wot well, all their will. For how were it possible while each of them almost would, if he might, be lord over all the remnant? Then many men under their princes in authority are in that case that privy malice and envy many bear them in heart, falsely speak them full fair, and praise them with their mouth, which, when there happeth any great fall unto them, bawl and bark and bite upon them like dogs.

Finally, the cost and charge, the danger and peril of war, wherein their part is more than a poor man's is, sith that matter more dependeth upon them; and many a poor plowman may sit still by the fire while they must arise and walk.

And sometime their authority falleth by change of their master's mind. And of that see we daily in one place or other ensamples such and so many that the parable of the philosopher can lack no testimony, which likened the servants of great princes unto the counters with which men do cast account. For like as that counter that standeth sometime for a farthing is suddenly set up and standeth for a thousand pound and after as soon set down eftsoon beneath to stand for a farthing again, so fareth it, lo, sometime with those that seek the way to rise and grow up in authority by the favour of great princes, that as they rise up high so fall they down again as low.

Howbeit, though a man escape all such adventures and abide in great authority till he die, yet then at the least wise every man must leave it at the last. And that which we call at last hath no very long time to it. Let a man reckon his years that are passed of his age ere ever he can get up aloft, and let him when he hath it first in his fist reckon how long he shall be like to live after, and I ween that then the most part shall have little cause to rejoice. They shall see the time likely to be so short that their honour and authority by nature shall endure beside the manifold chances whereby they may lose it more soon. And then, when they see that they must needs leave it, the thing which they did much more set their heart upon than ever they had reasonable cause, what sorrow they take therefore, that shall I not need to tell you. And thus it seemeth unto me, cousin, in good faith, that sith in the having the profit is not great and the displeasures neither small nor few and of the losing so many sundry chances, and that by no mean a man can keep it long, and that to part therefrom is such a painful grief, I can see no very great cause for which as an high worldly commodity men should great desire it.

That these outward goods desired but for worldly wealth be not only little good for the body, but are also much harm for the soul

THE TWELFTH CHAPTER

AND thus far have we considered hitherto in these outward goods that are called the gifts of fortune no farther but the slender commodity that worldly-minded men have by them. But now, if we consider farther what harm to the soul they take by them that desire them but only for the wretched wealth of this world, then shall we well perceive how far more happy is he that well loseth them than he that evil findeth them.

These things, though they be such as are of their own nature indifferent, that is to wit, of themself things neither good nor bad but are matter that may serve to the one or the other after as men will use them, yet need we little to doubt it but that they that desire them but for their worldly pleasure and for no farther godly purpose, the devil shall soon turn them from things indifferent unto them and make them things very naught. For though that they be indifferent of their nature, yet cannot the use of them lightly stand indifferent, but determinately must either be good or bad. And therefore he that desireth them but for worldly pleasure desireth them not for any good. And for better purpose than he desireth them, to better use is he not likely to put them, and therefore not unto good but consequently to naught.

As, for ensample, first consider it in riches. He that longeth for them as for things of temporal commodity and not for any godly purpose, what good they shall do him Saint

Paul declareth, where he writeth unto Timothy: *Qui volunt divites fieri incidunt in tentationem et in laqueum diaboli, et desideria multa inutilia et nociva, quæ mergunt homines in interitum et perditionem:* They that long to be rich fall into temptation and into the grin of the devil and into many desires unprofitable and noyous, which drown men into death and into perdition. And the Holy Scripture saith also in the twenty-first chapter of the Proverbs: *Qui congregat thesauros impingetur ad laqueos mortis:* He that gathereth treasures shall be shoved into the grins of death. So that whereas by the mouth of Saint Paul God saith that they shall fall into the devil's grin, He saith in the other place that they shall be pushed and shoved in by violence. And of truth, while a man desireth riches not for any good godly purpose but for only worldly wealth it must needs be that he shall have little conscience in the getting, but by all evil ways that he can invent shall labour to get them; and then shall he either niggardly heap them up together (which is, you wot well, damnable) or wastefully misspend them about worldly pomp, pride, and gluttony, with occasion of many sins more. And that is yet much more damnable.

As for fame and glory desired but for worldly pleasure, doth unto the soul inestimable harm. For that setteth men's hearts upon high devices and desires of such things as are immoderate and outrageous, and by help of false flatterers puff up a man in pride, and make a brittle man (lately made of earth, and that shall again shortly be laid full low in earth, and there lie and rot and turn again into earth) take himself in the meantime for a god here upon earth, and ween to win himself to be lord of all the earth.

This maketh battles between these great princes, and with much trouble to much people, and great effusion of blood, one king to look to reign in five realms that cannot well rule one. For how many hath now this great Turk, and yet aspireth to more? And those that he hath he ordereth evil, and yet himself worst.

* M 461

Then offices and rooms of authority, if men desire them only for their worldly fantasies, who can look that ever they shall occupy them well, but abuse their authority and do thereby great hurt? For then shall they fall from indifferency and maintain false matters of their friends, bear up their servants and such as depend upon them with bearing down of other innocent folk and not so able to do hurt as easy to take harm. Then the laws that are made against malefactors shall they make, as an old philosopher said, to be much like unto cobwebs, in which the little gnats and flies stick still and hang fast, but the great humble-bees break them and fly quite through. And then the laws that are made as a buckler in the defence of innocents, those shall they make serve for a sword to cut and sore wound them with, and therewith wound they their own souls sorer. And thus you see, cousin, that of all these outward goods which men call the goods of fortune there is never one that unto them which long therefore, not for any godly purpose but only for their worldly wealth, hath any great commodity to the body; and yet are they all in such case besides that very deadly destruction unto the soul.

Whether men desire these outward goods for their only worldly wealth, or for any good virtuous purpose, this persecution of the Turk against the faith will declare, and the comfort that both twain may take in the losing them thus.

THE THIRTEENTH CHAPTER

Vincent. Verily, good uncle, this thing is so plainly true that no man may with any good reason deny it; but I ween, uncle, also, that there will no man say nay. For I see no man that will for very shame confess that he desireth riches, honour, and renown, offices and rooms of authority for his only worldly pleasure. For every man would fain seem as holy as an horse. And therefore will every man say, and would it were so believed too, that he desireth these things, though for his worldly wealth a little so, yet principally to merit thereby through doing some good therewith.

Anthony. This is, cousin, very sure so, that so doth every man say. But first he that in the desire thereof hath his respect therein unto his worldly wealth, as you say but a little so, so much as himself weeneth were but a little, may soon prove a great deal too much. And many men will say so too that have principal respect unto their worldly commodity and unto Godward therein little or nothing at all; and yet they pretend the contrary, and that unto their own harm *quia Dominus non irridetur.* God cannot be mocked. And some peradventure know not well their own affection themself, but there lieth more imperfection secret in their affection than themself are well ware of, which only God beholdeth. And therefore saith the prophet unto God: *Imperfectum meum viderunt oculi tui:* Mine imperfection have Thine eyes beholden. For which the prophet prayeth: *Ab occultis meis munda me Domine:* From mine hid sins cleanse thou me, good Lord.

But now, cousin, this tribulation of the Turk, if he so persecute us for the faith that those that will forsake their faith shall keep their goods, and those shall lose their goods that will not leave their faith, this manner of persecution, lo, shall like a touchstone try them and shew the feigned from the true-minded, and teach also them that ween they mean better than they do indeed better to discern themself. For some there are that ween they mean well while they frame themself a conscience, and ever keep still a great heap of superfluous substance by them, thinking ever still that they will bethink themself upon some good deed whereon they will well bestow it once, or that else their executors shall. But now if they lie not unto themself, but keep their goods for any good purpose to the pleasure of God indeed, then shall they in this persecution, for the pleasure of God in keeping of His faith, be glad for to depart from them.

And therefore, as for all these things, the loss, I mean, of all these outward things that men call the gifts of fortune, this is, methinketh, in this Turk's persecution for the faith consolation great and sufficient, that sith every man that hath them either setteth by them for the world or for God. He that setteth by them for the world hath, as I have shewed you, little profit by them to the body and great harm unto the soul, and therefore may well (if he be wise) reckon that he winneth by the loss, although he lost them but by some common chance, and much more happy then while he loseth them by such a meritorious mean. And on the other side, he that keepeth them for some good purpose, intending to bestow them for the pleasure of God, the loss of them in this Turk's persecution for keeping of the faith can be no manner grief unto him, sith that by his so parting from them he bestoweth them in such wise unto God's pleasure that at the time when he loseth them by no way could he bestow them unto His high pleasure better. For though it had be peradventure better to have bestowed them well before, yet sith he kept them for some good purpose, he would not have left them unbestowed if he had foreknown the chance. But being now prevented so by persecution that he cannot bestow them in that other good way that he would, yet while he parteth from them because he will not part from the faith, though the devil's escheator violently take them from him, yet willingly giveth he them to God.

Another cause for which any man should be content to forgo his goods in the Turk's said persecution

THE FOURTEENTH CHAPTER

Vincent. I cannot in good faith, good uncle, say nay to none of this. And indeed unto them that by the Turk's overrunning of the country were happed to be spoiled and robbed and all their substance movable and unmovable bereft and lost already, their persons only fled and safe, I think that these considerations (considered therewith that, as you lately said, their sorrow could not amend their chance) might unto them be good occasion of comfort and cause them, as you said, make a virtue of necessity. But in the case, uncle, that we now speak of, that is to wit, where they have yet their substance untouched in their own hands and that the keeping or the losing shall hang both in their own hands by the Turk's offer upon the retaining or the renouncing of the Christian faith, here, uncle, I find it (as you said) that this temptation is most sore and most perilous. For I fear me that we shall find few of such as have much to lose that shall find in their hearts so suddenly to forsake their goods with all those other things afore rehearsed whereupon their worldly wealth dependeth.

Anthony. That fear I much, cousin, too; but thereby shall it well, as I said, appear that, seemed they never so good and virtuous before, and flattered they themself with never so gay a gloss of good and gracious purpose that they kept their goods for, yet were their hearts inwardly in the deep sight of God not sound and sure such as they should be, and as peradventure some had themself weened they had be, but like a puff ring of Paris, hollow, light, and counterfeit indeed.

And yet they being even such, this would I fain ask one of them. And I pray you, cousin, take you his person upon you and in this case answer for him. What letteth you, would I ask (for we will take no small man for a sample in this part nor him that had little to lose, for such one were, methink, so far from all frame that would cast away God for a little that he were not worthy to talk with), what letteth, I say therefore, your lordship, that you be not gladly content without any deliberation at all in this kind of persecution rather than to leave your faith to let go all that ever you have at once?

Vincent. Sith you put it, uncle, unto me, to make the matter the more plain, that I should play that great man's part that is so wealthy and hath so much to lose, albeit I cannot be very sure of another man's mind nor what another man would say, yet as far as mine own mind can conjecture I shall answer in his person what I ween would be his let.

And therefore to your question I answer, that there letteth me the thing that yourself may lightly guess, the losing of the manifold commodities which I now have: riches, and substance, lands and great possessions of inheritance with great rule and authority here in my country. All which things the great Turk granteth me to keep still in peace, and have them enhanced too, so that I will forsake the faith of Christ. Yea, I may say to you, I have a motion secretly made me farther, to keep all this yet better cheap, that is to wit, not be compelled utterly to forsake Christ nor all the whole Christian faith, but only some such parts thereof as may not stand with Mahomet's law; and only granting Mahomet for a true prophet and serving the Turk truly in his wars against all Christian kings, I shall not be letted to praise Christ also and to call Him a good man and worship Him and serve Him too.

Anthony.   Nay, nay, my lord, Christ hath not so great need of your lordship as rather than to lose your service He would fall at such covenants with you to take your service at halfs to serve Him and His enemy both. He hath given you plain warning already by Saint Paul that He will have in your service no parting fellow: *Quæ societas lucis ad tenebras? Quæ autem conventio Christi ad Belial?* What fellowship is there between light and darkness? Between Christ and Belial? And He hath also plainly shewed you Himself by His own mouth: *Nemo potest duobus dominis servire:* No man may serve two lords at once. He will have you believe all that He telleth you and do all that He biddeth you and forbear all that He forbiddeth you without any manner exception. Break one of His commandments and break all. Forsake one point of His faith and forsake all, as for any thanks you get of Him for the remnant. And therefore if you devise as it were indentures between God and you, what thing you will do for Him and what thing you will not do, as though He should hold Him content with such service of yours as yourself list appoint Him; if you make, I say, such indentures you shall seal both the parts yourself, and you get thereto none agreement of Him.

And this I say, though the Turk would make such an appointment with you as you speak of, and would when he had made it keep it, whereas he would not, I warrant you, leave you so when he had once brought you so far forth, but would little and little after ere he left you make you deny Christ altogether and take Mahomet in His stead. And so doth he in the beginning when he will not have you believe him to be God. For surely if he were not God he were no good man neither while he plainly said he was God.

But though he would never go so far forth with you, yet Christ will, as I said, not take your service to halfs, but will that you shall love Him with all your whole heart. And because that while He was living here 1500 year ago He foresaw this mind of yours that you have now with which you would fain serve Him in some such fashion as you might keep your worldly substance still, but rather forsake His service than put all your substance from you, He telleth you plain 1500 year ago His own mouth, that He will no such service of you, saying: *Non potestis Deo servire et mammonæ*, you cannot serve both God and your riches together. And therefore this thing stablished for a plain conclusion which you must needs grant if you have faith; and if you be gone from that ground of faith already, then is all our disputation, you wot well, at an end. For whereto should you then rather lose your goods than forsake your faith if you have lost your faith and let it go already? This point, I say therefore, put first for a ground between us both twain agreed, that you have yet the faith still and intend to keep it alway still in your heart, and are but in doubt whether you will lose all your worldly substance rather than forsake your faith in your only word. Now shall I reply to the point of your answer wherein you tell me the loathness of the loss and the comfort of the keeping letteth you to forgo them and moveth you rather to forsake your faith.

I let pass all that I have spoken of the small commodity of them unto your body and of the great harm that the having of them do to your soul. And sith the promise of the Turk made unto you for the keeping of them is the thing that moveth you and maketh you thus to doubt, I ask you first whereby you wot that when you have done all that he will have you do against Christ to the harm of your soul, whereby wot you, I say, that he will keep you his promise in these things that he promiseth you concerning the retaining of your well-beloved worldly wealth for the pleasure of your body.

Vincent. What surety can a man have of such a great prince but his promise, which for his own honour it cannot become him to break?

Anthony. I have known him, and his father afore him too, break more promises than five as great as this is that he should here make with you. Who shall come and cast it in his teeth, and tell him it is a shame for him to be so fickle and so false of his promise? And then what careth he for those words that he wotteth well he shall never hear? Not very much, although they were told him too. If you might come after and complain your grief unto his own person yourself, you should find him as shamefast as a friend of mine, a merchant, found once the sultan of Syria. To whom, being certain years about his merchandise in that country he gave a great sum of money for a certain office meet for him there for the while, which he scant had him granted and put in his hand but that ere ever it was aught worth unto him the sultan suddenly sold it to another of his own sect, and put our Hungarian out. Then came he to him and humbly put him in remembrance of his grant passed his own mouth and signed with his own hand. Whereunto the sultan answered him with a grim countenance: I will thou wit it, losel, that neither my mouth nor mine hand shall be master over me to bind all my body at their pleasure; but I will so be lord and master over them both that whatsoever the one say or the other write I will be at mine own liberty to do what me list myself, and ask them both no leave. And therefore go get thee hence out of my countries, knave.

Ween you now, my lord, that that sultan and this Turk being both of one false sect, you may not find them both like false of their promise?

Vincent. That must I needs jeopard, for other surety can there none be had.

Anthony. An unwise jeoparding, to put your soul in peril of damnation for the keeping of your bodily pleasures, and yet without surety thereof must jeopard them too. But yet go a little farther, lo. Suppose me that you might be very sure that the Turk would break no promise with you: are you then sure enough to retain all your substance still?

Vincent. Yea, then.

Anthony. What if a man should ask you how long?

Vincent. How long? As long as I live.

Anthony. Well, let it be so, then. But yet, as far as I can see, though the great Turk favour you never so much and let you keep your goods as long as ever you live, yet if it hap that you be this day fifty year old, all the favour he can shew you cannot make you one day younger to-morrow, but every day shall you wax older than other; and then within a while must you for all his favour lose all.

Vincent. Well, a man would be glad, for all that, to be sure not to lack while he liveth.

Anthony. Well, then, if the great Turk give you your goods, can there then in all your life none other take them from you again?

Vincent. Verily I suppose no.

Anthony. May he not lose this country again unto Christian men, and you with the taking of this way fall in the same peril then that ye would now eschew?

Vincent. Forsooth, I think that if he get it once he will never lose it after again in our days.

Anthony. Yes, by God's grace. But yet if he lose it after your days, there goeth your children's inheritance away again. But be it now that he could never lose it, could none take your substance from you then?

Vincent. No, in good faith, none.

Anthony. No? None at all? Not God?

Vincent. God? What yes, pardy, who doubteth of that?

Anthony. Who? Marry, he that doubteth whether there be any God or no. And that there lacketh not some such the prophet testifieth where he saith: *Dixit insipiens in corde suo non est Deus:* The fool hath said in his heart there is no God. With the mouth the most foolish will forbear to say it unto other folk, but in the heart they let not to say it softly to themself. And I fear me there be many more such fools than every man would ween there were, and would not let to say it openly too if they forbare it not more for dread or of shame of men than for any fear of God.

But now those that are so frantic foolish as to ween there were no God and yet in their words confess Him, though that, as Saint Paul saith, in their deeds they deny Him, we shall let them pass till it please God shew Himself unto them either inwardly by time by His merciful grace, or else outwardly, but over late for them, by His terrible judgment.

But unto you, my lord, sith you believe and confess, like as a wise man should, that though the Turk keep you promise in letting you keep your substance because you do him pleasure in the forsaking of your faith, yet God, whose faith you forsake and therein do Him displeasure, may so take them from you that the great Turk with all the power he hath is not able to keep you them, why will you be so unwise with the loss of your soul to please the great Turk for your goods while you wot well that God, whom you displease therewith, may take them from you too?

Besides this, sith you believe there is a God you cannot but believe therewith that the great Turk cannot take your goods from you without His will or sufferance, no more than the

devil could from Job. And think you then that if he will
suffer the Turk take away your goods, albeit that by the
keeping and confessing of His faith you please him, He will,
when you displease Him by forsaking His faith, suffer you
of those goods that you get or keep thereby to rejoice or enjoy
any benefit?

Vincent. God is gracious, and though that men offend
Him yet He suffereth them many times to live in prosperity
long after.

Anthony. Long after? Nay, by my troth, my lord, that
doth He no man. For how can that be that He should suffer
you live in prosperity long after when your whole life is but
short in all together, and either almost half thereof or more
than half, you think yourself, I dare say, spent out already
before? Can you burn out half a short candle and then have
a long one left of the remnant?

There cannot in this world be a worse mind than that a
man delight and take comfort in any commodity that he
taketh by sinful mean. For it is the very straight way
toward the taking of boldness and courage in sin, and finally
to fall into infidelity and think that God careth not nor
regardeth not what things men do here nor what mind we
be of.

But unto such minded folk speaketh Holy Scripture in this
wise: *Noli dicere peccavi et nihil mihi accidit triste; patiens
enim redditor est Dominus:* Say not, I have sinned and yet
there hath happed me none harm, for God suffereth before He
strike. But as Saint Austin saith, the longer that He tarrieth
ere He strike the sorer is the stroke when He striketh.

And therefore if ye will well do, reckon yourself very sure
that when you deadly displease God for the getting or the
keeping of your goods, God shall not suffer those goods to do
you good, but either shall He take them shortly from you
or suffer you to keep them for a little while to your more
harm, and after shall He, when you least look therefore, take
you away from them.

And then what a heap of heaviness will there enter into your heart, when you shall see that you shall so suddenly go from your goods and leave them here in the earth in one place, and that your body shall be put in the earth in another place, and (which then shall be most heaviness of all) when you shall fear (and not without great cause) that your soul shall first forthwith and after that at the final judgment your body to be driven down deep toward the centre of the earth, into the fiery pit and dungeon of the devil of hell, there to tarry in torment world without end.

What goods of this world can any man imagine whereof the pleasure and commodity could be such in a thousand year as were able to recompense that intolerable pain that there is to be suffered in one year, yea, or one day, or one hour either? And then what a madness is it for the poor pleasure of your worldly goods of so few years to cast yourself both body and soul into the everlasting fire of hell, whereof there is not minished the mountenance of a moment, by the lying there the space of an hundred thousand years. And therefore our Saviour in few words concluded and confuted all these follies of them that for the short use of this worldly substance forsake Him and His faith and sell their souls unto the devil for ever, where he saith: *Quid prodest homini si universum mundum lucretur, animæ vero suæ detrimentum patiatur?* What availeth it a man if he won all the whole world and lost his soul? This were, methinketh, cause and occasion enough to him that had never so much part of this world in his hand to be content rather to lose it all than for the retaining or increasing of his worldly goods to lose and destroy his soul.

Vincent. This is, good uncle, in good faith very true. And what other thing any of them that would not for this be content have for to allege in reason for the defence of their folly, that can I not imagine nor list not in this matter to play their part no longer. But I pray God give me the grace to play the contrary part indeed, and that I never for any goods or substance of this wretched world forsake my faith toward God, neither in heart nor tongue, as I trust in His great goodness I never shall.

This kind of tribulation trieth what mind men have to their goods, which they that are wise will at the fame thereof see well and wisely laid up safe before.

THE FIFTEENTH CHAPTER

Anthony. Methinketh, cousin, that this persecution shall not only (as I said before) try men's hearts when it cometh and make them know their own affections, whether they have a corrupt, greedy, covetous mind or not, but also the very fame and expectation thereof may teach them this lesson ere ever the thing fall upon them itself to their no little fruit, if they have the wit and the grace to take it in time while they may. For now may they find sure places to lay their treasure in so that all the Turk's army shall never find it out.

Vincent. Marry, uncle, that way they will, I warrant you, not forget as near as their wits will serve them. But yet have I known some that have ere this thought that they had hid their money safe and sure enough, digging it full deep in the ground, and have missed it yet when they came again and have found it digged out and carried away to their hands.

Anthony. Nay, from their hands, I ween ye would say, and it was no marvel, for some such have I known too. But they have hid their goods foolishly in such place as they were well warned before that they should not. And that were they warned by Him that they well knew for such one as wist well enough what would come thereon.

Vincent. Then were they more than mad. But did He tell them too, where they should have hid it to have it sure?

Anthony. Yea, by Saint Mary, did He, for else had he told them but half a tale. But He told them an whole tale, bidding them that they should in no wise hide their treasure in the ground, and He shewed them a good cause. For there thieves use to dig it out and steal it away.

Vincent. Why, where should they hide it then said He? For thieves may hap to find it out in any place.

Anthony. Forsooth, He counselled them to hide their treasure in heaven and there lay it up, for there it shall lie safe. For thither, He said, there can no thief come, till he have left his theft and be waxen a true man first. And He that gave this counsel wist what he said well enough. For it was our Saviour Himself which in the sixth chapter of Saint Matthew saith: *Nolite thesaurizare vobis thesauros in terra, ubi erugo et tinea demolitur, et ubi fures effodiunt et furantur. Thesaurizate autem vobis thesauros in cœlo, ubi nec erugo neque tinea demolitur, et ubi fures non effodiunt nec furantur. Ubi enim est thesaurus tuus, ibi est et cor tuum:* Hoard not up your treasures in earth where the rust and the moth fret it out and where thieves dig it out and steal it away. But hoard up your treasures in heaven where neither the rust nor the moth fret them out and where thieves dig them not out nor steal them away. For whereas is thy treasure there is thine heart too.

If we would well consider these words of our Saviour Christ we should, as methink, need no more counsel at all, nor no more comfort neither concerning the loss of our temporal substance in this Turk's persecution for the faith. For here our Lord in these words teacheth us, where we may lay up our substance safe before the persecution come.

If we put it into the poor men's bosoms there shall it lie safe. For who would go search a beggar's bag for money? If we deliver it to the poor for Christ's sake we deliver it unto Christ Himself. And then what persecutor can there be so strong as to take it out of His hand?

Vincent. These things are, uncle, undoubtedly so true that no man may with words wrestle therewith; but yet ever there hangeth in a man's heart a loathness to lack a living.

Anthony. There doth indeed in theirs that either never or

but seldom hear any good counsel thereagainst, and when
they hear it hearken it but as they would an idle tale, rather for
a pastime or for the manner sake than for any substantial intent and purpose to follow good advertisement and take any
fruit thereby. But verily if we would not only lay our ear
but also our heart thereto and consider that the saying of our
Saviour Christ is not a poet's fable nor an harper's song, but
the very holy word of Almighty God Himself, we would (and
well we might) be full sore ashamed in ourself and full sorry
too when we felt in our affection those words to have in our
hearts no more strength and weight, but that we remain still
of the same dull mind as we did before we heard them.

This manner of ours, in whose breasts the great good counsel of God no better settleth nor taketh no better root, may
well declare us that the thorns, and the briers, and the
brambles of our worldly substance grow so thick and spring
up so high in the ground of our hearts, that they strangle (as
the gospel saith) the word of God that was sown therein.
And therefore is God very good Lord unto us when He
causeth like a good husbandman His folk to come on field
(for the persecutors be His folk to this purpose) and with their
hooks and their stocking-irons grub up these wicked weeds
and bushes of our earthly substance, and carry them quite
away from us, that the word of God sown in our hearts may
have room therein and a glade round about for the warm sun of
grace to come to it and make it grow. For surely those words
of our Saviour shall we find full true: *Ubi est thesaurus tuus,
ibi est et cor tuum:* Whereas thy treasure is there is also thine
heart. If we lay up our treasure in earth, in earth shall be our
hearts. If we send our treasure into heaven, in heaven shall
we have our hearts. And surely the greatest comfort that any
man may have in his tribulation, is to have his heart in heaven.

If thine heart were indeed out of this world and in heaven,
all the kinds of torment that all this world could devise could
put thee to no pain here. Let us, then, send our hearts hence
thither in such manner as we may by sending thither our

worldly substance hence, and let us never doubt it but we shall (that once done) find our hearts so conversant in heaven with the glad consideration of our following the gracious counsel of Christ, that the comfort of His Holy Spirit inspired us therefore shall mitigate, minish, assuage, and in a manner quench the great furious fervour of the pain that we shall happen to have by His loving sufferance for our farther merit in our tribulation.

And therefore, like as if we saw that we should be within a while driven out of this land and fain to fly into another, we would ween that man were mad which would not be content to forbear his goods here for the while and send them into that land before him where he saw he should live all the remnant of his life; so may we verily think yet ourself much more mad (seeing that we be sure it cannot be long ere we shall be sent spite of our teeth out of this world) if the fear of a little lack or the love to see our goods here about us and the loathness to part from them for this little while which we may keep them here, shall be able to let us from the sure sending them before us into the other world, in which we may be sure to live wealthily with them if we send them thither, or else shortly leave them here behind us, and then stand in great jeopardy there to live wretches for ever.

Vincent. In good faith, good uncle, methinketh that concerning the loss of these outward things these considerations are so sufficient comforts that for mine own part, save only grace well to remember them, I would, methink, desire no more.

Another comfort and courage against the loss of worldly substance

THE SIXTEENTH CHAPTER

Anthony. Much less than this may serve, cousin, with calling and trusting upon God's help, without which much more than this cannot serve.

But the fervour of the Christian faith so sore fainteth now-adays and decayeth, coming from hot unto lukewarm and from lukewarm almost to key-cold, that men must now be fain as at a fire that is almost out to lay many dry sticks thereto and use much blowing thereat. But else would I ween, by my troth, that unto a warm faithful man one thing alone whereof we spake yet no word were comfort enough in this kind of persecution, against the loss of all his goods.

Vincent. What thing may that be, uncle?

Anthony. In good faith, cousin, even the bare remembrance of the poverty that our Saviour willingly suffered for us. For I verily suppose that if there were a great king that had so tender love to a servant of his, that he had, to help him out of danger, forsaken and left off all his worldly wealth and royalty, and become poor and needy for his sake, that servant could scant be founden that were of such an unkind villain courage that if himself came after to some substance would not with better will lose it all again than shamefully to forsake such a master.

And therefore, as I say, I do surely suppose that if we would well remember and inwardly consider the great goodness of our Saviour toward us not yet being His poor sinful servants but rather His adversaries and His enemies, and what wealth of this world that He willingly forsook for our sake, being indeed universal king thereof, and so having the power in His own hand to have used it if He had would, instead whereof (to make us rich in heaven) He lived here in neediness and poverty all His life, and neither would have authority, nor keep neither lands nor goods; the deep consideration and earnest advisement of this one point alone were able to make any kind Christian man or woman well content rather for His sake again to give up all that ever God hath lent them (and lent them hath He all that ever they have) than unkindly and unfaithfully to forsake Him. And Him they forsake if that for fear they forsake the confessing of His Christian faith.

And therefore, to finish this peace withal concerning the dread of losing our outward worldly goods, let us consider the slender commodity that they bring, with what labour they be bought, how little while they abide with whomsoever they abide longest, what pain their pleasure is mingled withal, what harm the love of them doth unto the soul, what loss is in the keeping (Christ's faith refused for them), what winning in the loss if we lose them for God's sake, how much more profitable they be well given than evil kept, and finally what unkindness it were if we would not rather forsake them for Christ's sake than unfaithfully forsake Christ for them, which while He lived for our sake forsook all the world, beside the suffering of shameful and painful death whereof we shall speak after.

If we these things, I say, will consider well, and will pray God with His holy hand to print them in our hearts, and will abide and dwell still in the hope of His help, His truth shall, as the prophet saith, so compass us about with a pavis that we shall not need to be afeard *ab incursu et demonio meridiano*, of this incursion of this midday devil, this open plain persecution of the Turk, for any loss that we can take by the bereaving from us of our wretched worldly goods, for whose short and small pleasure in this life forborne we shall be with heavenly substance everlastingly recompensed of God, in joyful bliss and glory.

Of bodily pain, and that a man hath no cause to take discomfort in persecution, though he feel himself in an horror at the thinking upon bodily pain.

THE SEVENTEENTH CHAPTER

Vincent. Forsooth, uncle, as for these outward goods, you have so farforth said that albeit no man can be sure what strength he shall have or how faint and how feeble he may hap to find himself when he shall come to the point, and therefore I can make no warranty of myself, seeing that Saint Peter so suddenly fainted at a woman's word, and so cowardly forsook his master for whom he had so boldly fought within so few hours before, and by that fall in forsaking well perceived that he had been too rash in his promise, and was well worthy to take a fall for putting so full trust in himself.   Yet, in good faith, methinketh now (and God shall, I trust, help me to keep this thought still) that if the Turk should take all that I have unto my very shirt except I would forsake my faith, and offer it me all again with five times as much thereto to fall into his sect, I would not once stick thereat, rather to forsake it every whit than of Christ's holy faith to forsake any point.

But surely, good uncle, when I bethink me farther on the grief and the pain that may turn unto my flesh, here find I the fear that forceth mine heart to tremble.

Anthony. Neither have I cause thereof to marvel, nor you, cousin, cause to be dismayed therefore.   The great horror and fear that our Saviour had in His own flesh against his painful Passion maketh me little to marvel.   And I may well make you take that comfort too, that for no such manner of grudging felt in your sensual parts, the flesh shrinking at the meditation of pain and death, your reason shall give over, but resist it and manly master it.   And though you would fain fly from the painful death and be loath to come thereto, yet may the meditation of His great grievous agony move you, and Himself shall (if you so desire Him) not fail to work with you therein, and get and give you the grace that you shall submit and conform your will therein unto His as He did His unto His Father, and shall thereupon be so comforted with the secret inward inspiration of His Holy Spirit as He was with the personal presence of that angel that after His agony came and comforted Him, that you shall as His true disciple follow Him, and with goodwill without grudge do as He did, and take your cross of pain and passion upon your back, and die for the truth with Him, and thereby reign with Him crowned in eternal glory.

And this I say to give you warning of the thing that is truth, to the intent when a man feeleth such an horror of death in his heart he should not thereby stand in outrageous fear that he were falling.   For many a such man standeth for all that fear full fast, and finally better abideth the brunt (when God is so good unto him as to bring him thereto and encourage him therein) than doth some other that in the beginning feeleth no fear at all.   And yet may it be, and most often so it is.   For God having many mansions, and all wonderful wealthful, in His Father's house, exalteth not every good man up to the glory of a martyr, but foreseeing their infirmity, that though they be of goodwill before and per-adventure of right good courage too, would yet play Saint Peter if they were brought to the point, and thereby bring their souls into the peril of eternal damnation, He provideth otherwise for them before they come thereat, and either findeth a way that men shall not have the mind to lay any hands upon them, as He found for His disciples when Him-self was willingly taken, or that if they set hand on them they shall have no power to hold them, as He found for Saint John the Evangelist which let his sheet fall from him, whereupon they caught hold, and so fled himself naked away and escaped from them, or though they hold him and bring him to prison too, yet God sometime delivereth them thence, as He did Saint Peter.   And sometime He taketh them to Him out of the prison into heaven, and suffereth them not to come to their torment at all, as He hath done by many a good holy man. And some He suffereth to be brought into the torments, and yet suffereth them not to die therein but live many years after and die their natural death, as He did by Saint John the Evangelist and by many another more, as we may well see both by sundry stories and in the epistles of Saint Cyprian also.

And therefore which way God will take with us we cannot tell.   But surely if we be true Christian men this can we well

tell, that without any bold warranties of ourself or foolish
trust in our own strength we be bounden upon pain of
damnation that we be not of the contrary mind, but that we
will with His help (how loath so ever we feel our flesh thereto)
rather yet than forsake Him or His faith afore the world
(which if we do He hath promised to forsake us afore His
Father and all His holy company of heaven), rather, I say,
than we would so do, we would with His help endure and sustain for His sake all the tormentry that the devil with all his
faithless tormentors in this world would devise. And then
when we be of this mind and submit our will unto His, and
call and pray for His grace, we can tell well enough that He
will never suffer them to put more upon us than His grace will
make us able to bear, but will also with their temptation
provide for us a sure way. For *fidelis est Deus*, saith Saint
Paul, *qui non patiatur vos tentari supra id quod potestis, sed dat
etiam cum tentatione proventum:* God is, saith the apostle,
faithful, which suffereth you not to be tempted above that you
may bear, but giveth also with the temptation a way out. For
either, as I said, He will keep us out of their hands (though
He before suffered us to be feard with them to prove our
faith withal, that we may have by the examination of our own
mind some comfort, in hope of His grace, and some fear of
our own frailty to drive us to call for grace), or else if we fall
in their hands (so that we fall not from the trust of Him nor
cease to call for His help) His truth shall (as the prophet saith)
so compass us about with a pavis that we shall not need to
fear this incursion of this midday devil. For either shall
these Turks his tormentors that shall enter this land and
persecute us, either they shall, I say, not have the power to
touch our bodies at all, or else the short pain that they shall
put unto our bodies shall turn us to eternal profit both in our
souls and in our bodies too. And therefore, cousin, to begin
with, let us be of good comfort. For sith we be by our faith
very sure that Holy Scripture is the very word of God and
that the word of God cannot be but true, and that we see that

by the mouth of His holy prophet and by the mouth of His blessed apostle also God hath made us so faithful promise, both that He will not suffer us to be tempted above our power but will both provide a way out for us, and that He will also round about so compass us with His pavis and defend us that we shall have no cause to fear this midday devil with all his persecution, we cannot now but be very sure (except we be very shamefully cowardous of heart, and toward God in faith out of measure faint, and in love less than lukewarm or waxen even key-cold), we may be very sure, I say, that either God shall not suffer the Turks to invade this land or, if they do, God shall provide such resistance that they shall not prevail or, if they prevail, yet if we take the way that I have told you we shall by their persecution take little harm, or rather none harm at all, but that that shall seem harm shall indeed be to us none harm at all, but good.   For if God make us and keep us good men, as He hath promised to do if we pray well therefore, then saith Holy Scripture: *Bonis omnia cooperantur in bonum :* Unto good folk all things turn them to good.

And therefore, cousin, sith that God knoweth what shall happen and not we, let us in the meanwhile with a good hope in the help of God's grace have a good purpose with us of sure standing by His holy faith against all persecutions.   From which if we should (which our Lord forbad) hereafter either for fear or pain, for lack of His grace least in our own default mishap to decline, yet had we both won the well-spent time in this good purpose before to the minishment of our pain, and were also much the more likely that God should lift us up after our fall and give us His grace again.

Howbeit, if this persecution come, we be by this meditation and well continued intent and purpose before the better strengthened and confirmed and much the more likely for to stand indeed.   And if it so fortune (as with God's grace at men's good prayers and amendment of our evil lives it may fortune full well) that the Turks shall either be well withstanden and vanquished, or peradventure not invade us at all.

then shall we pardy by this good purpose get ourself of God a very good cheap thank.

And on the other side, while we now think thereon (as not to think thereon in so great likelihood thereof, I ween no wise man can), if we should, for the fear of worldly loss or bodily pain framed in our own minds, think that we would give over, and to save our goods and our lives forsake our Saviour by denial of His faith, then whether the Turks come or come not, we be gone from God the while. And then if they come not indeed, or come and be driven to flight, what a shame should this be to us before the face of God in so shameful cowardous wise to forsake Him for fear of that pain that we never felt nor never was falling toward us.

Vincent. By my troth, uncle, I thank you. Methinketh that though you never said more in the matter, yet have you even with this that you have of the fear of bodily pain in this persecution spoken here already marvellously comforted mine heart.

Anthony. I am glad, cousin, if your heart have taken comfort thereby. But and if you so have, give God the thank and not me; for that work is His and not mine. For neither am I able any good thing to say but by Him, nor all the good words in the world, no not the holy words of God Himself, and spoken also with His own holy mouth, can be able to profit the man with the sound entering at his ear but if the Spirit of God therewith inwardly work in his soul. But that is His goodness ever ready to do, except the let be through the untowardness of our own froward will.

Of comfort against bodily pain, and first against captivity

The Eighteenth Chapter

AND therefore, now being somewhat in comfort and courage before whereby we may the more quietly consider everything (which is somewhat more hard and difficile to do when the heart is before taken up and oppressed with the troublous

affection of heavy sorrowful fear), let us examine the weight
and the substance of those bodily pains as the sorest part of
this persecution which you rehearsed before, which were
(if I remember you right) thraldom, imprisonment, painful
and shameful death.   And first let us (as reason is) begin with
the thraldom, for that was, as I remember, the first.

Vincent. I pray you, good uncle, say then somewhat
thereof.   For methinketh, uncle, that captivity is a marvellous heavy thing, namely when they shall (as they most
commonly do) carry us far from home into a strange uncouth
land.

Anthony. I cannot say nay but that some grief it is,
cousin, indeed.   But yet as unto me not half so much as it
would be if they could carry me out into any such unknown
country that God could not wit where nor find the mean to
come at me.   But in good faith, cousin, now if my trans-
migration into a strange country should be any great grief
unto me the fault should be much in myself.   For sith (I am
very sure) that whithersoever men convey me, God is no
more verily here than He shall be there, if I get (as I may if I
will) the grace to set mine whole heart upon Him and long
for nothing but Him, it can then make no great matter to my
mind whether they carry me hence or leave me here.   And
then if I find my mind much offended therewith that I am
not still here in mine own country, I must consider that the
cause of my grief is mine own wrong imagination whereby I
beguile myself with an untrue persuasion, weening that this
were mine own country whereas of truth it is not so.   For as
Saint Paul saith: *Non habemus hic manentem civitatem, sed
futuram inquirimus:* We have here no city nor dwelling
country at all, but we seek for one that we shall come to.
And in what country soever we walk in this world, we be but
as pilgrims and wayfaring men.

And if I should take any country for mine own it must
be the country to which I come and not the country from
which I came.   That country that shall be to me then for a

while so strange shall yet pardy be no more strange to me nor longer strange to me neither than was mine own native country when I came first into it. And therefore if that point of my being far from hence be very grievous to me, and that I find it a great pain that I am not where I would be, that grief shall great part grow for lack of sure setting and settling my mind in God where it should be. Which fault of mine when I mend, I shall soon ease my grief.

Now, as for all the other griefs and pains that are in captivity, thraldom, and bondage, I cannot deny but many there are and great. Howbeit, they seem yet somewhat (What say I somewhat? I may say a great deal), the more because we took our former liberty for more a great deal than indeed it was. Let us therefore consider the matter thus.

Captivity, bondage, or thraldom, what is it but the violent restraint of a man being so subdued under the dominion, rule, and power of another, that he must do what the other list to command him and may not do at his liberty such things as he list himself?

Now when we shall be carried away with a Turk and be fain to be occupied about such things as he list to set us, here shall we lament the loss of our liberty and think we bear an heavy burden of our servile condition, and so to do we shall have (I grant well) many times great occasion. But yet should we (I suppose) set thereby somewhat the less if we would remember well what liberty that was that we lost and take it for no larger than it was indeed. For we reckon as though we might before do what we would, but therein we deceive ourself. For what free man is there so free that can be suffered to do what him list? In many things God hath restrained us by His high commandment; so many, that of those things which else we would do I ween it be more than the half. Howbeit, because (God forgive us) we let so little therefore but do what we list, as though we heard Him not, we reckon our liberty never the less for that.

But then is our liberty much restrained by the laws made

by men for the quiet and politic governance of the people. And these would, I ween, let our liberty but a little neither, were it not for fear of the pains that fall thereupon.

Look, then, whether other men that have authority over us command us never no business which we dare not but do, and therefore do it full oft full sore against our wills. Of which things some service is sometime so painful and so perilous too, that no lord can lightly command his bondman worse nor seldom doth command him half so sore.

Let every free man that reckoneth his liberty to stand in doing what he list consider well these points, and I ween he shall then find his liberty much less than he took it for before.

And yet have I left untouched the bondage that almost every man is in that boasteth himself for free, the bondage, I mean, of sin which to be a very bondage I shall have our Saviour Himself to bear me good record. For He saith: *Omnis qui facit peccatum servus est peccati :* Every man that committeth sin is the thrall or the bondman of sin. And then, if this be thus (as it must needs be so, sith God saith it is so), who is there then that may make so much boast of his liberty that he should take it for so sore a thing and so strange to become through chance of war bond unto a man while he is already through sin become willingly thrall and bond unto the devil.

Let us look well how many things and of what vile wretched sort the devil driveth us to do daily through the rash braids of our blind affections which we be for our faultful lack of grace fain to follow and are too feeble to refrain. And then shall we find in our natural freedom our bond service such that never was there any man lord of any so vile a villain that ever would for very shame command him so shameful service.

And let us, in the doing of our service to the man that we be slave unto, remember what we were wont to do about the same time of the day while we were at our free liberty before, and were well likely if we were at liberty to do the like again, and we shall peradventure perceive that it were better for us to do this business than that.

Now shall we have great occasion of comfort if we consider that our servitude (though in the compt of the world it seem to come by chance of war) cometh yet in very deed unto us by the provident hand of God, and that for our great good, if we will take it well, both in remission of sins and also matter of our merit.

The greatest grief that is in bondage or captivity is this (as I trow), that we be forced to do such labour as with our goodwill we would not. But then against that grief Seneca teacheth us a good remedy: *Semper da operam, ne quid invitus facias*: Endeavour thyself evermore that thou do nothing against thy will, but the thing that we see we shall needs do let us use always to put our goodwill thereto.

Vincent. That is, uncle, soon said, but it is hard to do.

Anthony. Our froward mind maketh every good thing hard, and that to our own more hurt and harm. But in this case if we will be good Christian men we shall have great cause gladly to be content for the great comfort that we may take thereby while we remember that in the patient and glad doing of our service unto that man for God's sake, according to His high commandment by the mouth of Saint Paul, *Servi obedite dominis carnalibus*, we shall have our thank and our whole reward of God.

Finally, if we remember the great humble meekness of our Saviour Christ Himself, that He being very Almighty God, *humiliavit semetipsum formam servi accipiens*, humbled Himself and took the form of a bondman or slave rather than His Father should forsake us, we may think ourself very unkind caitiffs, and very frantic fools too, if, rather than to endure this worldly bondage for a while we would forsake Him that hath by His own death delivered us out of everlasting bondage of the devil, and will for our short bondage give us everlasting liberty.

Vincent. Well fare you, good uncle, this is very well said.

Albeit that bondage is a condition that every man of any courage would be glad to eschew and very loath to fall in, yet have you well made it open that it is a thing neither so strange nor so sore as it before seemed unto me, and specially far from such as any man that any wit hath should for fear thereof shrink from the confession of his faith.   And now, therefore, I pray you somewhat speak of imprisonment.

Of imprisonment, and comfort there against

THE NINETEENTH CHAPTER

Anthony.   That shall I, cousin, with goodwill.   And first, if we could consider what thing imprisonment is of his own nature we should not, methinketh, have so great horror thereof.   For of itself it is pardy but a restraint of liberty which letteth a man from going whither he would.

Vincent.   Yes, by Saint Mary, uncle, methinketh it is much more sorrow than so.   For beside the let and restraint of liberty it hath many more displeasures and very sore griefs knit and adjoined thereto.

Anthony.   That is, cousin, very true indeed, and those pains among many sorer than those thought I not after to forget.   Howbeit, I purpose now to consider first imprisonment, but as imprisonment only without any other incommodity beside; for a man may be pardy imprisoned and yet not set in the stocks nor collared fast by the neck, and a man may be let walk at large where he will and yet a pair of fetters fast riveted on his legs.   For in this country, ye wot well, and in Seville and Portugal too, so go there all the slaves.

Howbeit, because that for such things men's hearts hath such horror thereof, albeit that I am not so mad as to go about to prove that bodily pain were no pain, yet sith that because of these manner of pains we so specially abhor the state and condition of prisoners, we should, methinketh, well perceive that a great part of our horror groweth of our own fantasy, if we would call to mind and consider the state and condition of many other folk in whose state and condition we would wish ourself to stand, taking them for no prisoners at all that stand yet for all that in much part of the selfsame points that we abhor imprisonment for. Let us therefore consider these things in order.

And first (as I thought to begin), because those other kinds of griefs that come with imprisonment are but accidents thereunto, and yet neither such kinds of accidents as either be proper thereunto but that they may almost all fall unto a man without it, nor are not such accidents thereunto as are unseparable therefrom but that imprisonment may fall to a man and none of all them therewith; we will, I say, therefore begin with the considering what manner pain or incommodity we should reckon imprisonment to be of himself and of his own nature alone. And then in the course of our communication you shall as you list increase and aggrieve the cause of your horror with the terror of those painful accidents.

Vincent. I am sorry that I did interrupt your tale. For you were about (I see well) to take an orderly way therein. And as yourself have devised, so I beseech you proceed. For though I reckon imprisonment much the sorer thing by sore and hard handling therein, yet reckon I not the prisonment of itself any less than a thing very tedious, all were it used in the most favourable manner that it possibly might. For, uncle, if it were a great prince that were taken prisoner upon the field, and in the hand of a Christian king, which use in such case (for the consideration of their former estate and mutable chance of the war) to shew much humanity to them and in very favourable wise entreat them (for these infidel emperors handle oftentimes the princes that they take more villainously than they do the poorest men, as the great Tamberlane kept the great Turk when he had taken him, to tread on his back alway while he leapt on horseback); but as I began to say by the sample of a prince taken prisoner, were the imprisonment never so favourable, yet were it in my mind no little grief in itself for a man to be pinned up, though not in a narrow chamber, but although his walk were right large and right fair gardens too therein, it could not but grieve his heart to be restrained by another man within certain limits and bounds, and lose the liberty to be where him list.

Anthony. This is, cousin, well considered of you. For in this you perceive well that imprisonment is of himself and his own very nature alone nothing else but the retaining of a man's person within the circuit of a certain space narrower or larger as shall be limited to him, restraining his liberty from the further going into any other place.

Vincent. Very well said, as methinketh.

Anthony. Yet forgat I, cousin, to ask you one question.

Vincent. What is that, uncle?

Anthony. This, lo. If there be two men kept in two several chambers of one great castle, of which two chambers the one is much more large than the other, whether be they prisoners both, or but the one that hath the less room to walk in?

Vincent. What question is it, uncle, but that they be prisoners both (as I said myself before), although the one lay fast locked in the stocks and the other had all the whole castle to walk in?

Anthony. Me thinketh verily, cousin, that you say the truth. And then if prisonment be such a thing as yourself here agree it is, that is to wit, but a lack of liberty to go whither we list, now would I fain wit of you what any one man you know that is at this day out of prison.

Vincent. What one man, uncle? Marry, I know almost none other. For surely prisoner am I none acquainted with that I remember.

Anthony. Then I see well you visit poor prisoners seld.

Vincent. No, by troth, uncle, I cry God mercy. I send them sometime mine alms, but by my troth I love not to come myself where I should see such misery.

Anthony. In good faith, cousin Vincent, though I say it

before you, you have many good conditions; but surely, though I say it before you too, that condition is none of them. Which condition if you would amend, then should you have yet the more good conditions by one, and peradventure the more by three or four. For I assure you it is hard to tell how much good to a man's soul the personal visiting of poor prisoners doth.

But now sith ye can name me none of them that are in prison, I pray you name me some one of all them that you be (as you say) better acquainted with, men, I mean, that are out of prison. For I know, methinketh, as few of them as you know of the other.

Vincent. That were, uncle, a strange case. For every man is, uncle, out of prison that may go where he will, though he be the poorest beggar in the town. And in good faith, uncle (because you reckon imprisonment so small a matter of itself), the poor beggar that is at his liberty and may walk where he will is (as meseemeth) in better case than is a king kept in prison, that cannot go but where men give him leave.

Anthony. Well, cousin, whether every waywalking beggar be by this reason out of prison or no we shall consider further when you will; but in the meanwhile I can by this reason see no prince that seemeth to be out of prison. For if the lack of liberty to go where a man will be imprisonment, as yourself say it is, then is the great Turk by whom we so fear to be put in prison in prison already himself. For he may not go where he will. For an he might, he would into Portugal, Italy, Spain, France, Almaine, and England, and as far on another quarter too, both Prester John's land and the Grand Khan's too.

Now the beggar that you speak of, if he be, as you say he is by reason of his liberty to go where he will, in much better case than a king kept in prison because he cannot go but where men give him leave, then is the beggar in better case, not only than a prince in prison but also than many a prince out of prison too. For I am sure there is many a beggar that may without let walk farther upon other men's ground than many a prince at his best liberty may walk upon his own. And as for walking out abroad upon other men's, that prince might hap to be said nay and holden fast where that beggar with his bag and his staff should be suffered to go forth and hold on his way.

But forasmuch, cousin, as neither the beggar nor the prince is at free liberty to walk where they will, but that if they would walk in some place neither of them both should be suffered, but men would withstand them and say them nay, therefore if imprisonment be (as you grant it is) a lack of liberty to go where we list, I cannot see but, as I say, the beggar and the prince whom you reckon both at liberty be by your own reason restrained in prison both.

Vincent. Yea, but, uncle, both the one and the other have way enough to walk, the one in his own ground, the other in other men's, or in the common highway where they may walk till they be both weary of walking ere any man say them nay.

Anthony. So may, cousin, that king that had, as yourself put the case, all the whole castle to walk in, and yet you say not nay but that he is prisoner for all that, though not so straitly kept, yet as verily prisoner as he that lieth in the stocks.

Vincent. But they may go at the least wise to every place that they need or that is commodious for them, and therefore they do not will to go but where they may go. And therefore be they at liberty to go where they will.

Anthony. Me needeth not, cousin, to spend the time about the impugning every part of this answer. For letting pass by that though a prisoner were with his keeper brought into every place where need required, yet sith he might not when he would go where he would for his only pleasure, he were, ye wot well, a prisoner still. And letting pass over also this, that it were to this beggar need and to this king commodious to go into divers places where neither of them both may come, and letting pass also that neither of them both is lightly so temperately determined but that they both fain so would do indeed if this reason of yours put them out of prison and set them at liberty and make them free (as I will well grant it doth if they so do indeed), that is to wit, if they have no will to go but where they may go indeed, then let us look on our other prisoners enclosed within a castle, and we shall find that the straitest kept of them both, if he get the wisdom and the grace to quiet his own mind and hold himself content with that place, and long not, like a woman with child for her lusts, to be gadding out anywhere else, is by the same reason of yours, while his will is not longing to be anywhere else, he is, I say, at his free liberty to be where he will, and so is out of prison too.   And on the other side, if though his will be not longing to be anywhere else, yet because that if his will so were he should not so be suffered, he is therefore not at his free liberty, but a prisoner still.   So sith your free beggar that you speak of and the prince that you call out of prison too, though they be (which I ween very few be) by some special wisdom so temperately disposed that they have not the will to be but where they see they may be suffered to be, yet sith that if they would have that will they could not then be where they would, they lack the effect of free liberty, and be both twain in prison too.

Vincent.   Well, uncle, if every man universally be by this reason in prison already, after the very propriety of imprisonment, yet to be imprisoned in this special manner (which manner is only commonly called imprisonment) is a thing of great horror and fear both for the straitness of the keeping and the hard handling that many men have therein.   Of all which griefs and pains and displeasures in this other general imprisonment that you speak of we feel nothing at all.   And therefore every man abhorreth the one and would be loath to come into it, and no man abhorreth the other, for they feel none harm nor find no fault therein.   Wherefore, uncle, in good faith, though I cannot find answers convenient wherewith to avoid your arguments, yet to be plain with you and tell you the very truth, my mind findeth not itself satisfied in this point, but that ever methinketh that these things, wherewith you rather convince and conclude me than induce a credence and persuade me that every man is in prison already, be but sophistical fantasies, and that, except those that are commonly called prisoners, other men are not in any prison at all.

Anthony. Well fare thine heart, good cousin Vincent. There was, in good faith, no word that you spake since we first talked of these matters that half so well liked me as these that you speak now.   For if you had assented in words and in your mind departed unpersuaded, then if the thing be true that I say, yet had you lost the fruit.   And if it be peradventure false and myself deceived therein, then while I should ween that it liked you too, you should have confirmed me in my folly.   For in good faith, cousin, such an old fool am I that this thing, in the persuading whereof unto you I had weened I had quit me well and when I have all done appeareth to your mind but a trifle and a sophistical fantasy, myself have so many years taken for so very substantial truth, that as yet my mind cannot give me to think it any other.   Wherefore, lest I play as the French priest played (that had so long used to say *dominus* with the second syllable long, that at last he thought it must needs be so, and was ashamed to say it short), to the intent that you may the better perceive me or I the better myself, we shall here between us a little more consider the thing.   And hardly spit well on your hands and take good hold, and give it not over against your own mind.   For then were we never the nearer.

Vincent. Nay by my troth, uncle, that intend I not, nor nothing did yet since we began.   And that may you well perceive by some things which without any great cause, save for the further satisfaction of mine own mind, I repeated and debated again.

Anthony. That guise, cousin, hold on hardly still. For in this matter I purpose to give over my part, except I make yourself perceive both that every man universally is a very prisoner in very prison plainly without any sophistication at all, and that there is also no prince living upon earth but he is in worse case prisoner by this general imprisonment that I speak of than is many a lewd simple wretch by that special imprisonment that you speak of. And over this, that in this general imprisonment that I speak of men are for the time that they be therein so sore handled and so hardly, and in such painful wise that men's hearts have with reason great cause as sore to abhor this hard handling that is in this imprisonment, as the other that is in that.

Vincent. By my troth, uncle, these things would I fain see well proved.

Anthony. Tell me then, cousin, first, by your troth, if there were a man attainted of treason or of felony, and after judgment given of his death and that it were determined that he should die, only the time of his execution delayed till the king's further pleasure known, and he thereupon delivered to certain keepers and put up in a sure place out of which he could not scape, were this man a prisoner or no?

Vincent. This man, quoth he? Yea, marry, that he were in very deed if ever any man were.

Anthony. But now, what if for the time that were mean between his attainder and his execution he were so favourably handled that he were suffered to do what he would as he was while he was abroad, to have the use of his lands and his goods, and his wife and his children licence to be with him, and his friends leave at liberty to resort unto him, and his servants not forboden to abide about him, and add yet thereunto that the place were a great castle royal with parks and other pleasures therein, a very great circuit about. Yea, add yet (an ye will) that he were suffered to go and ride also, both when he would and whither he would, only this one point alway provided and foreseen, that he should ever be surely seen to and safely kept from scaping, so that took he never so much of his own mind in the meanwhile all other ways save scaping, yet he well knew that scape he could not, and that when he were called for, to execution and to death he should. Now, cousin Vincent, what would you call this man? A prisoner because he is kept for execution, or no prisoner because he is in the meanwhile so favourably handled, and suffered to do all that he would save scape. And I bid you not here be hasty in your answer, but advise it well that you grant no such thing in haste as you would after mislike by leisure and think yourself deceived.

Vincent. Nay, by my troth, uncle, this thing needeth no study at all in my mind; but that for all this favour shewed him and all this liberty lent him, yet being condemned to death and being kept therefore and kept with such sure watch laid upon him that he cannot escape, he is all that while a very plain prisoner still.

Anthony. In good faith, cousin, methinketh you say very true. But then one thing must I yet desire you, cousin, to tell me a little further. If there were another laid in prison for a fray and through the jailer's displeasure were bolted and fettered and laid in a low dungeon in the stocks where he might hap to lie peradventure for a while, and abide in the mean season some pain but no danger of death at all but that out again he should come well enough, which of these two prisoners stood in worse case? He that hath all this favour or he that is thus hardly handled?

Vincent. By our Lady, uncle, I ween that most part of men, if they should needs choose, had liefer be such prisoners in every point as he that so sorely lieth in the stocks than in every point such as he that at such liberty walketh about the park.

Anthony. Consider then, cousin, whether this thing seem any sophistry to you that I shall shew you now; for it shall be such as seemeth in good faith substantial true to me. And if it so happen that you think otherwise I will be very glad to perceive which of us both is beguiled.

For it seemeth to me, cousin, first, that every man coming
into this world here upon earth, as he is created by God so
cometh he hither by the providence of God. Is this any
sophistry first or not?

Vincent. Nay verily, this is very substantial truth.

Anthony. Now take I this also for very truth in my mind,
that there cometh no man nor woman hither into the earth
but that ere ever they come quick into the world out of the
mother's womb God condemneth them unto death by His
own sentence and judgment for the original sin that they
bring with them, contracted in the corrupted stock of our
forefather Adam. Is this, think you, cousin, verily thus or
not?

Vincent. This is, uncle, very true indeed.

Anthony. Then seemeth this true further unto me, that
God hath put every man here upon the earth under so sure
and under so safe keeping that of all the whole people living
in this wide world there is neither man, woman, nor child,
would they never so far wander about and seek it, that
possibly can find any way whereby they may scape from
death. Is this, cousin, a fond imagined fantasy or is it very
truth indeed?

Vincent. Nay, this is none imagination, uncle, but a thing
so clearly proved true that no man is so mad to say nay.

Anthony. Then need I no more, cousin. For then is all
the matter plain and open evident truth which I said I took
for truth, which is yet more a little now than I told you before
when you took my proof yet but for a sophistical fantasy
and said that, for all my reasoning that every man is a
prisoner, yet you thought that except these whom the common people call prisoners there is else no man a very prisoner
indeed. And now you grant yourself again for very substantial open truth that every man is here (though he be the
greatest king upon earth) set here by the ordinance of God in
a place (be it never so large), a place, I say, yet (and you say
the same) out of which no man can escape, but that therein is

every man put under sure and safe keeping to be readily set forth when God calleth for him, and that then he shall surely die. And is not then, cousin, by your own granting before, every man a very prisoner when he is put in a place to be kept to be brought forth when he would not, and himself not wot whither?

Vincent. Yes, in good faith, uncle. I cannot but well perceive this to be so.

Anthony. This were (you wot well) true, although a man should be but taken by the arm and in fair manner led out of this world unto his judgment. But now while we well know that there is no king so great but that all the while he walketh here, walk he never so loose, ride he with never so strong an army for his defence, yet himself is very sure (though he seek in the mean season some other pastime to put it out of his mind), yet is he very sure, I say, that escape can he not, and very well he knoweth that he hath already sentence given upon him to die, and that verily die he shall, and that himself, though he hope upon long respite of his execution, yet can he not tell how soon, and therefore (but if he be a fool) he can never be without fear that either on the morrow or on the selfsame day the grisly cruel hangman Death which from his first coming in hath ever hoved aloof and looked toward him and ever lien in a wait on him, shall amid among all his royalty and all his main strength neither kneel before him nor make him any reverence nor with any good manner desire him to come forth, but rigorously and fiercely grip him by the very breast and make all his bones rattle, and so by long and divers sore torments strike him stark dead in this prison, and then cause his body to be cast into the ground in a foul pit within some corner of the same, there to rot and be eaten with the wretched worms of the earth, sending yet his soul out further unto a more fearful judgment whereof at his temporal death his success is uncertain, and therefore, though by God's grace not out of good hope, yet for all that in the meanwhile in very sore dread and fear, and

peradventure in peril inevitable of eternal fire too. Methinketh therefore, cousin, that (as I told you) this keeping of
every man in this wretched world for execution of death is a
very plain imprisonment indeed; and that (as I say) such that
the greatest king is in this prison in much worse case in all his
wealth than many a man is by the other imprisonment, that is
therein sore and hardly handled. For where some of those
lie not there attainted nor condemned to death, the greatest
man of this world and the most wealthy in this universal
prison is laid in to be kept undoubtedly for death.

Vincent. But yet, uncle, in that case is the other prisoner
too, for he is as sure that he shall die pardy.

Anthony. This is very true, cousin, indeed, and well
objected to. But then you must consider that he is not in
danger of death by reason of the prison into which he is put
peradventure but for a light fray, but his danger of death is
by the other imprisonment by which he is prisoner in the great
prison of this whole earth, in which prison all the princes
thereof be prisoners as well as he. If a man condemned to
death were put up in a large prison, and while his execution
were respited he were, for fighting with his fellows, put up in a
strait place part of the same, he is in danger of death in that
strait prison, but not by the being in that, for therein is he
but for the fray. But his deadly imprisonment was the other,
the larger I say, into which he was put for death. So the
prisoner that you speak of is, beside the narrow prison, a
prisoner of the broad world, and all the princes thereof
therein prisoners with him; and by that imprisonment both
they and he in like danger of death, not by that strait imprisonment that is commonly called imprisonment, but by
that imprisonment which, because of the large walk, men call it
liberty, and which prison you therefore thought but a fantasy
sophistical to prove it any prison at all. But now may you,
methinketh, very plainly perceive that this whole earth is not
only for all the whole kind of man a very plain prison indeed
but also that every man without exception, even those that are

most at their liberty therein and reckon themself great lords
and possessioners of very great pieces thereof, and thereby
wax with wantonness so forgetful of their own state that they
ween they stand in great wealth, do stand for all that indeed,
by the reason of their imprisonment in this large prison of the
whole earth, in the selfsame condition that other do stand
which in the narrow prisons (which only be called prisons and
which only be reputed prisons in the opinion of the common
people) stand in the most fearful and in the most odious case,
that is to wit, condemned already to death.   And now, cousin,
if this thing that I tell you seem but a sophistical fantasy to
your mind I would be glad to know what moveth you so to
think.   For in good faith, as I have told you twice, I am no
wiser but that I verily ween that the thing is thus of very plain
truth in very deed.

THE TWENTIETH CHAPTER

Vincent.   In good faith, uncle, as for thus farforth I not only
can make with any reason no resistance thereagainst, but also
see very clearly proved that it can be none otherwise but that
every man is in this world a very prisoner, sith we be all put
here into a sure hold to be kept till we be put unto execution
as folk already condemned all to death.   But yet, uncle, the
strait keeping, collaring, bolting, and stocking, with lying in
straw or on the cold ground (which manner of hard handling is
used in these special prisonments that only be called commonly by that name) must needs make the imprisonment
which only beareth among the people that name much more
odious and dreadful than the general imprisoning, wherewith
we be every man universally prisoned at large, walking where
we will round about the wide world; in which broad prison out
of those narrow prisons there is with the prisoners no such
hard handling used.

Anthony.   I said I trow, cousin, that I purposed to prove you further yet that in this general prison, the large prison, I mean, of this whole world, folk be for the time that they be therein as sore handled and as hardly and wrenched and wrung and braked in such painful wise that our hearts (save that we consider it not) have with reason good and great cause to grudge against and (as farforth as pertaineth only to the respect of pain) as much horror to conceive against the hard handling that is in this prison, as the other that is in that.

Vincent.   Indeed, uncle, truth it is that this you said you would prove.

Anthony.   Nay, so much said I not, cousin, but I said I would if I could, and if I could not then would I therein give over my part.   But that, trust I, cousin, I shall not need to do, the thing seemeth me so plain.   For, cousin, not only the prince and king, but also, though he have both angels and devils that are jailers under him, yet the chief jailer over this whole broad prison the world is (as I take it) God; and that I suppose ye will grant me too.

Vincent.   That will I not, uncle, deny.

Anthony.   If a man be, cousin, committed unto prison for no cause but to be kept though there be never so great charge upon him, yet his keeper, if he be good and honest, is neither so cruel that would pain the man of malice nor so covetous that would put him to pain to make him seek his friends and to pay for a pennyworth of ease; else if the place be such that he be sure to keep him safe otherwise, or that he can get surety for the recompense of more harm than he seeth he should have if he scaped, he will never handle him in any such hard fashion as we most abhor imprisonment for.   But, marry, if the place be such as the keeper cannot otherwise be sure, then is he compelled to keep him after the rate the straiter.   And also if the prisoner be unruly and fall to fighting with his fellows or do some other manner of shrewd turns, then useth the keeper to punish him sundry wise in some of such fashions as yourself have spoken of.   So is it now, cousin, that God, the chief jailer, as I say, of this broad prison the world, is neither cruel nor covetous. And this prison is also so sure and so subtly builded that albeit that it lieth open on every side without any wall in the world, yet wander we never so far about therein, the way to get out at shall we never find, so that He neither needeth to collar us nor to stock us for any fear of scaping away. And therefore except He see some other cause than our only keeping for death, He letteth us in the meanwhile, for as long as He list to respite us, walk about in the prison and do therein what we will, using ourself in such wise as He hath by reason and revelation from time to time told us His pleasure.

And hereof it cometh, lo, that by reason of this favour for a time we wax, as I said, so wanton that we forget where we be, weening that we were lords at large, whereas we be indeed (if we would consider it) even silly poor wretches in prison. For, of very truth, our very prison this earth is; and yet thereof we cant us out, part by covenants that we make among us and part by fraud and part by violence too, divers parts diversely to ourself, and change the name thereof from the odious name of prison and call it our own land and our livelihood. Upon our prison we build; our prison we garnish with gold and make it glorious; in this prison they buy and sell; in this prison they brawl and chide; in this they run together and fight; in this they dice; in this they card; in this they pipe and revel; in this they sing and dance; and in this prison many a man reputed right honest letteth not for his pleasure in the dark privily to play the knave.

And thus while God, our king and our chief jailer too, suffereth us and letteth us alone, we ween ourself at liberty and we abhor the state of those whom we call prisoners, taking ourself for no prisoners at all.

In which false persuasion of wealth and forgetfulness of our own wretched state which is but a wandering about for a while in this prison of this world till we be brought unto the execution of death, while we forget with our folly both ourself and our jail and our under-jailers, angels and devils both, and our chief jailer God too, God that forgetteth not us but seeth us all the while well enough, and being sore discontent to see so shrewd rule kept in the jail (beside that He sendeth the hangman Death to put to execution here and there sometime by the thousands at once), He handleth many of the remnant, whose execution He forbeareth yet unto a farther time, even as hardly, and punisheth them as sore in this common prison of the world as there are any handled in those special prisons which for the hard handling used (you say) therein your heart hath in such horror and so sore abhorreth.

Vincent. The remnant will I not gainsay, for, methinketh, I see it so indeed. But that God, our chief jailer in this world, useth any such prisonly fashion of punishment, that point must I needs deny. For I neither see Him lay any man in the stocks or strike fetters on his legs or so much as shut him up in a chamber either.

Anthony. Is he no minstrel, cousin, that playeth not on an harp? Maketh no man melody but he that playeth on a lute? He may be a minstrel and make melody, you wot well, with some other instrument, some strange fashioned peradventure that never was seen before.

God, our chief jailer, as Himself is invisible, so useth He in His punishments invisible instruments, and therefore not of like fashion as the other jailers do, but yet of like effect and as painful in feeling as those. For He layeth one of His prisoners with an hot fever as evil at his ease in a warm bed as the other jailer layeth his on the cold ground; He wringeth them by the brows with a megrim; He collareth them by the neck with a quinsy; He bolteth them by the arm with a palsy that they cannot lift their hands to their head; He manacleth their hands with the gout in their fingers; He wringeth them by the legs with the cramp in their shins; He bindeth them to the bed board with the crick in the back, and layeth one there along and as unable to rise as though he lay fast by the feet in the stocks.

Some prisoner of another jail singeth, danceth in his two

fetters, and feareth not his feet for stumbling at a stone, while God's prisoner that hath his one foot fettered with the gout lieth groaning on a couch and quaketh, and crieth out if he fear there would fall on his foot no more but a cushion.

And therefore, cousin, as I said, if we consider it well we shall find this general prison of this whole earth a place in which the prisoners be as sore handled as they be in the other. And even in the other some make as merry too as there do some in this that are very merry at large out of that.

And surely, like as we ween ourself out of prison now, so if there were some folk born and brought up in a prison that never came on the wall nor looked out at the door nor never heard of other world abroad but saw some, for shrewd turns done among themself, locked up in straiter room and heard them only called prisoners that were so served and themself ever called free folk at large, the like opinion would they have there of themself then that we have here of ourself now. And when we take ourself for other than prisoners now, as verily be we now deceived as those prisoners should there be then.

Vincent. I cannot, uncle, in good faith say nay but that you have performed all that you have promised. But yet sith that for all this there appeareth no more but that as they be prisoners so be we too, and that as some of them be sore handled so be some of us too (sith we wot well for all this that when we come to those prisons we shall not fail to be in a straiter prison than we be now, and to have a door shut upon us where we have none shut on us now), this shall we be sure of at the least wise if there come no worse, and then may there come worse, ye wot well, it cometh there so commonly. Wherefore, for all this, it is yet little marvel though men's hearts grudge much thereagainst.

Anthony. Surely, cousin, in this you say very well. Howbeit, somewhat had your words touched me the nearer if I had said that imprisonment were no displeasure at all. But the thing that I say, cousin, for our comfort therein, is that our fantasy frameth us a false opinion by which we deceive ourself and take it for sorer than it is. And that do we by the reason that we take ourself before for more free than we be, and prisonment for a stranger thing to us than it is indeed. And thus far forth, as I said, have I proved truth in very deed. But now the incommodities that you repeat again, those, I say, that are proper to the imprisonment of their own nature, that is to wit, to have less room to walk in and to have the door shut upon us, these are, methinketh, so very slender and slight, that in so great a cause as to suffer for God's sake we might be sore ashamed so much as once to think upon them.

Many a good man there is, ye wot well, which without any force at all or any necessity wherefore he should so do suffereth these two things willingly of his own choice with much other hardness more. Holy monks, I mean, of the Charterhouse order such as never pass their cells but only to the church set fast by their cells, and thence to their cells again. And Saint Bridget's order, and Saint Clare's much like, and in a manner all close religious houses; and yet anchors and anchoresses most especially, all whose whole room is less than a meetly large chamber. And yet are they there as well content many long years together as are other men, and better too, that walk about the world. And therefore you may see that the loathness of less room and the door shut upon us, while so many folk are so well content therewith, and will for God's love live so to choose, is but an horror enhanced of our own fantasy. And indeed I wist a woman once that came into a prison to visit of her charity a poor prisoner there, whom she found in a chamber, to say the truth, meetly fair, and at the least wise it was strong enough; but with mats of straw the prisoner had made it so warm both under the foot and round about the walls that in these things for the keeping of his health she was on his behalf glad and very well comforted. But among many other displeasures that for his sake she was sorry for, one she lamented much in her mind, that he should have the chamber door upon him by night made fast by the jailer that should shut him in. For, by my troth, quoth she, if the door should be shut upon me I would ween it would stop up my breath. At that word of hers the prisoner laughed in his mind, but he durst not laugh aloud nor say nothing to her, for somewhat indeed he stood in awe of her and had his finding there much part of her charity for alms; but he could not but laugh inwardly, why he wist well enough, that she used on the inside to shut every night full surely her own chamber to her, both door and windows too, and used not to open them of all the long night. And what difference, then, as to the stopping of the breath whether they were shut up within or without?

And so surely, cousin, these two things that you speak of are neither other of so great weight that in Christ's cause ought to move a Christian man; and the one of the twain is so very a childish fantasy that in a matter almost of three chips (but if it were in chance of fire) never should move any man.

As for those other accidents of hard handling therein, so mad am I not to say they be no grief, but I say that our fear may imagine them much greater grief than they be. And I say that such as they be, many a man endureth them, yea and many a woman too, that after fare full well.

And then would I wit what determination we take, whether for our Saviour's sake to suffer some pain in our bodies sith He suffered in His blessed body so great pain for us, or else to give Him warning and be at a point rather utterly to forsake Him than suffer any pain at all. He that cometh in his mind unto this latter point (from which kind of unkindness God keep every man), comfort he none needeth, for he will flee the need. And counsel, I fear, availeth him little if grace be so far gone from him. But on the other side, if rather than to forsake our Saviour we determine ourself to suffer any pain at all, I cannot then see that the fear of hard handling should anything stick with us and make us so to shrink as we rather would forsake His faith than to suffer for His sake so much as imprisonment, sith the handling is neither such in prison but that many men many years, and many women too, live therewith and sustain it and afterward yet fare full well, and yet that it may well fortune that, beside the very bare imprisonment, there shall hap us none hard handling at all, nor that same haply but for a short while neither, and yet, beside all this, peradventure not at all.   And specially sith which of all these ways shall be taken with us lieth all in His will for whom we be content to take it, and which for that mind of ours favoureth us and will suffer no man to put more pain unto us than He well wotteth we shall be well able to bear.   For He will give us the strength thereto Himself, as you have heard His promise already by the mouth of Saint Paul: *Fidelis autem Deus est, qui non patietur vos tentari supra id quod potestis ferre, sed dat etiam cum tentatione proventum:* God is faithful, which suffereth you not to be tempted above that you may bear, but giveth also with the temptation a way out.   But now, if we have not lost our faith already before we come to forsake it for fear, we know very well by our faith that by the forsaking of our faith we fall into that state to be cast into the prison of hell, and that can we not tell how soon; but as it may be that God will suffer us to live a while here upon earth, so may it be that He will throw us into that dungeon beneath before the time that the Turk shall once ask us the question. And therefore if we fear imprisonment so sore we be much more than mad, that we fear not most the far more sore. For out of that prison shall no man never get and in this other shall no man abide but a while.

In prison was Joseph while his brethren were at large; and yet after were his brethren fain to seek upon him for bread.   In prison was Daniel, and the wild lions about him; and yet even there God kept him harmless and brought him safe out again.   If we think that He will not do the like wise for us let us not doubt but He will do for us either the like or better.   For better may He do for us if He suffer us there to die.

Saint John the Baptist was, you wot well, in prison while Herod and Herodias sat full merry at the feast and the daughter of Herodias delighted them with her dancing till with her dancing she danced off Saint John's head. And now sitteth he with great feast in heaven at God's board while Herod and Herodias full heavily sit in hell burning both twain, and to make them sport withal the devil with the damsel dance in the fire afore them.

Finally, cousin, to finish this piece with, our Saviour was Himself take prisoner for our sake, and prisoner was He carried, and prisoner was He kept, and prisoner was He brought forth before Annas, and prisoner from Annas carried unto Caiaphas. Then prisoner was He carried from Caiaphas unto Pilate, and prisoner was He sent from Pilate to King Herod, prisoner from Herod unto Pilate again, and so kept as prisoner to the end of His Passion.

The time of His imprisonment, I grant well, was not long, but as for hard handling which our hearts most abhor, He had as much in that short while as many men among them all in much longer time. And surely then if we consider of what estate He was and therewith that He was prisoner in such wise for our sake, we shall, I trow (but if we be worse than wretched beasts), never so shamefully play the unkind cowards as for fear of imprisonment sinfully to forsake Him, nor so foolish neither as by forsaking of Him to give Him the occasion again to forsake us, and with the avoiding of an easier prison fall into a worse, and instead of prison that cannot keep us long fall into that prison out of which we can never come, where the short prisonment would win us everlasting liberty.

The fear of shameful and painful death

THE TWENTY-FIRST CHAPTER

Vincent. Forsooth, uncle, our Lord reward you therefore, if we feared not farther beside imprisonment the terrible dart of shameful and painful death. As for imprisonment, I would verily trust that, remembering these things which I have here heard of you, rather than I should forsake the faith of our Saviour I would with help of grace never shrink thereat.

But now are we comen, uncle, with much work at the last unto the last and uttermost point of the dread that maketh *incursum et demonium meridianum,* this incursion of this mid-day devil. This open invasion of the Turk and his persecution against the faith seem so terrible unto men's minds, that although the respect of God vanquish all the remnant of the trouble that we have hitherto perused, as loss of goods, lands, and liberty, yet when we remember the terror of shameful and painful death, that point so suddenly putteth us in oblivion of all that should be our comfort that we feel (all men, I fear me, for the most part) the fervour of our faith wax so cold and our hearts so faint that we find ourself at the point to fall even therefrom for fear.

Anthony. To this I say not nay, cousin, but that indeed in this point is the sore pinch. And yet you see for all this that even this point too taketh increase or minishment of dread after the difference of the affections that are before fixed and rooted in the mind, so far forth that you see some man set so much by his worldly substance that he less feareth the loss of his life than the loss of lands. Yea, some man shall you see that abideth deadly torment and such as some other had liefer die than endure rather than he would bring out the money that he hath hid. And I doubt not but you have heard of many by right authentic stories that some for one cause, some for other, have not letted willingly to suffer death, divers in divers kinds, and some both with despiteful rebuke and painful torment too. And therefore, as I say, we may see that the affection of the mind toward the increase or decrease of dread maketh much of the matter.

Now are the affections of men's minds imprinted by divers means. One way by the mean of the bodily senses, moved by such things pleasant or displeasant as are outwardly through sensible worldly things offered and objected unto them. And this manner of receiving the impression of affections is common unto men and beasts. Another manner of receiving affections is by the mean of reason which both ordinately tempereth those affections that the bodily five wits imprint and also disposeth a man many times to some spiritual virtues very contrary to those affections that are fleshly and sensual. And those reasonable dispositions been affections spiritual and proper to the nature of man and above the nature of beasts. Now, as our ghostly enemy the devil enforceth himself to make us lean unto the sensual affections and beastly, so doth Almighty God of His goodness by His Holy Spirit inspire us good motions with aid and help of His grace toward the other affections spiritual, and by sundry means instructeth our reason to lean unto them, and not only to receive them as engendered and planted in our soul, but also in such wise water them with the wise advertisement of godly counsel and continual prayer, that they may be habitually radicate and surely take deep root therein. And after, as the one kind of affection or the other beareth the strength in our heart so be we stronger or feebler against the terror of death in this cause.

And therefore will we, cousin, assay to consider what things there are for which we have cause in reason to master the affection fearful and sensual, and though we cannot clean avoid it and put it away, yet in such wise to bridle it at the least that it run not out so far like an headstrong horse that spite of our teeth it carry us out unto the devil.

Let us, therefore, now consider and well weigh this thing that we dread so sore, that is to wit, shameful and painful death.

*Of Death considered by himself alone, as a bare leaving of this
life only*

THE TWENTY-SECOND CHAPTER

AND first I perceive well by these two things that you join
unto Death, that is to wit, shameful and painful, you would
esteem Death so much the less if he should come alone without
either shame or pain.

Vincent. Without doubt, uncle, a great deal the less. But
yet though he should come without them both by himself,
whatsoever I would, I wot well many a man would be for all
that very loath to die.

Anthony. That I believe well, cousin, and the more pity it
is; for that affection happeth in very few but that either the
cause is lack of faith, lack of hope, or finally lack of wit.
They that believe not the life to come after this and ween
themself here in wealth are loath to leave this, for then they
think they lose all. And thereof cometh the manifold foolish
unfaithful words which are so rife in our many mouths:
This world we know and the other we know not. And that
some say in sport and think in earnest: The devil is not so
black as he is painted; and let him be as black as he will, he
is no blacker than a crow. With many such other foolish
fantasies of the same sort.

Some that believe well enough, yet through the lewdness
of living fall out of good hope of salvation; and then though
they be loath to die I very little marvel. Howbeit, some that
purpose to mend and would fain have some time left them
longer to bestow somewhat better may peradventure be loath
to die also by and by. And that manner loathness, albeit
a very good will gladly to die and to be with God were
in my mind so thankful that it were well able to purchase
as full remission both of sin and pain, as peradventure
he were like if he lived to purchase in many years' penance;
yet will I not say but that such kind of loathness to die
may be before God allowable. Some are there also that

are loath to die that are yet very glad to die and long for to be dead.

Vincent.   That were, uncle, a very strange case.

Anthony.   The case, I fear me, cousin, falleth not very often, but yet sometime it doth, as where there is any man of that good mind that Saint Paul was which for the longing that he had to be with God would fain have been dead, but for the profit of other folk was content to live here in pain, and defer and forbear for the while his inestimable bliss in heaven: *desiderium habens dissolvi et esse cum Christo, multo magis melius, permanere autem in carne necessarium propter vos.*

But of all these kinds, cousin, of folks that are loath to die (except the first kind only that lacketh faith) there is, I suppose, none but that, except the fear of shame or sharp pain joined unto death should be the let, would else for the bare respect of death alone let to depart hence with goodwill in this case of the faith, well witting by his faith that his death taken for the faith should cleanse him clean of all his sins and send him straight to heaven.   And some of these (namely the last kind) are such that shame and pain both joined unto death were unlikely to make them loathe death or fear death so sore but that they would suffer death in this case with goodwill, sith they know well that the refusing of the faith for any cause in this world (were the cause never so good in sight) should yet sever them from God with whom (save for other folk's profit) they so fain would be.   And charity can it not be for the profit of the whole world, deadly to displease Him that made it.

Some are there, I say also, that are loath to die for lack of wit, which albeit that they believe the world that is to come and hope also to come thither, yet they love so much the wealth of this world and such things as delight them therein, that they would fain keep them as long as ever they might, even with tooth and nail.   And when they may be suffered in no wise to keep it no longer but that death taketh them therefrom, then if it may be no better they will agree to be (as soon as they be hence) hanced up in heaven, and be with

God by and by. These folk are as very idiot fools as he that had kept from his childhood a bag full of cherry stones and cast such a fantasy thereto that he would not go from it for a bigger bag filled full of gold.

These folk fare, cousin, as Æsop telleth in a fable that the snail did. For when Jupiter (whom the poets feign for the great God) invited all the poor worms of the earth unto a great solemn feast that it pleased him (I have forgot upon what occasion) upon a time to prepare for them, the snail kept her at home and would not come thereat. And when Jupiter asked her after wherefore she came not at his feast, where he said she should have been welcome and have faren well and should have seen a goodly palace and been delighted with many goodly pleasures, she answered him that she loved no place as well as her own house. With which answer Jupiter waxed so angry that he said, sith she loved her house so well she should never after go from home, but should always after bear her house upon her back wheresoever she went. And so hath she done ever since, as they say; and at the least wise I wot well she doth so now and hath done as long time as I can remember.

Vincent. Forsooth, uncle, I would ween the tale were not all feigned. For I think verily that so much of your tale is true.

Anthony. Æsop meant by that feigned fable to touch the folly of such folk as so set their fantasy upon some small simple pleasure, that they cannot find in their heart to forbear it neither for the pleasure of a better man nor for the gaining of a better thing. By which their fond froward fashion they sometime fall in great indignation and take thereby no little harm.

And surely such Christian folk as by their foolish affection which they have set, like the snail, upon their own house here, this earth, cannot for the loathness of leaving that house find in their heart with their goodwill to go to the great feast that God prepareth in heaven and of His goodness so gently calleth them to, belike, I fear me (but if they mend that mind in time), to be served as the snail was, and yet much worse too. For they be like to have their house here, the earth, bound fast upon their backs for ever, and not walk therewith where they will as the snail creepeth about with hers, but lie fast bound in the midst with the foul fire of hell about them.

For into this folly they bring themself by their own fault as the drunken man bringeth himself into drunkenness, whereby the evil that he doth in his drunkenness is not forgiven him for his folly but to his pain imputed to his fault.

Vincent. Surely, uncle, this seemeth not unlikely; and by their fault they fall in such folly indeed. And yet if this be folly indeed there are then some folk fools that ween themself right wise.

Anthony. That ween themself wise? Marry, I never saw fool yet that thought himself other than wise. For as it is one spark of soberness left in a drunken head when he perceiveth himself drunk and getteth him fair to bed, so if a fool perceive himself a fool that point is no folly but a little spark of wit. But now, cousin, as for these kind of fools, sith they be loath to die for the love that they bear to their worldly fantasies which they should by their death leave behind them and forsake, they that would for that cause rather forsake the faith than die would rather forsake it than lose their worldly goods, though there were offered them no peril of death at all. And then as touching those that are of that mind, we have, you wot well, said as much as yourself thought sufficient this afternoon herebefore.

Vincent. Verily, uncle, that is very true. And now have you rehearsed, as far as I can remember, all the other kinds of them that would be loath to die for any other respect than the grievous qualities of shame and pain joined unto death. And of all these kinds, except the kind of infidelity when no comfort can help but counsel only to the attaining of faith (which faith must be to the receiving of comfort presupposed and had ready before, as you shewed in the beginning of our communication the first day that we talked of the matter), but else, I say, except that one kind, there is none of the remnant of those that were before untouched which were likely to forsake their faith in this persecution for the fear and dread of death, save for those grievous qualities (pain, I mean, and shame) that they see well would come therewith. And therefore, uncle, I pray you give us some comfort against those twain. For in good faith, if death should come without them in such a case as this is, wherein by the losing of this life we should find a far better, mine own reason giveth me that, save for the other griefs going before the change, there would no man that wit hath anything stick at all.

Anthony. Yes, peradventure suddenly before they gather their wits unto them, and therewith well weigh the matter. But they, cousin, that will consider the matter well, reason grounded upon the foundation of faith shall shew them very great substantial causes for which the dread of those grievous qualities that they see shall come with death, shame, I mean, and pain also, shall not so sore abash them as sinfully to drive them therefrom. For the proof whereof let us first begin at the consideration of the shame.

Of the shame that is joined with the death in the persecution for the faith

THE TWENTY-THIRD CHAPTER

How can any faithful wise man dread the death so sore for any respect of shame, when his reason and his faith together may shortly make him perceive that there is therein no piece of very shame at all? For how can that death be shameful that is glorious? Or how can it be but glorious to die for the faith of Christ, if we die both for the faith and in the faith joined with hope and charity, while the Scripture so plainly saith: *Pretiosa in conspectu Domini mors sanctorum eius:* Precious is in the sight of God the death of His saints. Now if the death of His saints be glorious in the sight of God it can never be shameful in very deed, how shameful soever it seem here in the sight of men. For here we may see and be sure that not at the death of Saint Stephen only, to whom it liked Him to shew Himself with the heaven open over His head, but at the death also of every man that so dieth for the faith, God with His heavenly company beholdeth his whole passion and verily looketh on.

Now, if it were so, cousin, that ye should be brought through the broad high street of a great long city, and that all along the way that ye were going there were on the one side of the way a rabble of ragged beggars and madmen that would despise and dispraise you with all the shameful names that they could call you and all the villainous words that they could say to you, and that there were then all along the other side of the same street where you should come by a goodly company standing in a fair range, a row of wise and worship-ful folk allowing and commending you, more than fifteen times as many as that rabble of ragged beggars and railing madmen are, would you let your way by your will, weening that ye went unto your shame for the shameful jesting and railing of those mad foolish wretches? Or hold on your way with a good cheer and a glad heart, thinking yourself much honoured by the laud and approbation of that other honourable sort?

Vincent. Nay, by my troth, uncle, there is no doubt but I would much regard the commendation of those commendable folk and not regard a rush the railing of all those ribalds.

Anthony. Then, cousin, can there no man that hath faith account himself shamed here by any manner death that he suffereth for the faith of Christ, while how vile and how shameful soever it seem in the sight here of a few worldly wretches it is allowed and approved for very precious and honourable in the sight of God and all the glorious company of heaven which as perfectly stand and behold it as those peevish people do, and are in number more than an hundred to one. And of that hundred every one an hundred times more to be regarded and esteemed than of the other an hundred such whole rabbles. And now if a man would be so mad as for fear of the rebuke that he should have of such rebukeful beasts he would be ashamed to confess the faith of Christ, then with fleeing from a shadow of shame he should fall into a very shame and a deadly painful shame indeed. For then hath our Saviour made a sure promise that He will shew himself ashamed of that man before the Father of heaven and all His holy angels, saying in the ninth chapter of Saint Luke: *Qui me erubuerit et meos sermones, hunc Filius Hominis erubescet quum venerit in maiestate sua et Patris et sanctorum angelorum*: He that is ashamed of Me and My words, of him shall the Son of Man be ashamed when He shall come in the majesty of Himself and of His Father and of His holy angels. And what manner of shameful shame shall that be then? If a man's cheeks glow sometime for shame in this world they will fall on fire for shame when Christ shall shew Himself ashamed of them there.

To suffer the thing for Christ's faith that we worldly wretched fools ween were villainy and shame the blessed apostles reckoned for great glory. For they, when they were with despite and shame scourged and thereupon commanded to speak no more of the name of Christ, went their way from the council joyful and glad that God had vouchsafed to do them the worship to suffer shameful despite for the name of Jesu. And so proud were they of the shame and villainous pain put unto them, that for all the forbidding of that great council assembled they ceased not every day to preach out the name of Jesu still, not in the temple only, out of which they were set and whipped for the same before, but also, to double it with, went preaching the name about from house to house too.

I would, sith we regard so greatly the estimation of worldly folk, we would among many naughty things that they use regard also some such as are good. For it is a manner among them in many places that some by handicraft, some by merchandise, some by other kind of living, arise and come forward in the world. And commonly folk are in youth set forth to convenient masters under whom they be brought up and grow. But now whensoever they find a servant such as he disdaineth to do such things as he that is his master did while he was servant himself, that servant every man accounteth for a proud unthrift never like to come to good proof. Let us, lo, mark and consider this, and weigh well therewithal, that our Master Christ (not the Master only, but the Maker, too, of all this whole world) was not so proud to disdain for our sakes the most villainous and most shameful death after the worldly count that then was used in the world; and the most despiteful mocking therewith joined to most grievous pain, as crowning Him with sharp thorn that the blood ran down about His face; then they gave Him a reed in His hand for a sceptre, and kneeled down to Him and saluted Him like a king in scorn, and beat then the reed upon the sharp thorns about His holy head. Now saith our Saviour that the disciple or servant is not above his master; and therefore, sith our Master endured so many kinds of painful shame, very proud beasts may we well think ourself if we disdain to do as our Master did. And whereas He through shame ascended into glory, we would be so mad that we rather will fall into everlasting shame both before heaven and hell than for fear of a short worldly shame to follow Him into everlasting glory.

Of painful death to be suffered in the Turk's persecution for the faith

THE TWENTY-FOURTH CHAPTER

Vincent. In good faith, uncle, as for the shame ye shall need to take no more pain. For I suppose surely that any man that hath reason in his head shall hold himself satisfied with this. But of truth, uncle, all the pinch is in the pain. For as for shame, I perceive well now a man may with wisdom so master it that it shall nothing move him at all, so farforth that it is almost in every country becomen a common proverb that shame is as it is taken. But, by God, uncle, all the wisdom in this world can never so master pain but that pain will be painful, spite of all the wit in this world.

Anthony. Truth it is, cousin, that no man can with all the reason he hath in such wise change the nature of pain, that in the having of pain he feel it not; for but if it be felt it is pardy no pain. And that is the natural cause, cousin, for which a man may have his leg stricken off by the knee and grieve him not, if his head be off but half an hour afore. But reason may make a reasonable man (though he would not be so foolish as causeless to fall therein yet upon good causes, either of gaining some kind of great profit or avoiding some kind of great loss, or eschewing thereby the suffering of far greater pain) not to shrink therefrom and refuse it to his more hurt and harm, but for his far greater advantage and commodity content and glad to sustain it. And this doth reason alone in many cases where it hath much less help to take hold of than it hath in this matter of faith. For well you wot, to take a sour and a bitter potion is great grief and displeasure, and to be lanced and have the flesh cut is no little pain. Now, when such things shall be ministered unto a child or to some childish man either, they will by their own wills rather let their sickness or their sore grow unto their more grief till it become incurable than abide the pain of the curing in time, and that for faint heart joined with lack of discretion. But a man that hath more wisdom, though he would without cause no more abide the pain willingly than would the other, yet sith reason sheweth him what good he shall have by the suffering and what harm by the refusing, this maketh him well content and glad also for to take it.

Now then, if reason alone be sufficient to move a man to take pain for the gaining of worldly rest or pleasure and for the avoiding of another pain (though peradventure more, yet endurable but for a short season), why should not reason

grounded upon the sure foundation of faith and holpen also
forward with aid of God's grace (as it ever is undoubtedly
when folk for a good mind in God's name comen together
thereon, our Saviour saying himself: *Ubi sunt duo vel tres
congregati in nomine meo, ibi et ego sum in medio eorum:* Where
there are two or three gathered together in My name, there am
I also even in the very midst of them), why should not,
then, reason, I say, thus furthered with faith and grace, be
much more able first to engender in us such an affection, and
after by long and deep meditation thereof so to continue that
affection, that it shall turn into an habitual fast and deep-
rooted purpose of patient suffering the painful death of this
body here in earth for the gaining of everlasting wealthy
life in heaven and avoiding of everlasting painful death in
hell?

Vincent. By my troth, uncle, words can I none find that
should have any reason with them (faith alway presupposed,
as you protested in the beginning, for a ground), words, I say,
can I none find wherewith I might reasonably counterplead
this that you have said here already. But yet I remember the
fable that Æsop telleth of a great old hart that had fled from a
little bitch, which had made suit after him and chased him so
long that she had lost him and, as he hoped, more than half
given him over. By occasion whereof having then some time
to talk, and meeting with another of his fellows, he fell in
deliberation with him what were best for him to do, whether
to run on still and fly farther from her or turn again and fight
with her. Whereunto the other hart advised him to fly no
farther lest the bitch might happen to find him again at such
time as he should with the labour of farther fleeing be fallen
out of breath and thereby all out of strength too, and so should
he be killed lying, where he could not stir him, whereas if he
would turn and fight he were in no peril at all. For the man
with whom she hunteth is more than a mile behind her, and
she is but a little body scant half so much as thou, and thy
horns may thrust her through before she can touch thy flesh,

by more than ten times her tooth length. By my troth, quoth the other hart, I like your counsel well, and methinketh that the thing is even soothly such as you say. But I fear me when I hear once that urchin bitch bark I shall fall to my feet and forget all together. But yet an you will go back with me, then methink we shall be strong enough against that one bitch between us both. Whereunto the other hart agreed, and so they both appointed them thereon. But even as they were about to busk them forward to it, the bitch had found the foot again, and on she came yearning toward the place; whom as soon as the harts heard: they to go both twain apace.

And in good faith, uncle, even so I fear it would fare by myself and many other too, which though we think it reason that you say and in our minds agree that we should do as ye say, yea and do peradventure think also that we would indeed do as ye say, yet as soon as we should once hear those hell-hounds, these Turks, come yelping and bawling upon us our hearts should soon fall as clean from us as those other harts flee from the hounds.

Anthony. Cousin, in those days that Æsop speaketh of, though those harts and other brute beasts more had (if he say sooth) the power to speak and talk, and in their talking power to talk reason too, yet to follow reason and rule themself thereby, thereto had they never given them the power. And in good faith, cousin, as for such things as pertain toward the conducting of reasonable men to salvation, I think without help of grace men's reasoning shall do little more. But then are we sure, as I said afore, that as for grace, if we desire it God is at such reasoning alway present and very ready to give it; and but if that men will afterward willingly cast it away, He is ever still as ready to keep it and from time to time glad to increase it. And therefore biddeth us our Lord by the mouth of the prophet, that we should not be like such brutish and unreasonable beasts as were those harts, and as are horses and mules. *Nolite fieri sicut equus et mulus, quibus non est intellectus:* Be not you like an horse and a mule that hath none understanding. And therefore, cousin, let us never dread but that if we will apply our minds to the gathering of comfort and courage against such persecutions, and hear reason, and let it sink into our heart, and cast it not out again, vomit it not up, nor even there choke it up and stifle it with pampering and stuffing up our stomachs with a surfeit of worldly vanities, God shall so well work therewith that we shall feel strength therein, and not in such wise have all such shameful coward-ous hearts as to forsake our Saviour and thereby lose our own salvation and run into eternal fire for fear of death joined therewith though bitter and sharp, yet short for all that, and in a manner a momentary pain.

Vincent. Every man, uncle, naturally grudgeth at pain and is very loath to come to it.

Anthony. That is very truth; nor no man biddeth any man to go run into it but that if he be taken and may not flee. Then we say that reason plainly telleth us that we should rather suffer and endure the less and the shorter here than in hell the sorer and so far the longer too.

Vincent. I heard, uncle, of late, where such a reason was made as you make me now, which reason seemeth undoubted and inevitable unto me.   Yet heard I late, as I say, a man answer it thus.   He said that if a man in this persecution should stand still in the confession of his faith and thereby fall into painful tormentry, he might peradventure hap for the sharpness and bitterness of the pain to forsake our Saviour even in the midst, and die there with his sin and so be damned for ever.   Whereas by the forsaking of the faith in the begin-ning betime, and for the time, and yet not but in word neither, keeping it still nevertheless in his heart, a man may save him-self from that painful death, and after ask mercy and have it, and live long, and do many good deeds, and be saved as Saint Peter was.

Anthony.   That man's reason, cousin, is like a three-footed stool, so tottering on every side that whoso sit thereon may soon take a foul fall.   For these are the three feet of this tottering stool, fantastical fear, false faith, false flattering hope. First it is a fantastical fear that the man conceiveth that it should be perilous to stand in the confession of the faith at the beginning lest he might afterward through the bitterness of pain fall to the forsaking and so die there in the pain therewith out of hand and thereby be utterly damned. As though that if a man by pain were overcome and so forsook his faith, God could not or would not as well give him grace to repent again and thereupon give him forgiveness as him that forsook his faith in the beginning and did set so little by Him, that he would rather forsake Him than suffer for His sake any manner pain at all. As though the more pain that a man taketh for God's sake, the worse would God be to him. If this reason were not unreasonable, then should our Saviour not have said as He did: *Ne terreamini ab his qui occidunt corpus, et posthac non habent amplius quid faciant:* Fear not them that may kill the body, and after that have nothing that they can do farther. For He should by this reason have said: Dread and fear them that may slay the body, for they may by the torment of painful death (but if thou forsake Me betimes in the beginning, and so save thy life, and get of Me thy pardon and forgiveness after) make thee peradventure forsake Me too late, and so to be damned for ever.

The second foot of this tottering stool is a false faith. For it is but a feigned faith for a man to say to God secretly that he believeth Him, trusteth Him, and loveth Him, and then openly, where he should to God's honour tell the same tale and thereby prove that he doth so, there to God's dishonour as much as in him is flatter God's enemies and do them pleasure and worldly worship with the forsaking of God's faith before the world; and is either faithless in his heart too, or else wotteth well that he doth God this despite even before His own face. For, except he lack faith, he cannot but know that our Lord is everywhere present, and while he so shamefully forsaketh Him, full angerly looketh on.

The third foot of this tottering stool is false flattering hope.

For sith the thing that he doth when he forsaketh his faith for fear is by the mouth of God upon the pain of eternal death forboden, though the goodness of God forgiveth many folk the fault, yet to be bolder in offending for the hope of forgiving is a very false pestilent hope wherewith a man flattereth himself toward his own destruction. He that in a sudden braid for fear or other affection unadvisedly falleth, and after in labouring to rise again comforteth himself with hope of God's gracious forgiveness, walketh in the ready way toward his salvation. But he that with the hope of God's mercy to follow doth encourage himself to sin and therewith offendeth God first, I have no power to shut the hand of God from giving out His pardon where He list, nor would if I could, but rather help to pray therefore. But yet I very sore fear that such a man may miss the grace to require it in such effectual wise as to have it granted. Nor I cannot suddenly now remember any sample or promise expressed in Holy Scripture that the offender in such a kind shall have the grace offered after in such wise to seek for pardon that God (by His other promises of remission promised to penitents) bounden Himself to grant it. But this kind of presumption, under pretext of hope, seemeth rather to draw near on the one side (as despair doth on the other side) toward the abominable sin of blasphemy against the Holy Ghost. Against which sin, concerning either the impossibility or at the least the great difficulty of forgiveness our Saviour hath shewed Himself in the twelfth chapter of Saint Matthew and in the third chapter of Saint Mark where He saith that blasphemy against the Holy Ghost shall never be forgiven, neither in this world nor in the world to come. And where the man that you speak of took in his reason a sample of Saint Peter which forsook our Saviour, and got forgiveness after, let him consider again on the other side that he forsook Him not upon the boldness of any such sinful trust, but was overcomen and vanquished upon a sudden fear. And yet by that forsaking Saint Peter won but little, for he did but delay his trouble for a little while, you wot well.   For beside that he repented forthwith very sore that he so had done and wept therefore by and by full bitterly, he came forth at the Whitsuntide ensuing and confessed his Master again; and soon after that he was imprisoned therefore, and not ceasing so, was thereupon sore scourged for the confession of his faith, and yet after that imprisoned again afresh; and being from thence delivered, stinted not to preach on still until that after manifold labours, travels, and troubles, he was at Rome crucified and with cruel torment slain.

And in like wise, I ween, I might in a manner well warrant that there shall no man which denieth our Saviour once and after attaineth remission escape through that denying one penny the better cheap, but that he shall, ere he come in heaven, full surely pay therefore.

Vincent. He shall peradventure, uncle, afterward work it out in the fruitful works of penance, prayer, and alms deed done in true faith and due charity, and attain in such wise forgiveness well enough.

Anthony. All his forgiveness goeth, cousin, you see well, but by perhaps. But as it may be perhaps yea, so may it be perhaps nay; and where is he then? And yet, you wot well, by no manner hap he shall never hap finally to scape from death for fear of which he forsook his faith.

Vincent. No, but he may die his natural death and escape that violent death; and then he saveth himself from much pain, and so winneth therewith much ease. For evermore a violent death is painful.

Anthony. Peradventure he shall not avoid a violent death thereby; for God is without doubt displeased, and can bring him shortly to a death as violent by some other way.

Howbeit, I see well that you reckon that whoso dieth a natural death dieth like a wanton even at his ease. You make me remember a man that was once in a galley-suttle with us on the sea. Which while the sea was sore wrought and the waves rose very high, and he came never on the sea afore, and lay tossed hither and thither, the poor soul groaned sore and for pain he thought he would very fain be dead, and ever he wished: Would God I were on land that I might die in rest. The waves so troubled him there with tossing him up and down, to and fro, that he thought that trouble letted him to die because the waves would not let him rest. But if he might get once to land he thought he should then die there even at his ease.

Vincent. Nay, uncle, this is no doubt but that death is to every man painful. But yet is not the natural death so painful as is the violent.

Anthony. By my troth, cousin, methinketh that the death which men call commonly natural is a violent death to every man whom it fetcheth hence by force against his will. And that is every man which when he dieth is loath to die and fain would yet live longer if he might.

Howbeit, how small the pain is in the natural death, cousin, fain would I wit who hath told you. As far as I can perceive, those folk that commonly depart of their natural death have ever one disease and sickness or other, whereof if the pain of the whole week or twain in which they lie pining in their bed were gathered together into so short a time as a man hath his pain that dieth a violent death, it would, I ween, make double the pain that it is; so that he that naturally dieth ofter suffereth more pain than less, though he suffer it in a longer time. And then would many a man be more loath to suffer so long lingering in pain than with a sharper to be sooner rid. And yet lieth many a man more days than one in well near as great pain continually as is the pain that with the violent death riddeth the man in less than half an hour. Except a man would ween that whereas the pain is great to have a knife to cut his flesh on the outside from the skin inward, the pain would be much less if the knife might begin on the inside and cut from the midst outward.

Some we hear in their deathbed complain that they think they feel sharp knives cut a-two their heart-strings. Some cry out and think they feel within the brain-pan their head pricked even full of pins. And they that lie in a pleurisy think that every time they cough they feel a sharp sword swap them to the heart.

The consideration of the pains of hell, in which we fall if we forsake our Saviour, may make us set all the painful death of this world at right naught.

THE TWENTY-FIFTH CHAPTER

HOWBEIT, what should we need to make any such comparison between the natural death and the violent for the matter that we be in hand with here? We may put it out of doubt that he which for fear of the violent death forsaketh the faith of Christ putteth himself in the peril to find his natural death more painful a thousand times. For his natural death hath his everlasting pain so suddenly knit unto it, that there is not one moment of an hour between but the end of the one is the beginning of the other that after never shall have end. And therefore was it not without great cause that Christ gave us so good warning before, when He said as Saint Luke in the twelfth chapter rehearseth: *Dico autem vobis amicis meis, ne terreamini ab his qui occidunt corpus et post hac non habent amplius quid faciant. Ostendam autem vobis quem timeatis. Timete eum qui postquam occiderit habet potestatem mittere in gehennam. Ita dico vobis, hunc timete:* I say to you that are my friends, be not afeard of them that kill the body and which when that is done are able to do no more. But I shall shew you whom you should fear. Fear Him which when He hath killed hath in His power farther to cast him whom He killeth into everlasting fire. So I say to you, be afeard of Him.

God meaneth not here that we should nothing dread at all any man that can but kill the body; but he meaneth that we should not in such wise dread any such that we should for dread of them displease Him that can everlastingly kill both body and soul with a death ever dying and that shall yet never die. And therefore He addeth and repeateth in the end again the fear that we should have of Him, and saith: *Ita dico vobis, hunc timete :* So I say to you, fear Him.

Oh, good God, cousin, if a man would well weigh those words and let them sink, as they should do, down deep into his heart and often bethink himself thereon, it would, I doubt not, be able enough to make us set at naught all the great Turk's threats and esteem him not at a straw, but well content to endure all the pain that all the world could put upon us for so short while as all they were able to make us dwell therein, rather than by the shrinking from those pains (though never so sharp, yet but short) to cast ourself into the pain of hell, an hundred thousand times more intolerable and whereof there shall never come an end.

A woeful death is that death in which folk shall evermore be dying and never can once be dead. Whereof the Scripture saith: *Desiderabunt mori et fugiet mors ab eis :* They shall call and cry for death and death shall fly from them.

Oh, good Lord, if one of them were now put in choice of the both, they would rather suffer the whole year together the most terrible death that all the Turks in Turkey could devise than the death that they lie in for the space of half an hour. In how wretched folly fall, then, those faithless or feeble-faithed folk, that, to avoid the pain so far the less and so short, fall in the stead thereof into pain a thousand thousand times more horrible and of which terrible torment they be sure they shall never have end.

This matter, cousin, lacketh, as I believe, but either full faith or sufficient minding. For I think, on my faith, if we have the grace verily to believe it and often to think well thereon, the fear of all the Turk's persecution (with all this midday devil were able to make them do in the forcing us to forsake our faith) should never be able to turn us.

Vincent. By my troth, uncle, I think it is as you say. For surely if we would as often think on these pains of hell as we be very loath to do, and seek us peevish pastimes of purpose to put such heavy things out of our thought, this one point alone were able enough to make, I think, many a martyr.

The consideration of the joys of heaven should make us for Christ's sake abide and endure any painful death

THE TWENTY-SIXTH CHAPTER

Anthony. Forsooth, cousin, if we were such as we should be I would scant for very shame, in exhortation to the keeping of Christ's faith, speak of the pains of hell. I would rather put us in mind of the joys of heaven, the pleasure whereof we should be more glad to get than we should be to flee and escape all the pains in hell.

But surely God in the thing wherein He may seem most rigorous is marvellous merciful to us. And that is (which many men would little ween) in that He provided hell. For I suppose very surely, cousin, that many a man and woman too, of whom there now sit some, and more shall hereafter sit, full gloriously crowned in heaven, had they not first been afraid of hell would toward heaven never have set foot forward.

But yet undoubtedly, were it so that we could as well conceive in our hearts the marvellous joys of heaven as we conceive the fearful pains of hell (howbeit sufficiently we can conceive neither nother), but if we could in our imagination draw as much toward the perceiving of the one as we may toward the consideration of the other, we would not fail to be far more moved and stirred to the suffering for Christ's sake in this world for the winning of these heavenly joys than for the eschewing of all those infernal pains. But forasmuch as the fleshly pleasures be far less pleasant than the fleshly pains are painful, therefore we fleshly folk that are so drowned in these fleshly pleasures and in the desire thereof that we can almost have no manner savour or taste in any pleasure spiritual, have no cause to marvel that our fleshly affections be more abated and refrained by the dread and terror of hell than affections spiritual imprinted in us and pricked forward with the desire and joyful hope of heaven.

Howbeit, if we would somewhat set less by the filthy voluptuous appetites of the flesh, and would by withdrawing from them with help of prayer through the grace of God draw nearer to the secret inward pleasure of the spirit, we shall by the little sipping that our hearts should have here now, and that sudden taste thereof, have such an estimation of the incomparable and uncogitable joy that we shall have (if we will) in heaven by the very full draught thereof whereof it is written: *Satiabor quum apparuerit gloria tua:* I shall be satiate, satisfied, or fulfilled, when Thy glory, good Lord, shall appear (that is to wit, with the fruition of the sight of God's glorious Majesty face to face), that the desire, expectation, and heavenly hope thereof shall more encourage us, and make us strong to suffer and sustain for the love of God and salvation of our soul than ever we could be made to suffer here worldly pain, by the terrible dread of all the horrible pains that damned wretches have in hell.

Wherefore, in the meantime, for lack of such experimental taste, as God giveth here sometime to some of His special servants (to the intent we may draw toward the spiritual exercise too, for which spiritual exercise God with that gift as with an earnest penny of their whole reward after in heaven comforteth them here in earth, let us not so much with looking to have described what manner of joys they shall be as with hearing what our Lord telleth us in Holy Scripture how marvellous great they shall be, labour by prayer to conceive in our hearts such a fervent longing for them, that we may for attaining to them utterly set at naught all fleshly delight, all worldly pleasures, all earthly losses, all bodily torment and pain. Howbeit, some things are there in Scripture expressed of the manner of the pleasures and joys that we shall have in heaven, as where *Fulgebunt iusti sicut sol, et qui erudiunt ad iustitiam,*

tanquam scintillæ in arundineto discurrent: Righteous men
shall shine as the sun, and shall run about like sparkles of
fire among reeds.

Now tell some carnal-minded man of this manner pleasure,
and he shall take little pleasure therein and say he careth not to
have his flesh shine, he, nor like a spark of fire to skip about
in the sky.   Tell him that his body shall be impassible and
never feel harm.   Yet if he think then therewith, that he shall
never be an-hungered nor athirst, and shall thereby forbear all
his pleasure of eating and drinking; and that he shall never
have list to sleep, and thereby lose the pleasure that he was
wont to take in slugging; and that men and women shall
there live together as angels without any manner mind or
motion unto the carnal act of generation, and that he shall
thereby not use there his old filthy voluptuous fashion; he
will say he is better at ease already and would not give this
world for that.   For, as Saint Paul saith: *Animalis homo non
percipit ea qua sunt spiritus Dei. Stultitia enim est illi:* A
carnal man feeleth not the things that be of the spirit of God,
for it is foolishness to him.   But when the time shall come
that these foul filthy pleasures shall be so taken from him
that it shall abhor his heart once to think on them (whereof
every man hath among a certain shadow of experience in a
fervent grief of a sore painful sickness, while the stomach can
scant abide to look upon any meat; and as for the acts of the
other foul filthy lust, is ready to vomit if it hap him to think
thereon), when men shall, I say, after this life feel that horrible
abomination in their heart at the remembrance of these
voluptuous pleasures, of which abomination sickness hath
here a shadow (for which voluptuous pleasures he would here
be loath to change with the joys of heaven), when he shall, I
say, after this life have his fleshly pleasures in abomination
and shall of those heavenly joys which be set here so little by
have there a glimmering, though far from a perfect sight, O
good God, how fain will he then be, with how good will and
how glad will he then give this whole world if it were his, to

have the feeling of some little part of those joys. And therefore let us all, that cannot now conceive such delight in the consideration of them as we should, have often in our eyes by reading, often in our ears by hearing, often in our mouths by rehearsing, often in our hearts by meditation and thinking those joyful words of Holy Scripture by which we learn how wonderful huge and great those spiritual heavenly joys are of which our carnal hearts hath so feeble and so faint a feeling, and our dull worldly wits so little able to conceive so much as a shadow of the right imagination. A shadow, I say; for as for the thing as it is, that cannot only no fleshly carnal fantasy conceive, but over that no spiritual ghostly person peradventure neither that here is living still in this world. For sith the very substance essential of all the celestial joy standeth in blessed beholding of the glorious Godhead face to face, there may no man presume or look to attain it in this life. For God hath so said Himself: *Non videbit me homo et vivet:* There shall no man here living behold Me. And therefore we may well know that for the state of this life we be not only shut from the fruition of the bliss of heaven, but also that the very best man living here upon earth (the best man, I mean, being no more but a man) cannot, I ween, attain the right imagination thereof; but those that are very virtuous are yet in a manner as far therefrom as the born blind man from the right imagination of colours.

The words that Saint Paul rehearseth of the prophet Isaias, prophesying of Christ's incarnation, may properly be verified of the joys of heaven: *Oculus non vidit nec auris audivit, nec in cor hominis ascendit, quæ preparavit Deus diligentibus se.* For surely, for this state of this world, the joys of heaven are by man's mouth unspeakable, to man's ears not audible, to men's hearts uncogitable, so far forth excel they all that ever men have heard of, all that ever men can speak of, and all that ever any man can by natural possibility think on. And yet where the joys of heaven be such prepared for every saved soul our Lord saith yet by the mouth of Saint

John that He will give His holy martyrs that suffer for His sake many a special kind of joy. For he saith: *Vincenti dabo edere de ligno vitæ:* To him that overcometh I shall give him to eat of the tree of life. And also he that overcometh shall be clothed in white clothes. And I shall confess his name before My Father and before His angels. And also He saith: Fear none of those things that thou shalt suffer, etc., but be faithful unto the death, and I shall give thee the crown of life. He that overcometh shall not be hurt of the second death. He saith also: *Vincenti dabo manna absconditum, et dabo illi calculum candidum, et in calculo nomen novum scriptum quod nemo scit nisi qui accipit:* To him that overcometh will I give manna secret and hid, and I will give him a white suffrage, and in his suffrage a new name written which no man knoweth but he that receiveth it.

They used of old in Greece (where Saint John did write) to elect and choose men unto honourable rooms, and every man's assent was called his suffrage, which in some place was by the voices, in some place by hands. And one kind of those suffrages was by certain things that are in Latin called *calculi* because that in some places they used thereto round stones. Now saith our Lord that unto him which overcometh he will give a white suffrage; for those that were white signified approving, as the black signified reproving. And in those suffrages did they use to write the name of him to whom they gave their voice; and now saith our Lord that to him that overcometh he will in the suffrage give him a new name which no man knoweth but he that receiveth it.

He saith also: He that overcometh I will make him a pillar in the temple of My God, and he shall go no more out thereof, and I shall write upon him the name of My God, and the name of the city of My God, the new Jerusalem which descendeth from heaven from My God, and I shall write on him also My new name.

If we would dilate and were able to declare these special gifts with yet other more specified in the second and the third chapter of the Apocalypse, there would it appear how far those heavenly joys shall surmount above all the comfort that ever came in the mind of any man living here upon earth.

The blessed apostle Saint Paul that suffered so many perils and so many passions, he that saith of himself that he hath been *in laboribus pluribus, in carceribus abundantius, in plagis supra modum, etc.*, in many labours; in prisons ofter than other; in stripes above measure; at point of death oftentimes; of the Jews had I five times forty stripes save one; thrice have I been beaten with rods; once was I stoned; thrice have I been in shipwreck; a day and a night was I in the depth of the sea. In my journeys oft have I been in peril of flood, in peril of thieves, in peril by the Jews, in peril by the paynims, in perils in the city, in perils in desert, in perils in the sea, perils by false brethren; in labour and misery, in many nights' watch, in hunger and thirst, in many fastings, in cold and nakedness, beside those things that are outward, my daily instant labour, I mean my care and solicitude about all the churches. And yet saith he more of his tribulations which for the length I let pass. This blessed apostle, I say, for all these tribulations that himself suffered in the continuance of so many years, calleth it all the tribulations of this world, but light and as short as a moment in respect of the weighty glory that it after this world winneth us. *Id enim quod in præsenti est momentaneum, et leve tribulationis nostræ; supra modum in sublimitate æternum gloriæ pondus operatur in nobis, non contemplantibus nobis quæ videntur sed quæ non videntur; quæ enim videntur temporalia sunt, quæ autem non videntur æterna sunt:* This same short and momentary tribulation of ours that is in this present time worketh within us the weight of glory above measure, *in sublimitate*, on high; we beholding not these things that we see, but those things that we see not. For those things that we see be but temporal things, but those things that are not seen are eternal.

Now to this great glory can there no man come headless. Our head is Christ; and therefore to Him must we be joined, and as members of His must we follow Him if we will come thither. He is our guide to guide us thither and is entered in before us, and he, therefore, that will enter in after, *debet sicut ille ambulavit et ipse ambulare*, the same way that Christ walked, the same way must he walk. And what was the way by which He walked into heaven? Himself sheweth what way it was that His Father had provided for him, where he said unto the two disciples going toward the castle of Emmaus: *Nonne hæc oportuit pati Christum et ita intrare in gloriam suam?* Knew you not that Christ must suffer passion and by that way enter into His kingdom? Who can for very shame desire to enter into the kingdom of Christ with ease when Himself entered not into His own without pain.

The consideration of the painful death of Christ is sufficient to make us content to suffer painful death for His sake

THE TWENTY-SEVENTH CHAPTER

SURELY, cousin, as I said before, in bearing the loss of worldly goods, in suffering of captivity, thraldom, and imprisonment, and in the glad sustaining of worldly shame, that if we would in all those points deeply ponder the sample of our Saviour Himself, it were of itself alone sufficient to encourage every kind Christian man and woman to refuse none of all those calamities for His sake. So say I now for painful death also, that if we could and would with due compassion conceive in our minds a right imagination and remembrance of Christ's bitter painful Passion; of the many sore bloody strokes that the cruel tormentors with rods and whips gave Him upon every part of His holy tender body; the scornful crown of sharp thorns beaten down upon His holy head so straight and so deep that on every part His blessed blood issued out and streamed down; His lovely limbs drawn and stretched out upon the cross, to the intolerable pain of his forebeaten and sore beaten veins and sinews, new feeling with the cruel stretching and straining, pain far passing any cramp in every part of His blessed body at once; then the great long nails cruelly driven with hammers through His holy hands and feet; and in this horrible pain lift up and let hang with the peise of all His body bearing down upon the painful wounded places so grievously pierced with nails; and in such torment (without pity, but not without many despites) suffered to be pined and pained the space of more than three long hours till Himself willingly gave up unto His Father His holy soul. After which, yet to shew the mightiness of their malice after His holy soul departed, they pierced His holy heart with a sharp spear, at which issued out the holy blood and water whereof His holy sacraments have inestimable secret strength. If we would, I say, remember these things in such wise as would God we would, I verily suppose that the consideration of His incomparable kindness could not fail in such wise to inflame our key-cold hearts and set them on fire in His love that we should find ourself not only content but also glad and desirous to suffer death for His sake that so marvellous lovingly letted not to sustain so far passing painful death for ours. Would God we would here, to the shame of our cold affection, again toward God, for such fervent love and inestimable kindness of God toward us, would God we would, I say, but consider what hot affection many of these fleshly lovers have borne and daily do to those upon whom they dote. How many of them have not letted to jeopard their lives, and how many have willingly lost their lives indeed without either great kindness shewed them before (and afterward, you wot well, they could nothing win), but even that it contented and satisfied their mind, that by their death their lover should clearly see how faithfully they loved. The delight whereof imprinted in their fantasy not assuaged only but counterpoised also they thought all their pain. Of these affections with the wonderful dolorous affects following thereon not only old written stories, but over that I think in every country, Christian and heathen both, experience giveth us proof enough. And is it not then a wonderful shame for us for the dread of temporal death to forsake our Saviour that willingly suffered so painful death rather than He would forsake us; considering that beside that, He shall for our suffering so highly reward us with everlasting wealth. Oh, if he that is content to die for his love, of whom he looketh after for no reward and yet by his death goeth from her, might by his death be sure to come to her and ever after in delight and pleasure to dwell with her, such a lover would not let here to die for her twice. And how cold lovers be we then unto God if rather than die for Him once we will refuse Him and forsake Him for ever that both died for us before and hath also provided that if we die here for Him we shall in heaven everlastingly both live and also reign with Him. For, as Saint Paul saith: *Si compatimur et conregnabimus:* If we suffer with Him we shall reign with Him. How many Romans, how many noble courages of other sundry countries, have willingly given their own lives and suffered great deadly pains and very painful deaths for their countries and the respect of winning by their deaths the only reward of worldly renown and fame? And should we then shrink to suffer as much for eternal honour in heaven and everlasting glory? The devil hath also some so obstinate heretics that endure wittingly painful death for vainglory, and is it not then more than shame that Christ shall see His Catholics forsake His faith rather than suffer the same for heaven and very glory?

Would God, as I many times have said, that the remembrance of Christ's kindness in suffering His Passion for us, the consideration of hell that we should fall in by forsaking of Him, the joyful meditation of eternal life in heaven that we shall win with this short temporal death patiently taken for Him, had so deep a place in our breast as reason would they should and as, if we would do our devoir toward it and labour for it and pray therefore, I verily think they should. For then should they so take up our mind and ravish it all another way, that as a man hurt in a fray feeleth not sometime his wound, nor yet is not ware thereof till his mind fall more thereon, so farforth that sometime another man sheweth him that he hath lost an hand before he perceive it himself, so the mind ravished in the thinking deeply of those other things, Christ's death, hell, and heaven, were likely to minish and put away of our painful death four parts of the feeling either of the fear or the pain.   For of this am I very sure, if we had the fifteenth part of the love to Christ that He both had and hath unto us, all the pain of this Turk's persecution could not keep us from Him, but that there would be at this day as many martyrs here in Hungary as have been afore in other countries of old. And of this point put I nothing doubt but that if the Turk stood even here with all his whole army about him, and every of them all were ready at our hand with all the terrible torments that they could imagine, and (but if we would forsake the faith) were setting their torments to us, and to the increase of our terror fell all at once in a shout with trumpets, tabrets, and timbrels all blowen up at once, and all their guns let go therewith to make us a fearful noise; if there should suddenly then on the other side the ground quake and rive atwain, and the devils rise out of hell and shew themself in such ugly shape as damned wretches shall see them, and with that hideous howling that those hell-hounds should shriek lay hell open on every side round about our feet, that as we stood we should look down into that pestilent pit and see the swarm of silly souls in the terrible torments there; we would wax so feard of the sight, that as for the Turk's host we should scantly remember we saw them.   And in good faith, for all that, yet think I farther this, that if there might then appear the great glory of God, the Trinity in His high marvellous majesty, our Saviour in His glorious manhood sitting on his throne with his immaculate Mother and all that glorious company calling us there unto them, and that yet our way should lie through marvellous painful death before we could come at them; upon the sight, I say, of that glory there would, I ween, be no man that once would shrink thereat, but every man would run on toward them in all that ever he might, though there lay for malice to kill us by the way both all the Turk's tormentors and all the devils. And therefore, cousin, let us well consider these things, and let us have sure hope in the help of God. And then I doubt not but that we shall be sure that, as the prophet saith, the truth of His promise shall so compass us with a pavis, that of this incursion of this midday devil, this Turk's persecution, we shall never need to fear. For either if we trust in God well and prepare us therefore the Turk shall never meddle with us; or else, if he do, harm shall he none do us but instead of harm inestimable good. Of whose gracious help wherefore should be so sore now despair (except we were so mad men as to ween that either His power or His mercy were worn out already) when we see so many a thousand holy martyrs by His holy help suffered as much before as any man shall be put to now? Or what excuse can we have by the tenderness of our flesh when we can be no more tender than were many of them, among whom were not only men of strength, but also weak women and children? And sith the strength of them all stood in the help of God, and that the very strongest of them all was never able of themself, and with God's help the feeblest of them all was strong enough to stand against all the world, let us prepare ourself with prayer, with our whole trust in His help without any trust in our own strength. Let us think thereon, and prepare us in our mind thereto long before. Let us therein conform our will unto His, not desiring to be brought unto the peril of persecution (for it seemeth a proud, high mind to desire martyrdom), but desiring help and strength of God if He suffer us to come to the stress, either being sought, founden, and brought out against our wills, or else being by His commandment (for the comfort of our cure) bounden to abide.

Let us fall to fasting, to prayer, to alms deed in time, and give that unto God that may be taken from us. If the devil put in our mind the saving of our land and our goods, let us remember that we cannot save them long. If he fear us with exile and flying from our country, let us remember that we be born into the broad world and not like a tree to stick still in one place, and that whithersoever we go God shall go with us. If he threaten us with captivity, let us tell him again, better is it to be thrall unto man a while for the pleasure of God than by displeasing God be perpetual thrall unto the devil. If he threat us with imprisonment, let us tell him we will rather be man's prisoners a while here in earth than by forsaking the faith be his prisoners ever in hell. If he put in our minds the terror of the Turks, let us consider his false sleight therein, for this tale he telleth us to make us forget him. But let us remember well that in respect of himself the Turk is but a shadow; nor all that they all can do can be but a flea biting in comparison of the mischief that he goeth about. The Turks are but his tormentors, for himself doth the deed. Our Lord saith in the Apocalypse: *Ecce missurus est diabolus aliquos ex vobis in carcerem ut tentemini:* The devil shall send some of you to prison to tempt you. He saith not that men shall, but that the devil shall himself. For without question the devil's own deed it is to bring us by his temptation with fear and force thereof into eternal damnation. And therefore saith Saint Paul: *Non est nobis colluctatio adversus carnem et sanguinem sed, etc.:* Our wrestling is not against flesh and blood, etc.

Thus may we see that in such persecutions it is the midday devil himself that maketh such incursion upon us, by the men that are his ministers, to make us fall for fear. For till we fall he can never hurt us. And therefore saith Saint James: *Resistite diabolo et fugiet a vobis:* Stand against the devil and he shall flee from you. For he never runneth upon a man to seize on him with his claws till he see him down on the ground willingly fallen himself. For his fashion is to set his servants against us, and by them to make us for fear or for impatience to fall. And himself in the meanwhile compasseth us, running and roaring like a ramping lion about us, looking who will fall that he then may devour him. *Adver-*

sarius vester diabolus, saith Saint Peter, *tanquam leo rugiens circuit quærens quem devoret:* Your adversary the devil like a roaring lion runneth about in circuit, seeking whom he may devour.

The devil it is, therefore, that if we for fear of men will fall is ready to run upon us and devour us. And is it wisdom, then, so much to think upon the Turks that we forget the devil? What madman is he that when a lion were about to devour him, would vouchsafe to regard the biting of a little fisting cur? Therefore when he roareth out upon us by the threats of mortal men let us tell him that with our inward eye we see him well enough, and intend to stand and fight with him even hand to hand. If he threaten us that we be too weak, let us tell him that our captain Christ is with us, and that we shall fight with His strength, that hath vanquished him already. And let us fence us with faith and comfort us with hope, and smite the devil in the face with a firebrand of charity. For surely if we be of the tender loving mind that our Master was, and not hate them that kill us but pity them and pray for them with sorrow for the peril that they work unto themself, that fire of charity thrown in his face striketh the devil suddenly so blind that he cannot see where to fasten a stroke on us.

When we feel us too bold, remember our own feebleness. When we feel us too faint, remember Christ's strength. In our fear let us remember Christ's painful agony that Himself would for our comfort suffer before His Passion to the intent that no fear should make us despair, and ever call for His help such as Himself list to send us. And then need we never to doubt but that either He shall keep us from the painful death or shall not fail so to strength us in it that He shall joyously bring us to heaven by it. And then doth He much more for us than if He kept us from it. For as God did more for poor Lazarus in helping him patiently to die for hunger at the rich man's door than if He had brought him to the door all the rich glutton's dinner, so though He be gracious to a man whom he delivereth out of painful trouble, yet doth He much more for a man if through right painful death He deliver him from this wretched world into eternal bliss.   From which whosoever shrink away with forsaking his faith and falleth in the peril of everlasting fear, he shall be very sure to repent it ere it be long after.

For I ween that whensoever he falleth sick next he will wish that he had been killed for Christ's sake before.   What folly is it, then, for fear to flee from that death which thou seest thou shalt shortly after wish thou hadst died.   Yea, I ween almost every good Christian man would very fain this day that he had been for Christ's faith cruelly killed yesterday, even for the desire of heaven though there were none hell.   But to fear while the pain is coming, there is all our let.   But then if we would remember hell pain on the other side into which we fall while we flee from this, then should this short pain be no let at all.   And yet should we be more pricked forward, if we were faithful, by deep considering of the joys of heaven of which the apostle saith: *Non sunt condignæ passiones huius temporis ad futuram gloriam quæ revelabitur in nobis :* The passions of this time be not worthy to the glory that is to come which shall be shewed in us.   We should not, I ween, cousin, need much more in all this whole matter than that one text of Saint Paul if we would consider it well.   For surely, mine own good cousin, remember that if it were possible for me and you alone to suffer as much trouble as the whole world doth together, all that were not worthy of itself to bring us to the joy which we hope to have everlastingly.   And therefore, I pray you, let the consideration of that joy put out all worldly trouble out of your heart; and also pray that it may do the same in me.

And even thus will I, good cousin, with these words make a sudden end of mine whole tale and bid you farewell.   For now begin I to feel myself somewhat weary.

Vincent.   Forsooth, good uncle, this is a good end.   And it is no marvel though you be waxen weary, for I have this day put you to so much labour that, saving for the comfort that yourself may take of your time so well bestowed and for the comfort that I have myself taken (and more shall, I trust) of your good counsel given; else would I be very sorry to have put you to so much pain. But now shall our Lord reward and recompense you therefore and many shall, I trust, pray for you. For to the intent that the more may take profit by you I purpose, uncle, as my poor wit and learning will serve me, to put your good counsel in remembrance, not in our own language only, but in the Almaine tongue too. And thus praying God to give me and all other that shall read it the grace to follow your good counsel therein I shall commit you to God.

Anthony. Sith you be minded, cousin, to bestow so much labour thereon, I would it had happed you to fetch the counsel at some wiser man that could have given you better. But better men may set more things and better also thereto. And in the meantime I beseech our Lord breathe of His Holy Spirit into the reader's breast, which inwardly may teach him in heart, without whom little availeth all that all the mouths of the world were able to teach in men's ears. And thus, good cousin, farewell till God bring us together again, either here or in heaven. Amen.

FINIS

GLOSSARY

ACHORIANS, placeless folk
ACQUITE, to requite
ADVANCE, to extol, boast
ADVENTURE, chance; AT ADVENTURE, at random, recklessly
ADVERTISEMENT, advice, warning
AFFECTION, partiality
AFFIANCE, confidence
AFFLIGHT, afflicted
AGGRIEVE, to aggravate, oppress
AGRISE, to quail
ALAOPOLITANS, community of blind folk
ALLECTIVES, allurements
ALLIANT, akin
ALLOWING, praising
ALL-TO, soundly
ALMAINE, Germany, German
ALMOST, mostly
AMAUROTE, faint-seen
AMONG (adv.), between-whiles
ANCHORS, anchorets
ANELING, anointing
ANEMOLIANS, windy folk
ANYDER, waterless
APPAIRED, impaired
ARIENN, Aire-sur-Lys
ASSOIL, to absolve, pardon
AUNTERS, IN, if perchance
AVALE, to degrade, cast down
AVOUTRERS, AVOUTRY, adulterers, adultery

BANK, PINE, see PINE BANK
BAYARD, self-confident ignoramus
BEAR THE SWING, to have full control
BEHEST, promise
BESET, to employ
BOLT, to shackle
BRABBLING, contention
BRAID, fancy; startled movement
BRAKED, tortured

BRIM, much spoken of; fierce, raging
BRITTLE, frail, mortal
BUGS, bugbears
BUSK, to prepare, make ready; to hurry
BUTHRESCAS, very religious folk
BUT IF, if only; unless
BY AND BY, straightway
BY-CHANCE, unexpected opportunity

CANNED (THANKS), expressed
CANT, to divide, share, apportion
CAREFUL, full of cares
CAUTEL, quibble
CHAFFARE, barter, trade
CHEVEREL POINT, kid lace
CHEVING, faring, issue
CLEPED, called
CLOSE RELIGION, enclosed religious order
COCK A-HOOP, SET, to turn on the tap
COLLATION, dialogue
COMMODITY, convenience
COMMON, IN, in the abstract, as a class
COMPT, reckoning
CONCEITS, fancy dishes
CONCLUDE, to confute
CONDESCEND, to concede
CONFEDERED, joined, confederated
CONTINENTLY, continuously
CONVERSANT, habitually residing
CONVEYANCE, expression
COP HIGH, to a great height
CORPS, body
COURAGE, mind, spirit, temper
COVETISE, covetousness
COVIN, deceit, collusion
CUNNING, knowledgeable
CURED, cared for

425

CUSTOMABLE, accustomed, customary

CUSTOMERS, collectors of customs

DEAD LIFT, extremity
DEAL, bit, piece
DEMEANED, managed
DEPRAVE, to speak ill of
DEPREHEND, to detect
DEPURED, purified
DERIVE, to conduct through a channel
DISANNULLED, disproved
DISPICIONS, disputations
DISPROVE, to disapprove of
DISSEMBLE, to ignore
DIZZARDS, blockheads
DO COST, to incur expenses
DORS, drones
DOUCE, sweet, gentle
DRIFT, device, purpose
DRIVEL, drudge, menial
DULCELY, soothingly

EARNEST, weighty, important
EATH, easy
EFTSOONS, again, afterwards
EMBASING, debasing
EMBRAID, to upbraid
ENDANGER, to subject
ENGROSS, to monopolize
ENSURE, to assure
ENTREAT, to treat
ESPIAL, a spy
ESTEEMER, estimator
EXISTIMATION, repute

FAITOUR, cheat, impostor
FALL FAIR, to fall clear
FARCED, stuffed
FARDEL, bundle, load
FATIGATION, fatigue
FEAR, to deter
FEAT, nature, art, knack
FELL, spirited
FILE, to defile
FINDING, provision, supply
FLOCK-MEAL, in a flock
FODE, to delay, put off

FOINS, thrusts
FORBODEN, forbidden
FORBY, past
FORCE, to care; NO FORCE, no matter
FORTH, further
FORWEARIED, worn out
FRAME, advantage
FRAY, to frighten
FREMD, unrelated
FRUSTRATE, idle, purposeless
FUMISH, irritable, choleric

GALLEY-SCUTTLE, cook's galley
GALLOWS, fit for the gallows, vile
GALP, to vomit
GAMENERS, gamesters
GAR, to make
GEAR, means of living, goods
GENTLE, generous, courteous
GHOSTLY, spiritual, devout
GIGLOT, one addicted to inordinate mirth
GLEEK, a card game
GLORIOUS, haughty, boastful
GLOSS, disguise, pretence
GRAMERCY, a thank-you
GRIN, snare, trap
GRUDGE, grumble; to trouble
GUISE, practice

HANCED, raised, exalted
HAPT, wrapped
HARDLY, assuredly, with energy, firmly
HAUT, high, haughty
HAVER, possessor, owner
HAVIOUR, behaviour
HELM, helve, handle
HOVED, hovered
HYTHLODAY, nonsense-talker

INCONTINENT, forthwith
INDIFFERENT, just, impartial
INDUCE, to bring in
INFAMED, accused, disgraced
INSTINCT, instigation
INSTITUTE, educated, trained
INSTRUCT, instructed
INVENT, to discover

JAVEL, good-for-nothing
JET, to swagger

KEN, to know
KNOT, binding condition
KNOWLEDGE, to acknowledge

LAY, to impute, allege
LEAST, despoiled, deprived
LEFT, ceased
LET, hindrance, impediment; to hinder, forbear, refrain
LEWD, untrained, unlettered; perverse
LIEFUL, permissible
LIFT, DEAD, see DEAD LIFT
LOGICALS, subjects studied in a course of logic
LOSEL, worthless person
LOUTING, mocking

MACARIANS, happy folk
MAMMERING, state of doubt, hesitation
MANNER, TAKEN WITH THE, taken with stolen property on one's person
MASTERIES, feats of skill
MATCHED, associated
MAUGRE, in spite of
MEAN, means; moderate, intermediate
MEINIE, company
MENDS, amends
METE (p.p. MET), to measure
MINISHED, lessened
MINISHMENT, lessening
MISCREANT, unbelieving
MISHAP, to happen unfortunately
MISLIKE, to displease
MOUNTENANCE, amount, space
MOVE, to raise (a question)

NAMELY, especially, expressly
NEPHELOGETES, cloud folk
NIGGISH, niggardly
NOYOUS, vexatious, troublesome

OCCUPY, to make use of (money), carry on (craft), deal (with)

OUGHT, owned
OVERCHARGE, to overburden
OVERTHWART, perverse; across

PAINFUL, painstaking
PARALIPOMENON, the Book of Chronicles
PARDY, in truth, surely
PASS, to care (about), concern oneself (with); to surpass
PAVIS, large shield, defence, protection
PEASE, pea
PEEVISH, senseless, childish, silly
PEEVISHNESS, childishness, folly
PEISE, weight
PENNY-FATHERS, skinflints
PERCASE, perhaps
PERSECUTE, to pursue
PERSEVERE (trans.), to continue towards
PETITS, junior schoolboys
PICK A THANK, to curry favour
PILL, to pillage
PINE BANK, the rack
PINED, tormented
PINNED UP, confined
PLAT, plan
PLATFORM, ground plan
POLYERITES, very nonsensical folk
PORTAS, portable breviary
POSIL (pucelle), maid
POTESTATES, potentates
POTICARIES, apothecaries
POULTER, poulterer
PRAISE, to appraise
PRESENTLY, on the spot, at once
PRETENCE, design
PRETENDED, intended
PRETTILY, quietly
PREVENT, to forstall, prejudice
PRICK, point aimed at, target; to spur, ride
PROBABLE, worthy of support
PROCESS, discourse
PRONITY, proneness
PROOF, fulfilment, thriving
PROPONED, proposed
PUBLEN, poultry

QUAIL, to fail
QUAILED, enfeebled
QUICKNESS, animation, vigour

RAMPIER, to strengthen by a rampart
RAVIN, rapine, plunder
RECIDIVATION, relapse
RECULED, recoiled, retreated
REFRAIN, to restrain
RENEY, to renounce, abjure
REPROACHFUL, disgraceful
RIPE, to ripen, bring to a head
ROOM, space; office, employment
ROVERS, AT, at random
ROYALTY, magnificence, pomp
RUFFLE, disorder
RUSHBUCKLERS, swashbucklers

SAD, serious, sober
SCOURERS, scouts
SCRY, clamour
SECOND INTENTIONS, secondary concepts
SELD, seldom
SEMBLABLE, like
SENTENCE, opinion
SEVERAL, apart, separate
SHENT, blamed
SHOG, to shake, jog
SHREW, evil-disposed person
SHREWD, poor, unsatisfactory; shrewish, evil
SHREWDLY, harshly
SHREWDNESS, shrewishness
SIB, kin
SICKERLY, securely
SILLY, insignificant, harmless, simple
SITH, since
SKILL, to matter
SOILED, absolved, pardoned
SOLEMN, customary
SORT, number, company
SPILL, to ruin, destroy
SPRENT, sprinkled
STOCK, to set in the stocks

STOCKING IRONS, grubbing tools
STRAIT, narrow, strict; STRAITED SORE, hard put to it
SUBLEVATION, elevation
SUFFRAGES, prayers
SUIT, pursuit
SULLEN, standing aloof
SUITORS, followers
SURMOUNT, to extend
SWAP, to strike
SWING, BEAR THE, see BEAR THE SWING

TABLE, picture; TABLES, backgammon
TABRETS, small tabors
TAKE IN WORTH, to take in good part, be content with
TAPROBANE, Ceylon
THANK, PICK A, see PICK A THANK
THRONG, crowded
TRAIN, enticement, guile
TRANSLATING, transferring
TRIACLE, antidote

UNCOUTH, unknown
UNKIND, unnaturally bad
UNWIELDY, feeble
UPLANDISH, rustic
UTOPIA, nowhere

VERIFIED, maintained
VITAIL, victuals

WARE, aware, beware
WARED, spent, laid out
WIPED, defrauded
WITTILY, wisely, cleverly
WORTH, TAKE IN, see TAKE IN WORTH
WRITHEN, twisted
WRY, to turn, swerve

YEARNING, giving tongue

ZAPOLETES, great gadabouts